PHARMACY MANAGEMENT IN CANADA

WITH COMPLIMENTS

FROM THE
PROFESSIONAL AFFAIRS DIVISION

THE UPJOHN COMPANY
OF CANADA

Upjohn

Published by
Grosvenor House Press Inc.
for
The Upjohn Company of Canada

PHARMACY MANAGEMENT IN CANADA

General Editors

ANDRÉ ARCHAMBAULT, DPharm

JOHN A. BACHYNSKY, PhD

HAROLD J. SEGAL, PhD

Grosvenor House Press Inc.

Toronto – Montreal

The publisher wishes to express its gratitude to **The Upjohn Company of Canada** for an education grant which has helped make the publication of this book possible.

Canadian Cataloguing in Publication Data

Main entry under title:

Pharmacy management in Canada

Also issued in French under title: La Gestion d'une pharmacie au Canada.
Bibliography: p.
Includes index.
ISBN 0-919959-38-5

1. Pharmacy management – Canada.   I. Archambault, André.
II. Bachynsky, John.   III. Segal, Harold, 1941-

RS100.4.C3P43 1989   615.1'068   C89-094068-1

Published by

Grosvenor House Press Inc.
111 Queen Street East
Suite 456
Toronto, Ontario
M5C 1S2

Éditions Grosvenor Inc.
1456 rue Sherbrooke ouest
3ᵉ étage
Montréal, Québec
H3G 1K4

Cover design by Karen Paul
Printed and bound in Canada

CONTENTS

v

LIST OF CONTRIBUTORS

ANDRÉ ARCHAMBAULT, BASc, BPharm, DPharm (General Editor)
Dr. Archambault is the former Dean of the Faculty of Pharmacy and Vice-Rector of the University of Montreal, and currently Professor of Health and Pharmacy Administration. Since receiving his doctorate in Pharmacy from the University of Paris, he has been very involved in university administration, lecturing and working with national and international professional organizations. He is the author of numerous articles for scientific and professional journals.

JOHN A. BACHYNSKY, BSP, MSc, PhD (General Editor)
Dr. Bachynsky is Professor and Dean of the Faculty of Pharmacy and Pharmaceutical Sciences at the University of Alberta. He received a PhD in Pharmacy Administration from the University of Wisconsin, and has since served as President of both the Association of Faculties and the Association of Deans of Pharmacy of Canada. In 1988 he was appointed Vice-President of the Commonwealth Pharmaceutical Association and also received the Meritorious Service Award of the Canadian Pharmaceutical Association.

LINDA J. BROWN, BSc(Phr)
Linda Brown is the Deputy Registrar of the College of Pharmacists of British Columbia. After obtaining her pharmacy degree from the University of Texas, she spent ten years practicing in community pharmacy settings in British Columbia. As Communications Coordinator for the College of Pharmacists of British Columbia from 1980 to 1987, she was responsible for pharmacy security and drug diversion prevention programs.

DONALD M. CAMERON, BScPharm
Donald Cameron served as Registrar Treasurer of the Alberta Pharmaceutical Association for 25 years, and lectured for 18 of those years in Pharmacy Man-

agement and Administration and forensic pharmacy at the University of Alberta. A former President of the Alberta Pharmaceutical Association and owner/operator of his own pharmacy, Mr. Cameron retired in 1982 and has since marketed the Association's pharmacist insurance program. He is an honourary life member of both the Canadian and Alberta Pharmaceutical Associations.

GRAHAM CUNNINGHAM, CA

Graham Cunningham is a partner in G.G. Cunningham & Associates, a chartered accountancy firm in which he specializes in business advisory services. An instructor in the Business School at York University in Toronto since 1980, he is the co-author of TVOntario's home study course, "Start Your Own Business." He is editor of the Bank of Montreal's *Independent Business Review*, and his pharmacy-related business articles appear regularly in national publications.

LEROY C. FEVANG, BScPharm, MBA

Leroy Fevang is Executive Director of the Canadian Pharmaceutical Association. Prior to this appointment in 1978, he served as Registrar and Secretary-Treasurer of the College of Pharmacists of British Columbia, and lectured on pharmacy law and ethics at the Faculty of Pharmaceutical Sciences at the University of British Columbia. Among his many professional activities, he is a Board Member of the Pharmacy Examining Board of Canada and Chairman of the Chief Executive Officers of National Health Organizations.

DAVID W. FIELDING, BScPharm, MSc, EdD, PhC

Dr. Fielding is Associate Professor and Chairman of the Divisions of Clinical Pharmacy and Pharmacy Administration, Faculty of Pharmaceutical Sciences, University of British Columbia. For eleven years he was Director of Continuing Pharmacy Education at the University of British Columbia and is presently Associate Director of Research and Evaluation.

NORMA M. FREEMAN, BScPharm, MBA

Norma Freeman is a sessional lecturer on business topics at the University of Alberta's Faculty of Pharmacy. With degrees in Business Administration from Burnaby, British Columbia's Simon Fraser University, and in pharmacy from the University of Alberta, her experience combines community pharmacy practice, business administration, management and teaching.

JACQUES GAGNÉ, BA, BScPharm, MSc, PhD

Dr. Gagné is Dean of the Faculty of Pharmacy at the University of Montreal and an active member of numerous scientific and professional organizations. He received a PhD in Pharmacology from the University of Montreal in 1971. The former Administrator (1977-81) and Vice-President (1979-81) of the Ordre des Pharmaciens du Québec, Dr. Gagné also served as President of both the Association of Faculties and the Association of Deans of Pharmacy of Canada.

MARIANNE GREER, BSP, MCEd, PhD

Dr. Greer is an Assistant Professor of Pharmacy at the University of Saskatchewan. She received a PhD in Pharmacy Administration in 1986 from the University of Texas at Austin and has practiced in both hospital and community pharmacy in Alberta and Saskatchewan. Her research has focussed on patient education, pharmacy continuing professional education, and decision-making processes.

DONALD F. KYTE, BScPharm, MBA

Donald Kyte is General Manager of Pharmasave Drugs (Atlantic) Limited in Dartmouth, Nova Scotia. He has Pharmacy and MBA degrees from Dalhousie University. His professional activities include serving on the Tariff Committee of the Pharmacy Association of Nova Scotia, while community endeavours include being a director of Junior Achievement.

CLAUDE LAFONTAINE, BScPharm, PharmD

Dr. Lafontaine is a pharmacist and the owner of Claude Lafontaine Pharmacy in Montreal. He has a Pharmacy degree from the University of Montreal and a PharmD from the University of Paris. Dr Lafontaine serves as Student Supervisor of Clinical Pharmacy In Community Practice at the Faculty of Pharmacy, University of Montreal. He is a past member of the Board of Directors of L'Ordre des Pharmaciens du Québec, and past member of the Board of Directors and past vice-president of the Canadian Pharmaceutical Association.

JACQUES A. NADEAU, BScPharm, MS, MBA

Jacques Nadeau is Vice-President, Professional Services and Human Resources, for Cumberland Drugs in Montreal. He has held several pharmacy management positions in R&D, production, sales and marketing since receiving Masters degrees in radiopharmacy from the University of Southern California and business administration from McGill University. Mr. Nadeau is a former Director General and Secretary of the Ordre des Pharmaciens du Quebec.

KEN READY, BScPharm

Ken Ready is Associate Professor of Pharmacy and Director of Continuing Professional Education at the Faculty of Pharmacy, University of Saskatchewan. He operated his own pharmacy for thirty years, during which time he also lectured at the College of Pharmacy in Drugstore Management. He is President of the Pharmacy Examining Board of Canada and past President of both the Saskatchewan and Canadian Pharmaceutical Associations.

JOHN JAMES RYAN, DipPharm

John Ryan is Vice-President and General Manager of QS/1 Data Systems Ltd., a company specializing in computer software for pharmacies. A former pharmacy manager and a fulltime lecturer at the College of Pharmacy, Dalhousie University, Mr. Ryan is a past President of the Canadian Foundation for Pharmacy. He is an honourary life member of the Canadian Pharmaceutical Association, the Pharmacy Association of Nova Scotia and the Nova Scotia Pharmaceutical Society.

GLEN H. SCHOEPP, BScPharm

Glen Schoepp is Manager of St. Anthony's Clinic Pharmacy in Victoria, B.C. He is also a Clinical Instructor at the Faculty of Pharmaceutical Sciences, the University of British Columbia, Vancouver. He specializes in longterm care and home health care marketing.

HAROLD J. SEGAL, BScPharm, MS, PhD (General Editor)
Dr. Segal is Professor of Pharmacy Administration at the Faculty of Pharmacy, University of Toronto. A former community pharmacist, he earned his PhD from Purdue University in Pharmacy Administration. He is the author of a marketing textbook, several booklets on pharmacy management, and numerous journal articles. He also consults and lectures to provincial, national and international conferences on pharmacy management.

PIERRE TREMBLAY, Eng, MScA, MBA
Pierre Tremblay is Director of the Pharmacy Division of Les Ordinateurs Hypocrat Inc., an information company specializing in the area of health. He has worked for over 16 years in information services for pharmacists. His experience includes creating automated systems for both the office and commercial areas of a pharmacy.

WILLIAM R. WENSLEY, BScPhm, MScPhm, MBA
William Wensley is Registrar of the Ontario College of Pharmacists and a teacher of pharmacy law at the University of Toronto. Licensed as a pharmacist in Ontario, he holds a Masters degree in Pharmaceutical Manufacturing and Business Administration from the University of Toronto. He has served on many advisory committees to the Provincial Ministry of Health, including the Ontario Council of Health, the Drug Quality and Therapeutics Committee and the Pharmaceutical Inquiry of Ontario.

PREFACE

The Canadian Pharmaceutical Association (CPhA) is a national voluntary association of pharmacists dedicated to maintaining and improving the quality of health care both in Canada and throughout the world. All activities and efforts of the association are intended to advance pharmacy academically, scientifically and professionally.

Established in 1907, the CPhA has a long-standing reputation for promoting excellence in pharmacy. The CPhA encourages high professional standards in contemporary practice, and works to maintain the effective viability of the profession in Canada through education, research, lobbying and publishing.

The CPhA is pleased to endorse *Pharmacy Management in Canada*, and is grateful to The Upjohn Company of Canada and Grosvenor House Press for the opportunity to participate in the project. This comprehensive textbook of current pharmacy practice will not only provide much-needed, practical information for those just entering community practice, but will help to expand the knowledge of all pharmacists.

LEROY FEVANG
Executive Director
Canadian Pharmaceutical Association

FOREWORD

The Upjohn Company of Canada has been involved in the provision and support of education programs for health professionals for over a decade. Our participation in continuing pharmacy education programs at the provincial and national levels has involved the sponsorship of a variety of professional speakers' programs, pharmacy services studies, and the distribution of educational materials.

In the past few years, there has been a strong effort to incorporate the behavioural sciences as well as management and administrative studies into all aspects of pharmacy education and practice. Upjohn has focussed its continuing pharmacy education support in these subject areas to help address specific Canadian needs. *Pharmacy Management in Canada* is our latest contribution to pharmacy education. The authors and editorial board members of this textbook are recognized nationally as experts in their various disciplines. *Pharmacy Management in Canada* will be made available to both pharmacy students and practitioners. It is our desire that the management principles presented in this book will serve as a resource for the practitioner, whether he or she be a student, professor, or practising pharmacist. The ultimate result will be a more efficient, effective, and successful provision of health care by pharmacists for the Canadian public.

In summary, this book is an extension and reaffirmation of the on-going commitment of The Upjohn Company of Canada to continuing pharmacy education in Canada. We hope it will be a source of enrichment for you in your pharmacy management endeavours.

Upjohn is honoured to have the endorsement and support of the Canadian Pharmaceutical Association for this pharmacy management textbook.

The Professional Affairs Division
The Upjohn Company of Canada

PUBLISHER'S FOREWORD

Pharmacy Management in Canada is a first for the pharmacy community in this country. Previously, both pharmacy students taking management courses and practising community pharmacists had to rely on American publications for a complete reference source on the subject. Grosvenor House Press in association with The Upjohn Company of Canada has remedied the situation with this textbook.

The text uses the most recent statistical data available from the Canadian Pharmaceutical Association's 1986 Seventh Annual Survey of Community Pharmacy Operations. At the same time, teachers and students are constantly made aware of the inevitable changes taking place as we move into the 1990s.

We chose to publish a textbook produced by a "management team" comprised of pharmacy management authorities both to reflect their wide range of experience and to collect their ideas into a cohesive instructional/ reference book. Each author's unique voice and opinions will help stimulate class discussions and allow instructors to base lectures on specifically Canadian data and Canadian specialists' chosen approaches.

The text follows a chronological and thematic structure — from the decision to become a pharmacy owner or manager, to opening and managing a pharmacy, to expansion planning and retirement planning; from financial aspects to technology and innovations.

The publisher wishes to thank all those whose invaluable assistance helped make the book possible. We appreciate the support and advice of the editorial board: Dr. André Archambault, Dr. John A. Bachynsky,

Dr. Murray Brown, Mr. Leroy Fevang, Dr. Carl Hoffman, Mr. Dick Hoy, Dr. David Fielding, Dr. Jacques Gagné, Mr. Ken Ready, Mr. John Ryan and Dr. Harold Segal.

We thank the following critical reviewers: Randall E. Baxandall, pharmacist, Shoppers Drug Mart, Edmonton; K. Hibbert, programme officer, Small Businesses Loans Administration, Ottawa; David Milovanovic, associate, Canadian Pharmaceutical Education and Consulting Services Ltd., Scarborough; Barry Phillips, manager, Shoppers Drug Mart, Downsview; Glen H. Schoepp, manager, St. Anthony's Clinic Pharmacy, Victoria; Toby M. Symes, partner, Deloitte Haskins & Sells, Vancouver.

We also wish to express our gratitude to Darlene Zeleney, editor, and Linda Szostak and Lois Pike, editorial coordinators.

Grosvenor House Press, The Upjohn Company of Canada, the Canadian Pharmaceutical Association and the authors of *Pharmacy Management in Canada* encourage the comments and suggestions of all pharmacy instructors, students and practitioners who use this textbook. Your feedback will help us produce an even better second edition. Send suggestions to: Grosvenor House Press Inc., 111 Queen St. E., Suite 456, Toronto, Ontario M5C 1S2.

INTRODUCTION

Graduate pharmacists have a number of career options: some may choose hospital pharmacy if they wish to practise in an institutional environment; others may choose to teach and conduct research in a university setting. Federal and provincial governments, national and provincial pharmacy associations, and pharmaceutical manufacturers and wholesalers all provide employment for pharmacists. But the largest percentage of graduate pharmacists choose employment in community or retail pharmacy, where they contribute to society as valuable members of the health-care team. This book is directed to them.

The pharmacist who chooses to enter community-pharmacy practice may well decide, after gaining sufficient experience in the field, to become a pharmacy manager, to purchase a franchise, or to buy or establish an independent pharmacy. With any one of these decisions, the pharmacist is embracing a second specialization – that of business management. Effective pharmacy management calls for a broad base of knowledge, moulded to the idiosyncracies and special needs of pharmacy practice and retailing. Management is a creative and dynamic process that demands informed decision making and the ability to recognize and seize new opportunities as they arise. It involves planning, staffing, and organizing, as well as directing, coordinating, and controlling the various facets of the business in a manner that will ensure the pharmacy's profitability. The endeavour is both exciting and challenging: it requires the pharmacist to draw continually on acquired knowledge and skills in order to minimize the risks and maximize the benefits involved in business.

This book will guide the student through the process of establishing and operating a pharmacy, drawing throughout on proven management principles and techniques. It will also serve as a handbook or reference for the practising community pharmacist. The chapters are grouped in five sections: on getting started; on organizing resources; on operating the pharmacy; on the growth and expansion of the pharmacy; and on personal planning. A comprehensive directory of pharmacy-related organizations, as well as of the provincial drug plans, is provided at the end of the book, and a list of recommended readings appears at the end of each chapter for those who wish to explore a given topic in greater detail.

The first eight chapters, on getting started, discuss the full range of factors that a pharmacist contemplating the ownership and management of a pharmacy must take into consideration. Chapter 1 stresses the importance of a personal analysis before embarking on the venture of pharmacy ownership. Is adequate capital available? Does the pharmacist possess the personal traits that are essential for successful business ownership, such as entrepreneurship, leadership, perseverance, organizational ability, experience, physical energy, and the necessary management skills? Chapter 2 guides the pharmacist through the advantages and disadvantages of the different forms of business organization.

Chapters 3 to 8 explore, from various perspectives, the ways in which the inevitable pitfalls and risks of business ownership may be reduced or eliminated. The importance of location and the need for a thorough understanding of the competitive situation in the pharmacy's locality is emphasized. The financial aspects of getting started in business will be explained and, while cautions are made about the risks involved, assurances are also given that these risks can be minimized through careful planning. The pharmacist is encouraged to formulate a business plan, set goals and objectives and then develop strategies that will make it possible to achieve those goals. The capital needs that face the new pharmacy owner are identified and ways of meeting them explored.

Chapter 7 provides a discussion of regulatory and legal considerations and Chapter 8 describes the various types of insurance coverage required to minimize losses that may occur in the operation of the pharmacy.

Organizing resources – physical, human, and financial – is the important subject addressed in the next five chapters. Chapter 9 discusses how pharmacy design and layout can contribute to the professional atmosphere that is so important to a successful and profitable pharmacy business. Chapter 10 takes as its premise that harmonious human relationships are vital to every successful enterprise and stresses the importance of open, two-way communication between management and staff.

The single largest investment in a pharmacy is represented by its inventory, making the control of that asset one of the most critical of management functions. Chapter 11 shows how proper planning and control will keep the inventory investment to a minimum while at the same time promoting maximum sales and profit. Maximizing profit and the essentials of sound financial management and financial reporting are the subjects of Chapter 12. Chapter 13 describes the wealth of information available to managers and owners through valuable professional resources, both within and outside the pharmacy.

Chapters 14 through 21 – on operating the pharmacy – begin by emphasizing the importance of establishing policies and procedures to govern general business, personnel, and operational matters. The reader is then guided through a range of topics that together comprise the fundamental requirements of pharmacy operation. Theory and practical applications are presented in the discussions on merchandising and marketing (Chapter 15), setting retail prices (Chapter 16), deciding what professional and commercial services the pharmacy should provide (Chapter 17), and reviewing and evaluating the financial condition of the operation (Chapter 18). The necessity for adequate external and internal security is dealt with in Chapter 19 and Chapter 20 deals with the vital topic of computerization in pharmacy practice. Finally, the importance of the health-care team and of establishing strong relationships with members of other health professions is elaborated on in Chapter 21.

The growth and expansion of the pharmacy, examined in Chapters 22 to 25, illustrates opportunities for change and development in the profession. These topics emphasize the fact that new technologies can free pharmacists from routine technical tasks and allow them to devote more time to their professional duties and responsibilities. New service opportunities, occasioned both by societal trends and technical innovations, are discussed in detail in Chapter 23, while Chapter 24 explains how best to observe the social and professional environments to detect and capitalize on opportunities for change and growth. Chapter 25 offers a discussion of the criteria to consider in planning for expansion of the pharmacy practice.

The final chapters on personal planning, discuss continuing pharmacy education and the maintenance of professional competency (Chapter 26), and why it is crucial to develop personal financial goals and retirement plans and how those goals can be attained in the current financial environment (Chapter 27).

Among the many changes taking place in community-pharmacy practice today are the trends toward larger stores and the growth of pharmacy chains and various types of co-operative groups. Because of these developments, the future will hold increased opportunities for employment at the management level. In its treatment of pharmacy management, this book combines issues of concern for both owners and managers, on the premise that a manager can function effectively only in full awareness of the risks and challenges that confront the pharmacy owner.

The pharmacy owner-manager has a dual role as a businessperson and a professional. Professional concerns and responsibilities are woven into the fabric of our discussion of management issues, with an emphasis on the provision of a high calibre and full range of professional services and on the role of the pharmacist in the health-care team. Not to be forgotten, however, is the responsibility of the practising pharmacist to the profession itself. The pharmacy owner or manager's ongoing participation in professional associations and continuing-education programs (either as a participant or lecturer) will have a mutually beneficial effect: the pharmacist will be making a valuable contribution to the betterment of the profession while at the same time gaining personally through an exchange of ideas, concerns, and professional activities. Similarly, financial support of faculties of pharmacy and of organizations dedicated to the advancement of the profession, such as the Canadian Foundation for Pharmacy, is critical to the continuance of high professional standards in Canadian pharmacy. The essential point here is that practising pharmacists must perceive themselves as members of a professional community whose collective strength can only enhance each of its individual members.

A final note to the prospective owner or manager: while maintaining high standards of practice and ensuring the profitability and growth of the pharmacy are the two guiding principles of successful community-pharmacy practice, they are both rooted in one fundamental premise – namely, that no business can survive in the long run unless it is committed to ethical practices. The reputation of the pharmacy – and equally of its owner or manager – among customers and within the industry and the profession will depend in large part on the integrity and honesty of its management's approach in matters of business and health care.

Good pharmacy managers are not born. Pharmacists become effective managers by combining extensive reading, conscientious study, and years of experience. This textbook has been designed to incorporate the experiences of many of Canada's best authorities on pharmacy management. It will provide an invaluable resource for both current and future pharmacists.

1

ALTERNATIVES IN COMMUNITY-PHARMACY PRACTICE

INTRODUCTION

Contemporary pharmacy practice exists in a myriad of settings. Most obvious are the rural versus the urban settings and the community versus the institutional practice settings. Community practices can be categorized by their physical location, size, merchandise mix, and service offering. For example, a traditional community-pharmacy practice could be described as having a merchandise mix balanced between professional and non-professional products. Included in the professional-products mix are prescription medications and companion non-prescription drug products that lend themselves to sale with pharmacist involvement. Non-professional products are those that can be purchased in other retail outlets as well as in pharmacies, and tend to fall into the traditional areas of health and beauty aids, paper goods, sunglasses, cosmetics, magazines, greeting cards, and giftware.

Outgrowths of the traditional community pharmacy are the smaller, more service-oriented pharmacy and its opposite – the larger, self-service pharmacy. The smaller, more service-oriented pharmacy is characterized by its physical size, merchandise mix (limited to more professional items), and its personal service. It is usually located in a medical building. The larger, self-service pharmacy practice emphasizes merchandising. In this type of practice, physical size is pronounced, there is a large dependence on customer self-service for a wide range of non-professional items, and the pharmacy department is a relatively small part of the total operation. It should be remembered that in the middle of this spectrum is the

1

traditional community pharmacy, characterized by its balance of professional and non-professional products, a mix of personal service and self-service, and a physical size ranging from about 3000 to 6000 square feet (tending in recent years, on average, toward the higher end of the spectrum). Community pharmacies can be found in shopping malls or plazas, as well as in smaller strip plazas or in self-standing buildings located in shopping areas within residential communities.

Not to be left out is the area of institutional pharmacy practice. In this type of setting, pharmacists emphasize "clinical pharmacy," which focusses on monitoring patients' needs for strictly pharmaceutical care. While the majority of pharmacists who choose this career option are situated in hospitals, some may be found in extended-care facilities such as old-age homes and nursing homes. Institutionally based pharmacists also practise in specialized settings such as mental-health hospitals, drug and alcohol treatment centres, and provincial and federal prisons.

Pharmacists operate in all of these settings and facilities to meet consumer needs and demand. In other words, all types and locations of commercial pharmacy practice exist because the marketplace supports them. If there were no demand or if there were a change in the nature of the demand for the products and services offered, pharmacy settings would also have to change in order to meet the altered consumer demand – or simply disappear for lack of sales.

Each of these practice alternatives implies a particular emphasis within the role that the pharmacist adopts. For example, the pharmacist in a small prescription-oriented pharmacy may provide a great deal of patient counselling with each prescription dispensed, as well as with the sale of non-prescription drug products. This may occur as a matter of course. On the other hand, a pharmacist in a merchandise-oriented pharmacy may provide basic counselling on prescription-drug use, and advice on non-prescription drugs only in direct response to a patient's inquiry.

In each of the above cases, the emphasis in the pharmacist's role is somewhat different and in each case a particular image or perception of that role is left with the patient. In this way, a style or pattern of practice emerges that is identifiable with a pharmacy setting. Similarly, as young pharmacists undertake practice in one type of setting or another, they are influenced by the role model that is provided, and may elect to remain in that setting. Thus, the influence of role models can play a large part in an individual pharmacist's long-term career path.

EMPLOYMENT WITH A FIRM

Pharmacists' career opportunities can be described as falling into one of two categories: self-employed or employed by another pharmacist or firm.

Many pharmacists enjoy the status of being an employee, with the defined responsibilities that are assumed within a job description. Employee status usually allows a person to leave the trials and tribulations of work within the environment of the practice and to enjoy non-working hours pursuing other activities of interest. This lifestyle appeals to certain types of individuals and can provide sufficient rewards for a satisfying career.

On the other hand, some employed pharmacists may seek other avenues of growth through their work. One opportunity is to become responsible for the work of other employees by becoming a supervisor. This type of responsibility involves certain management skills, which can be learned either on the job or by taking appropriate courses.

As supervisory skills of communication, interviewing, leadership, introducing change, and discipline are mastered in practice, the pharmacist-supervisor may be ready for the next step – management. As a manager, the pharmacist's administrative skills and responsibilities increase further.

Again, much is learned on the job and valuable experience is gained, but it is often by trial and error. And, because of the potentially high cost of trial-and-error learning in this position, it may be more productive to engage in some sort of formal training or education in the area of business management – and, in this instance, how it relates to a pharmacy practice. If formal training is not practical in a given situation, the on-the-job learning process could be supplemented by selected reading or correspondence courses.

Depending on the circumstances, varying degrees of managerial expertise may be required of a pharmacist. Given the responsibility of managing a pharmacy, for example, one would need all the skills of an owner. If the pharmacy were part of a chain organization, the number of employees and the amount of inventory involved might be considerably greater than in a smaller but independently owned pharmacy. On the other hand, the chain-pharmacy manager may be able to rely on corporate guidelines and manuals, while the independent owner has only his or her own knowledge and experience at hand.

For pharmacists who have become managers and who have adjusted well to the demands of the job but are still searching for an element of greater independence, a franchise may be the answer. A franchise is not a new method of operating a business, but its application to pharmacy ownership was popularized only in the late 1960s.

FRANCHISING

The first franchise system is credited to the Singer Sewing Machine Company. Later, soft-drink manufacturers, major oil companies, and automobile manufacturers adopted the concept. Franchising gained wide acceptance in the 1950s and 1960s as fast-food outlets were introduced to the market.[1]

In a publication entitled *Franchise Opportunities Handbook*, the U.S. Department of Commerce defined "franchise" as follows:

> Franchising is a form of licensing by which the owner (franchisor) of a product, service, or method obtains distribution at the retail level through affiliated dealers (the franchisees).
>
> The product, method, or service being marketed is identified by a brand name and the franchisor maintains control over the marketing methods employed.
>
> In many cases, the operation resembles that of a large chain with trademarks, uniform symbols, equipment, storefronts, and standardized services or products, and maintains uniform practices as outlined in the franchise agreement.[2]

There are basically three types of franchise. One is oriented to the selling of product lines such as cosmetics, candy, or vitamins. Another is a flexible franchise program or agreement distinguished by few demands to stock specific products, but a strong management approach that provides extensive consulting services to help establish the business, plan its retail strategy, and provide ongoing advice. (This type of franchise is often promoted by a full-line, full-service wholesale.)

The third type of franchise involves a more structured, well-defined merchandising program and often functions as a "turnkey" operation. This means that the franchisor undertakes all that is necessary to establish the operation, and the franchisee simply opens the door and begins doing business. In pharmacy, the best known example of this type of franchise is the Shoppers Drug Mart operation, established by Koffler Stores Limited in Toronto.

The system was developed by Murray B. Koffler and represented an entirely new approach to organizing and financing a retail pharmacy. In this particular approach, the franchisor develops the site, negotiates the lease, designs the layout, installs fixtures and equipment, and finances the start-up and pre-opening costs. The pharmacy is then leased to a pharmacist-franchisee who assumes all expenses, including inventory, wages, general overhead, and rent. The franchisee pays a franchise fee to the parent organization for establishing the business and for the man-

---

[1] For further information about franchising, see *Minding Your Own Business*, Vol. 3 (Chapter 1: Buying a Franchise), Federal Business Development Bank, Ottawa. Also, information should be available from the small business development branch of your provincial ministry of trade (for example, *Starting a Small Business in Ontario*, Ministry of Industry, Trade and Technology, Government of Ontario).

[2] As quoted in *American Druggist Merchandising* 168, no. 2 (15 July 1973):39

agerial expertise that it will provide for the duration of the franchise agreement.

The individual pharmacist-franchisee is offered all the benefits of a chain operation, with an opportunity to operate his own retail business: the onus is on the franchisee to make the business succeed. In this sense, the franchisee is a cross between a manager and an owner. One aspect of franchising that might be considered a disadvantage is that management style, procedures, and policy are to a large extent governed by the parent organization.

The Association of Canadian Franchisors (ACF)[3] is an organization that promotes and protects ethical franchising in Canada. Although it deals with franchising in general, much of the information it provides can be applied to the area of retail pharmacy. For example, the association produces an information package, available at minimal cost, that contains a booklet entitled "Investigate Before Investing"; the ACF Code of Ethics; an Evaluation Checklist; "How to Retain a Franchise Consultant"; listings of expert consultants, specialist lawyers, and bank contacts; a calendar of franchise programs and events; and leads to other sources of information.

As an option to ownership, a franchise provides many of the benefits of independent operation, with less risk and a less onerous initial financial obligation. At the same time, it provides the backup resources of experience, access to managerial information, and a continuing source of promotional and educational programs. Studies show that franchises have a lower failure rate than independently owned firms.

Just as some pharmacists are not interested in assuming managerial responsibilities, not all pharmacists will be comfortable in a franchise situation. A typical profile of an ideal franchisee has been described as follows:

> From 30 to 50 years old
> Happily married
> Shows leadership qualities
> Healthy
> No history of substance abuse
> Evidence of being a good financial manager
> Good references[4]

Although this description applies to an industry entirely unrelated to pharmacy, it is quite reasonable to assume that pharmacy franchisors would look for similar qualities in potential pharmacist-franchisees. Fur-

---

[3] The Association of Canadian Franchisors is located at 88 University Avenue, Suite 600, Toronto, Ontario M5J 1T8.

[4] Adapted from *Franchise Journal*; as quoted in *American Druggist Merchandising* 168, no. 2 (15 July 1973):39.

thermore, these characteristics are not inappropriate for the pharmacist who has entrepreneurial aspirations.

ENTREPRENEURSHIP

An entrepreneur may be described as someone who organizes a business, assuming all the inherent risks, for the purpose of obtaining a profit. The emphasis here is on the risk-taking element, as this is what distinguishes the entrepreneurial role from other administrative and managerial roles that are available to pharmacists.

The pharmacist-entrepreneur differs from the pharmacist-franchisee in that the latter has an umbrella of protection provided by the franchising organization. It is in the interest of that organization to assure the continued success of the franchisee because of the potential revenue to be derived from future sales. Thus, this monitored ownership greatly enhances the opportunity for success and reduces the risk assumed by the franchisee.

Conversely, the entrepreneur is on his own. The challenge facing the pharmacist who elects to become an independent owner of a practice is the balancing of the professional and managerial skills required to operate the business. The pharmacist-owner must be a skilled merchandiser, manager of people, and financial manager, with an acute awareness of the environment. And not to be forgotten is the fact that the independent owner must assume full financial risk.

The independence of being one's own boss brings with it the burden of responsibility. Payrolls must be met, rent or mortgage payments come due monthly, suppliers expect payment, staff must be supervised, and customer/patient demands must be satisfied. Because too many wrong decisions can lead to business failure, the pharmacist who wants to become an entrepreneur should conduct a self-analysis before making any such commitment, answering questions such as the following:

1. Have you had sufficient experience in a pharmacy practice?
2. Have you supervised staff?
3. Have you managed a pharmacy practice?
4. Are you willing to risk your savings?
5. Do you have a strong desire to make money?
6. Are you prepared to work long hours?[5]

A pharmacist who answers yes to most or all of these questions is likely a good candidate to become a successful owner. And with suc-

---

[5] Adapted from *Starting a Small Business in Ontario*, Ministry of Industry, Trade, and Technology, Government of Ontario, p.2.

cessful ownership, certain expectations can be realized: the opportunity to practise your profession as you define it; to receive an income based on your ability to provide products and services of your choosing in response to the demands of your clientele; and to introduce products and innovative services without seeking approval from others.

BECOMING AN OWNER

There are essentially three ways to become a pharmacy owner: (1) by purchasing part ownership and becoming a junior partner of an established pharmacy; (2) by purchasing an existing pharmacy practice outright; or (3) by establishing a new practice. Each of these approaches to ownership has its advantages and disadvantages.

Purchasing Part Ownership

Purchasing part ownership is usually an opportunity that is made available to a younger pharmacist who has worked in a particular practice for a period of time. Of the three ownership options, it requires the smallest initial capital investment. It can pave the way for buying out the remaining owner(s), because it gives the younger pharmacist some time to accumulate capital through savings and profit sharing. Another advantage of this approach is that the junior partner can learn on the job from the current owner/manager and establish his own rapport with the clientele. It allows for a gradual, smooth transfer of ownership and is attractive to older owners who wish to ease themselves out of practice and into retirement.

On the flip side of the coin is the problem that while this small investment can bring substantial future benefits, it may not provide for any immediate authority. Personality problems or a reluctance on the part of the current owner to give up control of his business can create obstacles for the junior partner. The degree of compatibility can, on the other hand, be determined in the early stages of the employer-employee relationship, before any purchase arrangement is made legally binding.

Advice from accountants and lawyers about entering into this type of arrangement can be valuable by helping to determine the manner in which payments for the purchase of the pharmacy are made. For example, there are certain advantages to both buyer and seller in extending payments over a longer term: monthly payments, including interest, are reduced for the buyer and, in turn, involve lower income-tax rates for the seller.

Purchasing an Established Pharmacy

Buying a known entity has an advantage over establishing a new practice in that the financial risk is smaller: the existing pharmacy has financial records that can be critically analyzed before a commitment is made. It also provides the opportunity to secure a good location, usually the major single criterion of success in operating a retail business of any sort. Since most newly established businesses experience a lag time before becoming profitable, purchasing an existing business virtually eliminates this difficulty. In other words, there should be a sufficient cash flow to sustain the business from the first day of assuming ownership. This advantage is reinforced by having an identified clientele that is comfortable with the pharmacy's products and services. As a result, it can be assumed that this client base will continue to use the pharmacy for its health-care needs. In addition, an established pharmacy will have a stable, if not growing, prescription practice, with a reasonable number of repeatable prescriptions on file.

These latter considerations – a loyal clientele and repeatable prescription business – are largely aspects of an intangible asset called goodwill. In an accounting sense, goodwill is the factor that raises the purchase price of a business over the appraised value of its physical assets, such as inventory, fixtures, and equipment. In part, goodwill has been described as "a measure of the probability that a patient will continue to be a patient" of a particular (medical) practice.[6] Applying this concept to pharmacy, one must consider the outcome of an owner-pharmacist selling his practice. Once the sale is completed, the former owner's services may no longer be available at that location, but patients will continue to utilize the services offered for other reasons. There is goodwill, but its value in a pharmacy practice must be carefully assessed. It is not surprising that the seller of a practice traditionally argues that the goodwill is of high dollar value, while the purchaser tries to minimize that claim. An approach to estimating the value of goodwill is discussed in Chapter 4.

Purchasing an established pharmacy has some disadvantages. Among them is the chance of overpaying for the assets and for goodwill. Another consideration is the state of the fixtures and equipment. If they are old, they may be inadequate for current operations and may require replacement. This may prove costly. Inventory may be old and unsalable and should be inspected critically before agreement is made to purchase it as is. Staff requirements should be assessed carefully, and if necessary, changes made.

Decisions about staffing changes should be made cautiously, as it is

[6]J. Marmer, "Value of Goodwill Hard to Measure in Partnership," *The Medical Post*, 4 September 1973, p.29.

difficult to predict whether dismissing employees with longevity will create ill will among the established clientele or have just the opposite effect. Finally, the purchase of an established pharmacy practice may or may not include the building in which it is situated. As you will learn in Chapter 4, a sizable investment in real estate in the initial stages of ownership can represent too great a drain on finances, and it may be preferable to take on a lease. If the building is not part of the purchase, it is important to clarify the terms of the existing lease. In any such discussions with the seller, the potential buyer should involve his lawyer and accountant for advice.

Establishing a New Practice

The opportunity to establish a new pharmacy practice allows one to purchase (or lease) new fixtures and equipment that can be custom ordered to suit a particular style and image. Similarly, inventory can be selected by type and amount compatible not only with one's budget, but with the style of practice chosen. New staff can be hired and policies and procedures developed without concern for creating conflict with policies that were in place in an established operation. Finally, a lease can be negotiated that is in the best interest of the new enterprise.

The disadvantage of establishing a new practice is the amount of risk that the owner must assume. There is a sizable capital outlay and assumption of debt. Indeed, it may be difficult to raise sufficient capital if one is lacking in security or collateral, has little or no demonstrated business experience, or cannot identify an agreeable loan guarantor. For this reason, financial planning must begin some years in advance of attempting to enter into independent practice. In addition, the so-called best locations – in shopping centres or medical buildings – may simply not be available to pharmacists who lack superior credit ratings. Finally, among the major disadvantages of starting a new pharmacy is the time lag between the initial opening of the enterprise and the point at which it breaks even and then starts to become profitable. Depending on factors such as customer traffic, availability of prescriptions, and debt load, this period of time can vary greatly. For example, some pharmacy owner/managers expect it to last four or five years. If it takes longer than that to become profitable, the practice should be critically examined to discover what the problem(s) might be. Such questions can usually be answered by conducting a business feasibility study, including a location analysis and sales forecast,[7] when the issue of profitability becomes problematic.

Notwithstanding the disadvantages of independent ownership, many

---

[7] Location analysis is the subject of Chapter 3 and financial forecasting is discussed in Chapters 4, 5, and 12.

would argue that the opportunity, excitement, and rewards that come with it are well worth the effort.

SUMMARY

There are many alternatives from which graduate pharmacists can select a career. Once a decision is made, there are a number of choices available that involve an assumption of responsibility or capital risk.

Depending on one's ambition, expectations from practising pharmacy, and desired lifestyle, opportunities for employment or self-employment abound. As the pharmacist learns new skills and applies them on the job, new career paths will also open up. Supervisory positions lead to managerial positions and, if greater independence is desired, opportunities to operate a franchise or become a junior partner or outright owner/manager are certainly possible.

There is no easy formula for success. Skills learned formally or on the job, and enhanced by experience, are invaluable. If these are combined with hard work, a reasonable amount of capital, and common sense, pharmacists may be expected to continue to operate successful and rewarding practices.

RECOMMENDED READING

American Druggist Merchandising 168, no. 2 (15 July 1973):39.

Association of Canadian Franchisors, "Investigate Before Investing." Toronto: ACF [88 University Avenue, Suite 600, Toronto, Ontario M5J 1T8].

Federal Business Development Bank. *Minding Your Own Business*. Vol. 3. Toronto: FBDB, 1982.

Tindall, W. "Educating Future Entrepreneurs." *NARD Journal* (September 1985), pp. 48-51.

Check with your provincial ministry of trade and commerce or consumer and commercial relations, which is likely to offer publications in the area of small business ownership and franchising (for example, Ontario, Ministry of Industry, Trade and Technology, *Starting a Small Business in Ontario*, 1984; Ministry of Consumer and Commercial Relations, *Franchising Facts*).

2

FORMS
OF
BUSINESS ENTERPRISE

INTRODUCTION

In addition to being a profession, community-pharmacy practice is a business. Because this is a basic fact, it is important to recognize that businesses do not operate themselves – people operate them. What then is business and who are these people?

Business has been defined as "all profit-seeking activities and enterprises that provide goods and services necessary to an economic system."[1] The two key elements of this definition – profitability and the provision of goods and services necessary to an economy – are applicable to pharmacy practice.

First, profit is important because, unless a practice is financially viable, it is of no value to anyone. Profits provide the basis on which pharmaceutical services are delivered. Because pharmacists have historically made themselves available to answer questions and provide their clientele with services and suggestions regarding health care that might be unavailable elsewhere, pharmacy clients have come to expect it. However, these services rarely, if ever, generate income and as a result are supported out of the profits earned by the business.

In addition, profits reinvested into the business allow new equipment and fixtures to be purchased, inventory to be replenished, repairs made, and bonuses and raises paid. Profits also create new jobs. In short, if a

[1] A.H. Appelbaum, M.D. Beckman, L.E. Boone, and D.L. Kurtz, *Contemporary Canadian Business* (Toronto: Holt, Rinehart and Winston of Canada Limited, 1984), p.8.

pharmacy practice is not profitable, it falters and closes, thus depriving a segment of the population of pharmaceutical care.

Second, certain goods and services are unique to pharmacy. In the case of prescription medication and certain non-prescription products, this exclusivity is regulated by law. It is considered to be in the public interest to have these products distributed in a controlled manner by individuals with specialized education and training. Related or companion services, such as initiating and maintaining medication histories, patient counselling, and monitoring a patient's compliance, are becoming increasingly important pharmacy services.

The products and services provided by pharmacies are certainly necessary to our economic system. This system is based on free enterprise, which allows firms to operate in a competitive atmosphere that, in turn, allows for success or failure depending in part on factors of supply and demand. Community pharmacies participate in this system as part of the private sector, since they are owned and operated by individuals who contribute to the economy by creating jobs, providing steady employment, paying taxes, and distributing products and services that are essential to maintaining health among the country's citizens and for which there is invariably a strong demand. Total sales generated by community pharmacies in 1986 are estimated to have been approximately $7.465 billion.[2]

Businesses, including pharmacies, in a free enterprise system are usually originated by entrepreneurs. Essentially, an entrepreneur is a person prepared to take a risk upon identifying an opportunity to generate a profit. This usually involves organizing capital and personnel into one of three or four recognized forms of business enterprise: the sole proprietorship, the general or limited partnership, and the corporation.

SOLE PROPRIETORSHIP

A sole (or single) proprietorship is the original and simplest form of business ownership. Its advantages and disadvantages are set out in Table 2.1.

Legally, the business and its proprietor are one and the same. As the proprietorship is wholly owned by one individual, its assets, earnings, and debts are those of the proprietor. This is an easy form of business to initiate, usually requiring only the registration of the firm's name with provincial authorities (simply a mechanism to prevent two different firms from using the same name. There is an exception to this, in that registration is not required if the business uses the proprietor's name). In the case of a pharmacy, however, all permits and licences required under the

[2] In 1986, there were 5733 pharmacies in Canada, with average annual sales of $1302 million.

provincial Pharmacy Act have to be obtained before the firm can legally open. As each province has its own Pharmacy Act, it would be necessary to investigate the applicable regulations before opening the business. Also, a sole proprietorship can be discontinued simply by closing it up. In this form of organization, all decisions rest with the owner, who, consequently, is in absolute control. All the rewards of the enterprise accrue to the owner.

However, since the business is considered to be inseparable from its owner, that is, since the earnings of the business are viewed as the owner's personal income, on which he or she pays the tax, all business profits are taxed at the personal tax rate. If the income of the business is very small, this could be a tax advantage, in that a lower rate of taxation than the lowest corporate rate may apply. Also, any losses incurred by the business can be offset against personal income, whether it derives from the business or other sources. However, with greater earnings, a sole proprietorship is at a tax disadvantage, because it is not eligible for the small business tax rate that applies only to corporations.[3]

Table 2.1 ADVANTAGES AND DISADVANTAGES OF THE SOLE
PROPRIETORSHIP

Advantages	Disadvantages
Greatest freedom from regulation	Unlimited liability
Owner in direct control	Difficult to raise capital
Tax advantages if earnings are low	Tax disadvantages with growth in earnings
All profits belong to the owner	Difficult to retain key employees
	Lack of continuity

Source: Adapted from W.F. Shane, Starting a Small Business in Ontario (Toronto: Government of Ontario, Ministry of Industry, Trade and Technology, 1984), p.51.

A sole proprietorship has some further disadvantages. The most important is unlimited liability. This means that if the business incurs financial obligations that it cannot meet, the owner is required to pay them out of personal assets. This could involve having to sell personal property such as a home or cottage. Some sole proprietors protect themselves from such an eventuality by signing all their assets over to family members or close friends – in itself a potentially risky business.

The financial resources of a proprietorship are limited to the owner's personal wealth and, possibly, borrowed funds. As a result, initial capital for the enterprise may also be limited because financial institutions are

[3]Jack D. James, Starting a Successful Business in Canada. 9th ed. (Vancouver: International Self-Counsel Press Ltd., 1986), pp. 10-11, 14-15.

reluctant to loan large sums when there is little or no collateral beyond the owner's personal assets.

Furthermore, since expansion and growth in a sole proprietorship may be constrained by limited financing, it can be difficult to retain effective employees. There is seldom any opportunity for promotion, perhaps few fringe benefits, and often little job security. Consequently, good employees leave either to start their own businesses or take other jobs that offer more potential for growth. Finally, proprietorships have a limited life span, terminating upon the bankruptcy, retirement, or death of the proprietor.

PARTNERSHIPS

Partnerships take one of two forms: general partnership or limited partnership. Partnerships are essentially groupings of two or more people coming together to operate a business. The partners become co-owners through a voluntary legal agreement that usually defines the nature of the business. The major difference between a general and a limited partnership is that in a general partnership, each partner is individually liable for the business debts, while in a limited partnership, there are general partners and limited partners – the latter being liable only to the amount of capital that they invest. Limited partners must refrain from taking an active role in the management of the business; otherwise, they may be deemed to be general partners and, as such, must assume unlimited debt liability. Limited partnerships are required to register with the appropriate provincial government department. It is important, in general, to be aware of and check current provincial legislation as stipulated in each province's Partnerships Registration Act. In addition, some provincial Pharmacy Acts have provisions regarding partnerships of pharmacists with non-pharmacists in pharmacy practice, which must be thoroughly explored.

Partnerships are easy to organize, provide an opportunity to bring together diverse skills, and, by pooling partners' financial resources, gather more of the capital needed to initiate the enterprise. In addition, partnerships may have a better chance of securing financing than sole proprietorships, since lending institutions have recourse to the unlimited liability of each general partner as opposed to that of a single owner.

In order to prevent misunderstanding between or among partners, it is important to have a written and signed partnership agreement. This agreement, completed with the assistance of a lawyer, should identify the roles and responsibilities of each partner. This may provide some legal protection for general partners who would otherwise have to assume debt because of the unauthorized actions of another partner. Also, the name of the business should be registered with provincial authorities.

Although the unlimited liability of general partners affords the advantage of easier access to financing, it can also be one of the biggest disadvantages of a partnership. It can be the source of conflicts between partners, lack of continuity, and complexities in dissolving the business. The partnership ceases to exist when one partner is unwilling or unable to continue, which can occur through disagreement, illness, or death. In such cases, the equity of that partner is sold to another individual, and the partnership agreement must be renewed. This may not be as simple as it seems.

To preserve the successful make-up of the partnership, any new partner, in addition to having capital, must be acceptable to and compatible with the existing partner(s). Even if these criteria are satisfied, the original partnership agreement might specify that the existing partner(s) have the first option to buy the interest of the partner who is leaving the business. If this occurs, each remaining partner will have a greater equity in the firm. If nothing else, this situation should serve to illustrate the importance of a partnership agreement that clearly sets out such contingencies.

A summary of the advantages and disadvantages of a partnership appears in Table 2.2.

Table 2.2   ADVANTAGES AND DISADVANTAGES OF A PARTNERSHIP

Advantages	Disadvantages
Easily formed	Each general partner has
Management skills or interests	unlimited financial liability
of partners can be	Potential for personality conflicts
complementary	Lack of continuity in the business
Opportunity to raise a greater	Potential for complicated
amount of initial capital	dissolution

CORPORATIONS AND LIMITED COMPANIES

The corporation, as a legal entity, exists with the legal rights and privileges of an individual. Corporations are granted charters upon incorporation, either by federal or provincial legislation, that set out the regulations by which the corporation must operate.

Ownership of a corporation is represented by stock or shares in the firm. The shares can be held publicly or privately. Publicly held corporations have their shares traded (bought and sold) on the open market, for example, at stock exchanges in major financial centres. Privately held corporations, such as those established by families or other small groups of people, rarely trade their shares. When they do, it is usually within the confines of the original group of shareholders.

The major advantage of incorporation is limited liability. Shareholders are not financially liable for the business beyond the cost of the shares they have purchased. Corporations are sometimes called limited companies to indicate the limited liability of the shareholders. An incorporated pharmacy will usually identify itself as "XYZ Pharmacy Limited," "XYZ Ltd.," or "XYZ Pharmacy Company Ltd."

Corporations – large ones at least – can more easily obtain personnel with specialized managerial skills because the firm is perceived to offer stability and long-term careers. Similarly, employees can specialize in a particular area or function because of the large size of the firm. Corporate ownership can also generate more capital through increased investor participation; that is, it can raise money by selling more shares in its ownership. It does this successfully because ownership can be divided into small units (shares) and can attract many investors, each with a modest amount of money.

The stability and the financial strength of corporations allow them to borrow funds more easily and, often, obtain more favourable rates than are available to smaller firms, including sole proprietorships and partnerships. It must be remembered, however, that not all corporations are large and that small businesses can also be organized in this way.

There are disadvantages to the corporate form of enterprise that should be noted. Incorporation is the most expensive form of ownership to establish and involves the greatest number of legal restrictions. Because each province has slightly different laws of incorporation, it is wise to use the services of a lawyer in order to avoid pitfalls unseen by the layman. Keep in mind, however, that legal fees and incorporation costs levied by the provinces add to the total cost of establishing this type of business entity. It should also be pointed out that, in the province of Quebec, pharmacies must be operated as sole proprietorships.

As legal entities, corporations are subject to taxation on profits earned. Canadian-controlled private corporations are eligible for a special small business tax rate, ranging from 16 to 23 percent depending on the province, that applies to income under $200,000 per year; above that amount, the firm will be taxed at the full corporate rate of approximately 46 percent.[4] Taxation is different for sole proprietorships and partnerships because the income or earnings of these businesses are treated as personal income and taxed accordingly. Within the corporate structure, certain methods of tax deferment and tax savings are available that do not apply in other forms of enterprise (these are discussed in greater detail in Chapter 27). Also, since corporate tax rates on retained earnings (profits reinvested in the corporation) above certain amounts are lower than personal

[4] The income-tax rates cited here are applicable at the time of writing and include surtaxes (temporary taxes that are periodically imposed by the provincial and federal governments). Also, note that the basic tax rates can change with each federal budget.

tax rates for similar income levels, many small businesses choose this form of organization.

Other disadvantages of incorporation centre around its legal requirements. For example, the corporate charter may restrict the corporation to certain types of activity. In addition, various reports about business operations must be filed with specific government departments.

Table 2.3 summarizes the advantages and disadvantages of the corporation as a form of business enterprise.

Table 2.3   ADVANTAGES AND DISADVANTAGES OF A CORPORATION

Advantages	Disadvantages
Limited liability	Closely regulated by government
Greater opportunity for specialized management functions	Expensive to organize
	Activity restricted as per charter
Ownership easily transferred	Required record keeping can be extensive
Existence is continuous	
Legal entity	
Easier to raise capital	
Possible tax advantages	

COLLECTIVE OWNERSHIP

No discussion of forms of enterprise would be complete without mentioning the concept of collective ownership. This form of business is popularly known as a co-operative or simply a co-op. It is a banding together of interested parties to buy or sell products or services. In western Canada, for example, wheat and dairy farmers form co-ops to market their produce more effectively. In Ontario, the largest drug wholesaler, Drug Trading Company Limited, is a co-op supported by its member pharmacists, who share in the firm's profits in proportion to their individual purchases from the wholesaler. In consumer co-operatives, members buy a share in the co-op and receive a rebate based on their purchases. Some large co-ops may operate pharmacies for the benefit of their members. Today, co-ops can be big businesses and must face the same constraints as the businesses with which they compete.

SUMMARY

Determining the legal form of one's business is a critical decision. The prospective pharmacist-owner must consider the advantages and disadvantages among the major forms of private business – the sole proprietorship, partnership, and corporation – in the light of his or her own business and professional objectives. Not to be taken lightly are the issue of liability and the relative potential for continuity and longevity of the business.

RECOMMENDED READING

Applebaum, A.H.; Beckman, M.D.; Boone, L.E.; and Kurtz, D.L. *Contemporary Canadian Business*. Toronto: Holt, Rinehart and Winston of Canada Limited, 1984.

Eckert, Lee A.; Ryan, J.D.; Ray, Robert J.; and Bracey, Robert J. *Canadian Small Business: An Entrepreneur's Plan*. Toronto: Harcourt Brace Jovanovich, Canada, 1987.

James, Jack D. *Starting a Successful Business in Canada*. 9th ed. Vancouver: International Self-Counsel Press Ltd., 1986.

3

LOCATION ANALYSIS

INTRODUCTION

As many retailing experts will tell you, the key to a successful business is location. Community pharmacies are unique among retail enterprises because of their peculiar mix of commercial and professional products, and their varied sizes, layout formats, and approaches to merchandising. The choice of location for a community pharmacy will depend on the nature of its objectives: a professional-oriented pharmacy is more likely to locate in a residential neighbourhood and attract a clientele interested in receiving professional services as well as pharmaceutical products, whereas a merchandise-oriented pharmacy might locate in a major thoroughfare to attract clientele looking for a wider variety of products. Therefore, rather than having a fixed formula for selecting a location, it is more useful to explore certain methods and techniques for evaluating alternative locations. In this way, new sites can be assessed and existing ones re-evaluated.

Each time a lease is renewed, a pharmacy owner "locates his practice," and each time a pharmacist who owns the building in which his practice is established turns the key in the lock, he too "locates" his practice. This may seem oversimplified, but the point is that a subconscious decision is being made because of an unwillingness to move. The astute businessperson analyzes location periodically, taking the same care that was applied in locating the pharmacy the first time. The need for relocation may arise because additional space is required, the existing location is no longer adequate, rent has increased to an unreasonable rate relative to sales, a lease cannot be renewed, or the building is destroyed by fire or otherwise damaged.

Location analysis has been described as a hierarchy of decisions focussing on a region, a market area, a trading area, and, finally, a site.[1] This method can be applied to locating a community pharmacy in Canada.

REGION

Regional analysis simply divides the country into regions that represent broad geographic areas. For example, Canada can be divided into the regions of British Columbia, the Prairies, Ontario, Quebec, and Atlantic Canada. These regions are distinct in their economies, attitudes, and consumption behaviour. Although they share many characteristics with their colleagues across Canada, pharmacists will usually locate their practices in the region where they received their pharmacy education and practical training, as they will hold a licence in a particular province within that region.

MARKET AREA

The basic information about a market area that is of interest to both retail business and professional practice is its population. Population data are readily obtainable from the Canadian Census. The Decennial Census, originated in 1851, is conducted every ten years (most recently in 1981) to enable a redistribution of seats in the House of Commons. In 1956, the Quincennial Census – occurring every five years between Decennial Censuses – was introduced to track statistical information on demographic and socio-economic developments. The most recent was completed in 1986 and is so detailed that population characteristics are available by city block for large cities. These data are often accumulated into census tracts that describe a small section of the city, typically with a population of approximately 4000.[2]

Two terms that are used in the censuses require explanation: Census Agglomeration (CA) and Census Metropolitan Area (CMA). A CA is a large urbanized core with adjacent urban and rural areas that have a high

---

[1] W.R. Davidson, S.J. Sweeney, and R.W. Stampfl, *Retailing Management*, 6th ed. (Toronto: John Wiley and Sons, 1988), p. 235.

[2] For a full description of a census tract, see the *Dictionary of the 1986 Census*, Catalogue 99-101. Population data by census tract includes income, occupation, education, housing, family structure, mobility, and so on. Census data published by Statistics Canada are available at many local libraries and at Statistics Canada's User Advisory Centres in major cities across Canada.

Table 3.1 THE TOP TEN CMA'S IN CANADA, 1986

CMA	Population (thousands)
Toronto	3427.2
Montreal	2921.4
Vancouver	1380.7
Ottawa-Hull	819.3
Edmonton	785.5
Calgary	671.3
Winnipeg	625.3
Quebec	603.3
Hamilton	557.0
St. Catharines-Niagara	343.3

Source: Canada Year Book 1988 (Ottawa: Statistics Canada 11-402 E/1987), pp. 2-4.

degree of economic and social integration with that core. Essentially, a CA is the main labour market of an urban area of at least 10,000 population. When a CA reaches a population of 100,000 it becomes a CMA, which in turn refers to the main labour market area of an urban area of at least 100,000 people. Table 3.1 lists the top ten of Canada's 25 CMA's as of 1986. These data can be used to describe a central city and its surrounding area by population density.

In addition to CMA's, the census recognizes a smaller category – the municipality – that is also based on population. There are 144 municipalities in Canada with populations over 25,000. Of these 144, 68 experienced rates of growth higher than the national average – a good indicator of location potential for any small business, including a pharmacy.

Table 3.2 lists some categories of information that are useful to consider when analyzing the location potential of a geographic area or unit such as a municipality. Such data should be available from local Chambers of Commerce, census tables, banks, and local governments. In addition, much can be gleaned from close observation of the area and its surroundings.

It is important to research the general population parameters of an area, such as size, growth, and density, which characterize a unit base. Such factors can determine the density of consumer traffic in an area and are therefore critical to the success of a pharmacy. Within these parameters, target markets of pediatric or geriatric populations, which represent the potential for specialized services and products, can be identified. Transportation networks are also important to consider. For example, the cost and scheduling of public transit may affect the ability of potential clients to get to the market area under consideration. Economic characteristics of the area – its diversity of industry or its dependence on only one type or source of employment – must also be examined closely.

ble 3.2   GEOGRAPHIC DATA TO CONSIDER IN LOCATION
ANALYSIS

Data Categories

General population parameters
Target-market parameters
Transportation networks
Economic characteristics
Purchasing power
Potential sales of specialized products
Degree of competition
Compatibility of nearby businesses
Environment uniqueness
Area rental costs
Retail improvement trends (permits issued for remodelling, expansion,
etc.)

Source: Adapted from W.R. Davidson, D.J. Sweeney, and R.W. Stampfl, *Retailing
Management,* 6th ed. © 1988 John Wiley and Sons, p. 240.

Related to this concept, and equally important, is information on the
disposable income and spending patterns of the population.

It should be obvious that if a particular geographic location is attractive to one pharmacist, it may also appeal to another. In other words,
consider the degree and intensity of competition in the area now, as well
as what it might be in the future. The uniqueness of the surrounding
area, in terms of its health-care facilities or extended- care facilities (such
as nursing homes) and the presence of retirement communities or new
subdivisions, is an important aspect to explore. Finally, the occupancy
cost or rent that will be demanded in the area must be considered in light
of the pharmacy's expected sales levels.

It should of course be mentioned that zoning by-laws must be investigated to determine if they are restrictive or compatible. A real estate
agent specializing in retail business properties can clarify local by-law
regulations and, in addition, assist in the rental of the premises.

No single category of information should sway a decision; rather,
the balance of all the indicators must be carefully considered. Furthermore, available information that pertains more specifically to pharmacies
should be explored. An example of such information is the nature of
consumer spending on health services and products. Table 3.3 shows
selected annual per capita expenditures, by province, for "drugs and
appliances."With this kind of information, the pharmacist will be better
equipped to identify the optimal geographic area (in this case, at least
the optimal province) in which to locate.

Table 3.3 SELECTED PER CAPITA HEALTH EXPENDITURE BY
PROVINCE, 1985†

	All Drugs and Appliances	Prescribed Drugs	Non-Prescribed Drugs	Eye-glasses	Hearing Aids	Other
Newfoundland	$174.47	$ 95.12	$61.14	$15.55	$1.04	$1.62
Prince Edward Island	216.53	108.64	79.25	23.82	2.88	1.95
Nova Scotia	235.34	128.60	77.11	20.70	5.19	3.74
New Brunswick	187.01	107.49	53.32	20.72	1.86	3.62
Quebec	161.97	57.44	72.43	23.13	2.14	6.82
Ontario	216.18	102.76	78.33	28.29	2.62	4.18
Manitoba	195.16	69.59	87.15	27.67	2.81	7.94
Saskatchewan	192.32	70.29	86.98	24.66	4.19	6.19
Alberta	182.72	78.02	62.78	23.14	2.92	15.86
British Columbia	202.76	94.36	68.35	31.73	3.77	4.55

†Provisional Data

Source: National Health Expenditures in Canada 1975-1985, (Ottawa: Health and Welfare
Canada, November 1987), pp. 40-104.

While national or regional pharmacy chains are able to maintain a
listing of specific potential market areas ranked in order of location priority, individual pharmacists do not have the resources for such detailed
analysis. Nonetheless, individual pharmacists can avail themselves of
similar procedures in selecting specific pharmacy locations within the
general geographic market areas they have chosen.

Selecting a precise location within a chosen market area necessitates
narrowing down the geographic area further, according to the scope of
commercial services provided either in unplanned business districts or in
areas planned for shopping and personal services. The choice between
an unplanned and planned area will partly be determined by the nature
and objectives of the pharmacy.

Unplanned Business Districts

Unplanned business districts come into existence through the "unco-
ordinated site decisions of individual merchants,"[3] and include:
1. Central business districts that contain a high concentration of retail
   businesses, offices, and services and have a high traffic flow.

[3] W.R. Davidson, D.J. Sweeney, and R.W. Stampfl, *Retailing Management*, 6th ed. (Toronto:
John Wiley and Sons, 1988), p. 242.

2. Secondary business districts and strong street districts where the former may service portions of the central city core or suburbs and the latter are located on arterial routes into and out of the central core.
3. Neighbourhood stores found in clusters and characterized by convenience stores and service outlets for a particular residential area. Neighbourhood pharmacies are found here, along with other independent retailers.

Shopping Areas

Planned shopping areas or shopping centres evolved as cities grew and became surrounded by suburban housing developments. Shopping centres are differentiated primarily by size, location, and the class of merchandise sold. They can be small, with a few stores situated along one side of a street in what is called a strip layout. This type of centre is oriented toward the sale of convenience goods, such as foods, sundries, and drugs and of personal services, such as laundry, dry cleaning, and barber shops. Larger strip centres may have an anchor store – a major tenant, usually a supermarket, to attract traffic to the centre.

Community shopping centres are the next step up in size. In addition to convenience stores, these centres usually contain a small department store and sporting goods, jewellery, and discount stores. They usually service a fairly well-defined neighbourhood or housing development and are located at intersections of major arterial roads.

Regional and super-regional shopping centres are the largest in size. They are found at intersections of, or along, major expressways. There are several large full-line department stores that serve as anchors and the other stores sell a wide variety of convenience, shopping, and specialty goods.

The last two categories of shopping centres are often referred to as malls or plazas.

TRADING AREA

Once location decisions are made regarding regional and market areas, it is necessary to select a particular trading area. This involves identifying sub-areas within market areas that contain target-market populations. At this stage of location analysis, it is necessary to consider the type of retail operation that is desired – a destination store or an intercept store. Destination stores generate most of their own traffic; that is, customers consciously choose the store as their destination, whether as a result of promotional efforts, breadth of merchandise, services offered, or store personality. Any one of these factors or some combination of them can create a destination store. Outlets such as supermarkets, discount stores, national department stores, and pharmacies can belong to this category.

Intercept stores are generally located between the people in the trading area and their traditional source of goods or services. The principle of business interception simply involves intercepting customers or pulling them off the beaten path. Pharmacies, for example, could be located between residential areas and medical clinics or physicians' offices. The principle of interception would be at work when patients stopped in on their way home to fill the prescription they received at the physician's office.

Locations within a trading area can benefit by sharing the customer traffic of retail outlets that are already well established there. Banks, beer and wine stores, and food stores may attract people to an area, but, once there, those consumers will also patronize other businesses.

Another principle to consider in location analysis is that of suscipient business, which holds that a store need not generate its own traffic nor depend on neighbouring stores for its customers; rather, its location in a place where people circulate for reasons other than shopping brings in its business.[4] An example is the busy newsstand located in a hotel, a train or bus station, or an airport. Pharmacies, too, may be found in locations such as the underground shopping complexes of large office buildings. They serve the working population of these specific sites and do not rely on attracting people directly from their homes or on their way from a physician's office.

In fact, pharmacies operate and derive satisfactory sales volume in all locations and situations described here. A pharmacist analyzing a location must take them all into account.

SITE CONSIDERATION

Among the actual sites that should be considered for the pharmacy are shopping complexes, free-standing buildings, and empty land on which to build. An important consideration in site selection is the relationship of cost to productivity.

The physical characteristics of the space in a building under consideration should be scrutinized. The shape of the space, its width and depth, the absence of supporting pillars, exposed pipes, and duct work, and its general appearance are all factors determining the effectiveness of the space for sales purposes and the cost that will be involved to furnish it. Windows at the front of the building that would offer passersby a view of the interior are an important feature as well. The position of entry and exit doors and whether they are located above, at, or below ground

[4] As discussed in R.L. Nelson, "Principles of Retail Location," in R.D. Gist, ed., *Management Perspectives in Retailing* (New York: John Wiley and Sons Inc., 1967), p.226.

level will also serve to attract or discourage people from entering the pharmacy.

Parking is a key concern: is the site relatively accessible from the parking lot and is the lot itself convenient for passing traffic? Although the traffic that passes by a site en route to and from work is a less valuable site asset than shopping traffic, it is still important to remember that people are more likely to stop on their way home than on their way to work. Hence, one-way streets should be assessed carefully. The prospective owner should conduct counts of both pedestrian and automobile traffic at each site under consideration.

Principles of proximity must not be ignored. Proximity to anchor stores in malls and plazas is important with regard to pedestrian traffic. The distance from medical clinics, outpatient departments of hospitals, and physicians' offices will have a direct bearing on prescription sales as well. (If we can assume that general practitioners write approximately 20-25 prescriptions per day, then a rough calculation based on the number of physicians' offices and the number of competing pharmacies in the area can help to estimate the percentage of the prescriptions that may be expected at a given location.) Nearness to bus, streetcar, and subway stops will also add to ambulatory traffic and hence to the number of potential customers.

Obstacles to pedestrian traffic can make a site less desirable. Accessibility to a site could be jeopardized by busy driveways or wide or congested streets that have to be crossed; by sidewalks that end abruptly; by excessive noise, odour, or unsightliness in the vicinity of the site; and by natural barriers such as ravines or rivers that would cause people to have to take lengthy detours.

TECHNIQUES TO ASSESS SITE LOCATIONS

Techniques used to assess site locations range from quite basic rules of thumb to sophisticated mathematical formulations. The retail industry is rife with rules of thumb that have evolved from observed relationships between store performance and certain specific criteria. They are useful as general guidelines and as aids to decision making.

The use of ratios as rules of thumb is fairly common. One such ratio is sales per square foot. In Canadian pharmacies in 1986, the average sales per square foot were $503, with the front shop generating $327 per square foot and the prescription department, $1711.[5] Other ratios include the number of prescriptions per patient and the average price per prescription. Such data help to estimate prescription sales.

[5] "Annual Survey of Community Pharmacy Operations," Canadian Pharmaceutical Association, 1988, Table 3, p.7.

Another rule of thumb deals with convenience and distance. It suggests that the average consumer's travel time to a retail destination is ten minutes or less. Therefore, to estimate the trading area of a particular site, simply drive in several directions from the proposed site for ten minutes and mark the boundaries on a map. Once this is done, census tract data can be used to estimate the population of the trading area and, with this information in hand, a rough estimate of the potential prescription sales at the site can be made with the aid of such statistics as given in Table 3.3. Say, for example, the proposed site is located in Nova Scotia. From Table 3.3, we see that per capita expenditures on prescription drugs in Nova Scotia in 1985 were $128.60. Let us say that the prospective owner has determined the population of the trading area to be approximately 7500. The potential prescription sales for all pharmacies in the trading area would therefore be approximately $128.60 × 7500 = $964,500. Let us say further that three pharmacies (including the one at the site under consideration) are located in or near the trading area. The potential prescription sales at any one of the pharmacies would therefore be roughly $964,500 ÷ 3 = $321,500. Adjustments should be made to the estimate to reflect (1) other unique features of the trading area, such as level of income and average age of the population (for example, a trading area with a high percentage of senior citizens would have higher per capita prescription sales than the provincial average) and (2) apparent advantages or disadvantages of the proposed site (for example, proximity to a medical clinic) and of the planned pharmacy (for example, in pricing, shopping convenience, and range of services to be offered). Similar calculations can be made for potential non-prescription product sales as listed in Table 3.3 as well. As a further check, such estimates can be compared to published industry averages, as you will see in Chapter 4.

Surveys are sometimes used in assessing site locations to determine the types of products purchased by the respondents in the area, the frequency of pharmacy patronage or visits to a physician, and the distance normally travelled to retail outlets. Such information is then used to evaluate the potential of the trading area.

One of the early mathematical models used to analyze site location was developed in 1929 by William J. Reilly. His approach has since been referred to as a gravitational model because it attempts to explain the patterns in which potential consumers gravitate toward an identified site. Reilly's work formalized empirical observations about consumer shopping movements between cities. The basic principle of his model is that a retail centre's attraction for a consumer is directly related to the size of the retail centre and inversely related to the consumer's distance from the centre. In other words, a larger centre suggests a greater assortment of products and therefore holds more attraction for the consumer. Distance, however, represents a cost in time and/or money; thus the farther the shopping centre is from the consumer, the less attraction it holds.[6]

In the early 1940s the theory was further refined by Paul D. Converse, who made it possible to calculate the approximate distance between two competing cities that held equal attraction for consumer shopping. Finally, in the 1960s, David Huff reformulated the model in probabilistic terms because the original model, designed to identify the market areas of competing cities, was unable to develop accurate estimates for individual store sites. Huff's model, however, has also been criticized as inaccurate, in that "individual store size per se has not been found to have great influence or drawing power."[7] Size, then, is a more important factor with regard to shopping centres.

PHARMACY RELOCATION

Relocating a pharmacy practice is just as important as locating it initially. Reasons to relocate can be as simple as a lack of sales growth; exhausting the renewable options on a lease; outgrowing the space; being displaced by fire or physical damage to the premises; or a changing trading or market area that makes the present location less than ideal.

A voluntary decision to relocate should be based on an analysis of the practice. If a different site within the area is being considered, it should be compared carefully to the present site. Information from the practice can be used to aid in the comparison. For example, an analysis of prescription files will identify the location of major prescribers and patients, and personal charge accounts, if kept, will identify the location of non-prescription clients. If charge or credit card courtesies have not been extended, a free draw that requires customers' names and addresses can be used to determine where they live. If it is found that the proposed site is closer to the majority of patients and physicians, the decision to relocate will clearly become easier.

Regardless of the method used to determine the ongoing advantages of the trading area and the present site, there are several factors that should be considered: Has the population for prescriptions shifted relative to the current site? Have the physicians moved from the area? Has the surrounding neighbourhood deteriorated? Has a major industry shut down or moved away? If a major change is identified, the merits of a potential new trading area must be carefully examined, and the owner must make the decision whether or not to relocate. In addition, the activity of competing pharmacies must be taken into consideration: for example, is there

---

[6] For the mathematical formula of Reilly's model, see H.A. Smith, *Principles and Methods of Pharmacy Management*, 3rd ed. (Philadelphia: Lea & Febiger, 1986), p.113.

[7] As cited in David L. Huff, "Defining and Estimating a Trading Area," in R.D. Gist, ed., *Management Perspectives in Retailing* (New York: John Wiley and Sons Inc., 1967), p.195.

Figure 3.1 LOCATION ANALYSIS WORKSHEET

1. Define trading area of the proposed site by:
   a. driving ten minutes in each direction from the site _____
   b. marking boundaries on a map _____
   c. listing census tracts within the identified boundaries _____

2. Population estimate:

Census tract and population		Percentage of tract in trading area		Estimated trading area population
a. _____	×	_____	=	_____
b. _____	×	_____	=	_____
c. _____	×	_____	=	_____
			Total	_____

3. Estimated pharmaceutical and related expenditures in trading area:
   Trading area population × Per capita expenditures
   = Estimate of purchases†

prescribed medication	_____
non-prescribed medication	_____
other pharmacy-related merchandise	_____
Total	$_____

4. Estimated market share:

Estimate of total purchases in trading area		Number of pharmacies in trading area		Potential purchases at proposed site store
$ _____	÷	_____	=	$ _____

Adjust the resulting estimate upward or downward to reflect the peculiarities of the trading area and of the proposed site (see pp. 24-5).

† For example, see Health and Welfare Canada, *National Health Expenditures in Canada 1975-1985*, 85 November 1987, Table 6: "Total Health Expenditures by Category, Canada, 1975-1985," p. 32.

Source: Adapted from V. Cardinale, "Are You Living Up to Your Full Market Potential?" *Drug Topics* (6 January 1986), p.28.

a risk that another pharmacy might open on the site or in the area under consideration, with the effect of diminishing your existing clientele? Good judgment, based on as much information as can be collected and tempered by reasonable advice from one's advisers, should lead to the correct decision.

The worksheet in Figure 3.1 and the Location Analysis Checklist on

LOCATION ANALYSIS CHECKLIST

1. Demographic variables (percentage estimates):
   predominant age groups: specific needs:
   pediatric _____   language _____
   geriatric _____   products _____
   young families _____
   Ethnicity (specify)

   _____

2. Economic variables:
   per capita income   _____
   average family income   _____
   predominant industry   _____
   agricultural: _____ one crop   _____ diversified
   industrial base: _____ one industry   _____ diversified

3. Institutions (commercial, professional):
   number and types _____
   supportive or competitive _____
   schools _____
   hospitals, clinics, extended-care facilities _____
   proximity to proposed site _____

4. Parking:
   street   _____
   lots   _____
   width of curb cuts   _____
   proximity to proposed site   _____

5. Traffic:
   ambulatory   _____
   vehicles   _____
   public transportation   _____
   location of stops and stations _____
   transfer points   _____
   shelters   _____
   one-way streets   _____
   congested streets   _____
   crosswalks   _____

6. Other observations or comments:

   _____
   _____
   _____

Source: Adapted from V. Cardinale, "Are You Living Up to Your Full Market Potential?" *Drug Topics* (6 January 1986), p.28.

p. 30 might be useful in summarizing the attributes of various locations. Although simple in approach, these forms do allow for a ready comparison of sites. And, as one gains experience in this type of analysis, such aids can be revised and refined to suit specific needs.

Summary

One of the most important determinants of the success of a business is its location. There are many factors to consider in selecting the best location for a particular business or professional practice.

All methods of location analysis take into consideration such variables as population, disposable income, the distance customers must travel to reach the site, and traffic patterns. It is important to remember that periodic analyses of an existing site should be conducted and compared to alternative locations. Periodic location analysis will help to keep the business attuned to the movements and needs of its clientele and may prevent competitors from gaining a foothold in the trading area.

Recommended Reading

Canada. Department of Health and Welfare. *National Health Expenditures in Canada 1975-1985*. Ottawa: Health and Welfare Canada, November 1987.

Canada. Statistics Canada. *Canada Year Book 1988*. Ottawa, 1987.

Cardinale, V. "Are You Living Up to Your Full Market Potential?" *Drug Topics* (6 January 1986), p. 28.

Davidson, W.R.; Sweeney, D.J.; and Stampfl, R.W. *Retailing Management*. 6th ed. Toronto: John Wiley and Sons, 1988.

Gist, R.D., ed. *Management Perspectives in Retailing*. New York: John Wiley and Sons Inc., 1967.

Smith, H.A. *Principles and Methods of Pharmacy Management*. 3rd ed. Philadelphia: Lea & Febiger, 1986

4

STARTING OUT:
FINANCIAL CONSIDERATIONS

INTRODUCTION

To have any measure of financial control over their businesses, pharmacy owners and managers must be familiar with various types of financial statements. As a foundation to this knowledge, an understanding of the basics of accounting, in the form of the income statement and balance sheet, is critical. Only from here can one progress to reading such statements and analyzing and interpreting them. In fact, it is necessary to gain some familiarity with financial statements at the very outset, since they are integral to the financial planning process.

Financial statements, then, can be used as analytical tools to understand the operation of a business, to detect and correct financial problem areas, and to plan growth and expansion. They are also essential in estimating the start-up costs involved in establishing a new pharmacy or estimating the value of an established pharmacy that is under consideration for purchase.

It is important to take into consideration the limitations of the data when reading financial statements. Any limitations in the form, reliability, age, or completeness of the financial information must temper the outcome of its use. The use of past-performance data as a guide to future expectations must also be approached cautiously.

Figure 4.1
INCOME STATEMENT
AVERAGE CANADIAN PHARMACY LIMITED
DECEMBER 31, 1986

	1985†		1986‡	
	(dollars)	(percent of total sales)	(dollars)	(percent of total sales)
Sales				
Prescription sales	$ 480,813	40.2%	$ 562,805	43.2%
OTC sales	227,090	19.0%	212,608	16.3%
Cosmetic sales	59,129	5.0%	57,572	4.4%
Other sales	427,621	35.8%	469,205	36.0%
Total Sales	$1,194,650	100.0%	$1,302,190	100.0%
Cost of Goods Sold	$ 833,204	69.7%	$ 915,139	70.3%
Gross Margin	$ 361,459	30.3%	$ 387,051	29.7%
Expenses				
Owner/manager salary	$ 48,424	4.0%	$ 46,197	3.5%
Employee wages	125,894	10.5%	141,327	10.9%
Rent	28,694	2.4%	30,150	2.3%
Heat, light, power	5,501	0.5%	5,725	0.4%
Acct., legal, prof. fees	5,967	0.5%	5,516	0.4%
Taxes and licences	4,323	0.4%	5,505	0.4%
Insurance	3,308	0.3%	3,544	0.3%
Interest paid	7,722	0.6%	7,805	0.6%
Repairs	4,430	0.4%	5,041	0.4%
Delivery	4,212	0.4%	4.951	0.4%
Advertising	15,513	1.3%	15,303	1.2%
Depreciation for fixtures	9,238	0.8%	9,947	0.8%
Bad debts	840	0.07%	602	0.0%
Telephone	2,820	0.2%	3,109	0.2%
Miscellaneous	34,204	2.9%	39,749	3.1%
Total Expenses	$ 301,090	25.2%	$ 324,471	24.9%
Profit (or net income) before tax	$ 60,359	5.1%	$ 62,580	4.8%
Other Income	$ 8,624	0.7%	10,377	0.8%
Total Income (before tax)	$ 68,983	5.8%	$ 72,957	5.6%

† Averages of 342 pharamcies surveyed
‡ Averages of 313 pharmacies surveyed

Source Figure 4.1, 4.2: Seventh Annual Survey of Community Pharmacy Operations, Canadian Pharmaceutical Association.

INCOME STATEMENT AND BALANCE SHEET

Financial statements provide a picture of the financial status of a business. Basically, they comprise an income statement (profit and loss statement) and a balance sheet.

The financial statement reflects the pharmacy's income, expenses, profit, assets, and liabilities over a period of time – usually a fiscal year of twelve months. (There are also several types of monthly financial statements, which are discussed in Chapter 12.) The progress of a business can be analyzed by comparing data in current-year financial statements with those in previous years' statements, as well as with published industry averages. Financial ratios, which will be discussed in Chapter 18, can also be calculated from financial-statement data and are similarly compared with previous ratios of the business and with past industry averages to gauge progress.

The basic formats of an income statement and balance sheet are shown in Figures 4.1 and 4.2. The data represented are the averages of 313 pharmacies reporting to the Seventh Annual Survey of Community Pharmacy Operations, for fiscal year 1986. Both dollar figures and percentages (based on total sales in the income statement and on total assets in the balance sheet) are reported. Data from a previous fiscal year – the 1985 averages of 342 pharmacies – are also given.

The income statement in Figure 4.1 shows sales by selected product categories. The cost of goods sold is usually calculated by adding the value of the beginning inventory to the cost of the pharmacy's purchases through the course of the year, then subtracting the ending inventory value. Hypothetical data are used for purchases in the following example (in practice, purchase data would normally come from suppliers' invoices):

Beginning Inventory	$ 194,262
plus Purchases	926,610
Total Value of Goods Available for Sale	1,120,872
minus Ending Inventory	205,733
Cost of Goods Sold	$ 915,139

The difference between sales and the cost of goods sold is the gross margin (sometimes referred to as gross profit). Gross margin can also be expressed as the sum of expenses and profit. The point to note is that the gross margin must be sufficient to cover expenses and leave an amount for profit.

Expenses are normally listed as illustrated in Figure 4.1. It is interesting to recalculate the expense percentages using total expenses as a base, as shown in Table 4.1. This serves to demonstrate the significance of several of the expense categories, specifically, salaries, rent, and "mis-

Figure 4.2
BALANCE SHEET
AVERAGE CANADIAN PHARMACY LIMITED
DECEMBER 31, 1986

	1985†		1986‡	
	(dollars)	(percent of total assets)	(dollars)	(percent of total assets)
Current Assets				
Cash	$ 34,884	9.8%	$ 57,525	14.0%
Accounts receivable	42,124	11.9%	49,884	12.1%
Inventory	194,262	54.6%	205,733	50.0%
Prepaid expenses	8,861	2.5%	9,918	2.4%
Total Current Assets	$280,131	78.8%	$323,060	78.6%
Fixtures and equipment	$ 75,504	21.2%	$ 88,129	21.4%
Total Assets	$355,635	100.0%	$411,189	100.0%
Current Liabilities				
Accounts payable	$ 93,540	26.3%	$106,518	25.9%
Notes payable < 1 yr.	28,123	7.9%	36,179	8.8%
Accrued expenses	22,470	6.3%	18,032	4.4%
Total Current Liabilities	$144,133	40.5%	$160,729	39.1%
Notes payable > 1 yr.	47,633	13.4%	55,129	13.4%
Total Liabilities	$191,766	53.9%	$215,858	52.5%
Owner's Equity *(Net Worth)*	163,869	46.1%	195,331	47.5%
Total Liabilities *& Net Worth*	$355,635	100.0%	$411,189	100.0%

† Averages of 342 pharmacies surveyed
‡ Averages of 313 pharmacies surveyed

cellaneous," and the need to monitor them carefully, as they account for 79.3 percent of total expenses.

Of the expenses listed, perhaps the least familiar to those who are inexperienced in accounting procedures is depreciation. Because fixed assets (including fixtures, equipment, and buildings) deteriorate or become obsolete over time, the owners of those assets may deduct a certain percentage of their original cost from annual income for a period of time, from acquisition of the asset to the time of its disposal or replacement.

Table 4.1   EXPENSES CALCULATED AS A PERCENTAGE OF TOTAL
EXPENSES

Expense Item	Percent of Sales	Percent of Total Expenses
Owner/manager salary	3.5	14.2
Employee wages	10.9	43.5
Rent	2.3	9.3
Heat, light, power	0.4	1.8
Acct., legal, professional fees	0.4	1.7
Taxes and licences	0.4	1.7
Insurance	0.3	1.1
Interest paid	0.6	2.4
Repairs	0.4	1.5
Delivery	0.4	1.5
Advertising	1.2	4.7
Depreciation for fixtures	0.8	3.1
Bad debts	0.0	0.2
Telephone	0.2	1.0
Miscellaneous	3.1	12.3
	24.9	100.0

Such deductions are represented as an expense on the income statement, and the declining value of the assets will be reflected accordingly in the annual balance sheets. As you will see in Chapter 5, it is important to remember that depreciation is a *non-cash* expense. Several methods of computing depreciation over the life of an asset exist; the pharmacy's accountant should determine the optimal method to be applied.

"Other income," may be the income from investments held by the business (interest or dividends), sales generated from lottery sales or a post office, or gains from the realization of extraordinary items, such as profits realized on the sale of fixed assets.

An expanded view of an income statement appears in Figure 4.3 and illustrates the four variables that affect profit: unit price, unit volume (i.e., number of units sold), unit cost, and expenses. By manipulating one or more of these variables, profit performance can be affected. In addition, it is important to note that unit price, unit volume, and unit cost affect gross margin, thus providing three opportunities to improve profit, whereas expense control provides only one.

The balance sheet indicates the financial position of a firm as of the date that appears on it (see Figure 4.2). Balance sheets, like income statements, are prepared periodically – at least annually – and contain comparative figures from the previous accounting period.

The balance sheet represents the basic accounting equation:

assets = liabilities + owner's equity.

Assets are those items that are owned by the business – in other words, all of the business's resources; *liabilities* (also called creditors' equity) are the debts of the business; and *owner's equity* is the personal capital contributed by the owners, together with accumulated earnings retained in the business, commonly known as retained earnings. All assets are, in other words, attributed to claims of creditors or owners; conversely, the claims of creditors and owners must be balanced by total assets. Assets can be current, meaning that they can be converted into cash within a twelve-month period, or non-current (fixed), meaning that they can be converted to cash but over a longer period of time. Included among non-current or fixed assets are fixtures, delivery vehicles, and buildings. The largest asset in a pharmacy practice is usually its inventory, which represents over one-half of total assets.

Liabilities are also categorized as current or long term, with similar constraints of payment: current liabilities will be paid within a year and

Figure 4.3
EXPANDED INCOME STATEMENT

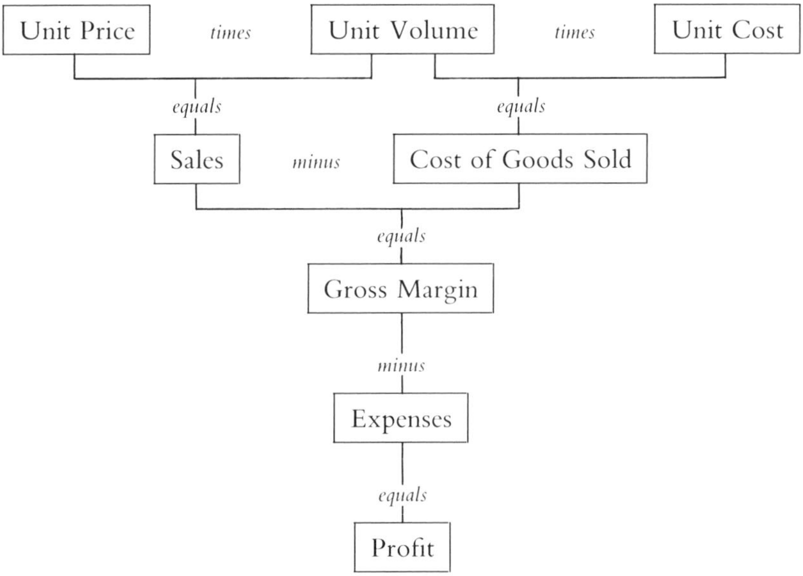

Source: Adapted from W.R. Davidson, D.J. Sweeney, and R.W. Stamfl, *Retailing Management*, 6th ed. © 1988 John Wiley and Sons, p. 169.

long-term liabilities are paid over a longer period of time. Current liabilities include accounts payable, i.e., the amount that the pharmacy owes
on purchases obtained on credit from its suppliers. In addition, short-
term notes payable are a current liability. These are loans provided by
lending institutions for the purchase of seasonal merchandise and are
expected to be repaid upon demand. Long-term liabilities include such
items as a mortgage on the building and loans incurred in the purchase
of the business, generally for the purchase of fixed assets.

Owner's (or shareholders') equity or net worth is the difference between total assets and total liabilities. It represents the owner's or shareholders' claim to the assets that remain after debts to creditors have been
discharged; hence, the owner's interest is equal to the *net* assets of the
business.

Finally, the profits of the firm (as a corporation) can be distributed
to the shareholders as cash dividends or they can be reinvested in the
business as retained earnings. Retained earnings are used for expansion
of the business.

An expanded view of a balance sheet appears in Figure 4.4. The
advantage of expressing a financial statement as a flow chart is that it
can be a useful visual aid in presenting current data and speculating on
future data by posing "what if" questions. Each rectangle can be split
diagonally, with current data inserted in one section and forecast data in
the other. In addition, while the usual method of reading the chart is
from left to right, according to the usual flow, reading it from right to
left (starting with anticipated financial outcomes) allows some insight
into what the assets and liabilities must be in order to arrive at the
expected outcomes. In this way, the flow chart can be used as a planning
aid.

Establishing a New Pharmacy

Estimating Start-Up Costs

To establish a new pharmacy, the prospective owner must first undertake
to forecast its financial operations and viability and to determine the
initial investment that will be required. This is accomplished by projecting the owner's anticipated sales and estimated expenses in earning
those sales in the form of an income statement. In this process, industry
averages can be used as a guideline for forecasting a working plan. As
you will see in Chapter 5, financial forecasting is critical throughout the
life of the pharmacy practice, but, over time, the practice will have
generated its own financial history from which projections can be made.
The discussion in Chapter 5 will also introduce you to operational planning, a critical part of business financial planning. Our aim in this chapter

Figure 4.4
EXPANDED BALANCE SHEET

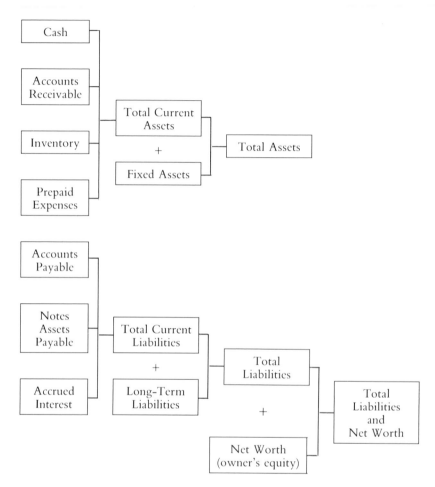

Source: From the NACA Bulletin, 1952 Conference Proceedings © 1952 by the National Association of Cost Accountants. As reprinted in C.A. Kline, Jr., and Howard L. Hessler, "The DuPont Chart System for Appraising Operating Performance," in W.E. Thomas, Jr., ed., *Readings in Cost Accounting, Budgeting and Control*, 2nd ed. (n.p. = South-Western Publishing Co., 1960), p. 797.

is to describe one approach to estimating start-up costs that can later be integrated as a step in operational planning.

Industry averages for Canadian pharmacies can be found in the Survey of Community Pharmacy Operations, published annually by the Canadian Pharmaceutical Association. In the absence of historical financial data, the prospective owner can refer to the industry averages as an aid in his or her investigation of the costs involved in opening a new pharmacy. The data must, of course, be selected by the province or region that is most applicable to the site of the pharmacy under consideration. Forecasts of financial activity are known as projected statements, meaning that they are hypothetical or anticipatory. (They are also referred to as "pro-forma" or "forecast" statements.)

There are no rigid guidelines for preparing a projected income statement. On the other hand, common sense and judgment, together with thorough and astute research, are critical in making the estimates as reliable as possible. For example, if the pharmacy is to service an elderly population, the number of prescriptions dispensed is likely to be greater than if the predominant clientele were young and healthy. Having conducted the research necessary for location analysis, the prospective owner will have a good sense of the particular characteristics of the trading area that will call for adjustments to industry averages in the estimating process.

The projected income statement is constructed around an estimate of expected total sales for the period being planned, based on results of location analysis, comparison with industry averages, and the size and type of the proposed pharmacy.[1] This figure then serves as a base and is taken as 100 percent. Other items on the income statement may be calculated as a percentage of this total sales figure. Examine Figure 4.5 to see how this principle is put into practice in our sample pro-forma income statement. Read the statement following the sequence of numbered annotations in the right-hand column. Notice that we have used the 1986 industry-average percentages from Figure 4.1 as our base.

Where known data exist or can be determined (rent, for example), they should always be used in lieu of estimates. Salaries and wages can be projected by determining the type and number of employees to be hired and researching current rates of pay. Current costs of utilities can also be researched and projected. As a check, the resulting percentages of total sales represented by your projections can be compared to the corresponding percentages in the industry averages.

As you can see, we have grouped all expenses except salaries, rent, and utilities under the category "other," and based our projection on the percentage of total sales represented by these expense items in the industry averages. This is therefore a very rough estimate, and, in practice, should

[1] Review the discussion of estimating potential prescription sales in the trading area in Chapter 3, p. 27.

Figure 4.5
AVERAGE PHARMACY LIMITED
SAMPLE PROJECTED INCOME STATEMENT
DECEMBER 31, 19—

Total Sales	$844,907	100.0%	2. Based on prescriptions representing 43.2% of total sales (1986 industry average)
Prescription sales	365,000	43.2%	1. Based on dispensing 50 prescriptions daily at ave. price of $20; a conservative estimate, as sales in the first year are normally below average.
Other	479,907	56.8%	3. Calculated difference between total sales and prescription sales
Cost of Goods Sold	593,970	70.3%	4. Based on discussions with suppliers, and industry averages
Gross Margin	250,937	29.7%	5. Calculated difference between total sales and cost of goods sold. Owner would strive to *exceed* industry-average gross margin percentage, but it is reasonable to assume this may not occur in the first year.
Expenses Salaries	119,132	14.1%	6. Based on estimates of salaries
Rent	20,278	2.4%	7. Based on landlord's lease
Utilities	4,225	0.5%	8. Based on estimate of utilities costs
Other	65,903	7.8%	9. Based on industry averages
Total Expenses	209,538	24.8%	10. Calculated sum of expenses
Profit *(before tax)*	41,399	4.9%	11. Calculated difference between gross margin and total expenses. Again, over time, the owner would expect profit to exceed industry average.
Other Income	6,759	0.8%	12. Based on industry averages
Total Income *(before tax)*	$ 48,158	5.7%	13. Calculated sum of profit and other income

be adjusted and fine-tuned to reflect research into current costs for some of the items involved (for example, licences and insurance). An important point to note is that one item included under "other" is interest payments. It is clear that this amount will require adjustment once you have completed your projections and can judge the amount of money that you actually need to borrow to finance the pharmacy. And, of course, this will require reworking your projected statement to achieve desired financial outcomes. Once again, this will be discussed in greater detail in the following chapter.

Once you have gained a sense of the costs involved for an average year of the proposed pharmacy's operation and of the gross margin required to cover expenses and provide an acceptable level of profit, it is necessary to consider the actual costs involved in the *initial* investment in the pharmacy. From the projected income statement, it will be necessary to develop pro forma monthly income and cash-flow statements (to be discussed in detail in Chapter 5) in order to estimate the amount of working capital that will be required for, say, the first three months of operation. Working capital, in this context, refers to the funds needed to cover expenses in addition to interest payments or other financing costs, until the pharmacy becomes profitable and can meet these obligations out of its own revenues. Sufficient working capital for at least the first three-month period should be in hand at the outset of the venture.

Expenses for the initial period should be adjusted upward to reflect the cost of first and last months' rent deposits, possible required deposits on utilities, fees for licences and permits, initial legal and accounting fees, and higher advertising costs connected with the opening of the new business.

In addition to working capital, the prospective owner must plan for a large initial outlay of capital in two areas: (1) inventory and (2) fixtures and equipment. The financing costs (whether to financial institutions or suppliers) for funds borrowed to cover these investments will be added to the expenses in the income statement. The prospective owner must explore payment terms with suppliers of merchandise and of fixtures and equipment: downpayments of a certain percentage of the costs will be required and repayment schedules for the balance will be negotiated. Such arrangements will affect the amount of funds that must be borrowed at the outset. It is also possible to lease rather than buy fixtures and equipment: as you will learn in Chapter 6, this approach can represent a major form of financing.

Suppliers of drugs and merchandise can offer invaluable assistance in determining the products and quantities to stock in the pharmacy in its first year of operation. The estimate for cost of goods sold for the projected income statement can be derived through discussions with suppliers, analysis of market demand in the trading area, and comparison with industry averages. Suppliers can also help with the critical selection of the *initial* inventory that will be required. The size of the investment in initial inventory will vary significantly with each operation. However, a useful way of checking that the estimated initial investment is reasonable is to divide the cost-of-goods-sold figure from your projected income statement by a basic rate of inventory turnover of four (meaning that the store's entire inventory is expected to be sold and replenished four times in the course of the year). Using the amount for cost of goods sold from our sample statement in Figure 4.5, we would thus obtain an initial inventory value of $593,970 ÷ 4 = $148,493. To ensure that such estimates are not exceeded in actuality, new owners must select merchandise very carefully during the first year, focussing on product lines that are known to be salable, and making cautious investments into less proven lines. Suppliers can provide statistics on the rates of sale of the products they distribute and these should be investigated thoroughly by the new pharmacy owner.

Fixtures and equipment include all of the shelving (gondolas) needed for the store, special display fixtures, magazine and card racks, signs, carpeting, cash registers, computers, dispensary equipment, and reference library materials. The costs for these items will depend on their quality and on the prices that can be negotiated with various suppliers. It is wise to conduct extensive research into current market prices to arrive at a reliable estimate of these costs, balancing requirements for the desired image of the pharmacy with critical cost considerations.

Calculating the Break-Even Point

Another useful tool in financial planning is break-even analysis, a test that determines the degree of business volume at which total sales equal total expenses, or, in other words, at which sales equal fixed costs plus variable costs. A break-even analysis should be conducted before proceeding ahead in any business venture. There are several approaches to calculating the break-even point: a rough calculation will be presented here and, later in the book, a more sophisticated and detailed approach will be introduced (see Chapter 18).

The rough estimate is calculated by dividing total estimated expenses by the estimated gross margin percentage. Hence, using the figures from our sample projected income statement in Figure 4.5, we arrive at a break-even point of $209,538 ÷ 0.297 = $705,515, meaning that the pharmacy must achieve sales of at least $705,515 to avoid a financial loss. Since we believe that the pharmacy's sales in the first year will exceed this amount, we are encouraged to proceed.

However, a second test that should be made is the calculation of the "profit point" to determine whether the proposed pharmacy can make a reasonable profit. For an established, thriving pharmacy operation, a reasonable profit is 25 percent of the gross margin. The profit point is calculated by the same formula used to determine the break-even point, except that the gross margin percentage is reduced by 25 percent. Hence,

$$\frac{\$209,538}{0.297 - (0.25 \times 0.297)} = \frac{\$209,538}{0.223} = \$939,632.$$

The resulting profit point is thus in the area of $940,000. This is equivalent to 25 percent of the gross margin, as you can see from the following reconciliation:

Sales	$940,000
Gross Margin (29.7%)	279,180
less Total Expenses	209,538
Profit	$ 69,642, or 25% of gross margin.

If it is feasible for sales to reach $940,000 within the first three to five years of the pharmacy's operation, the prospective owner is further assured that it is sensible to proceed with the new pharmacy practice. Some will argue that this goal is too ambitious, but many well-run pharmacies are indeed achieving profits in excess of our guideline of 25 per cent of gross margin. Note that the industry averages do not reflect such profits because, as averages, they include statistics from pharmacies that are unprofitable, whether through poor management, detrimental shifts in their markets, or newness in business.

Buying an Established Pharmacy

Estimating the Value of a Pharmacy

If the prospective owner is planning to purchase an established pharmacy, the task at hand is to estimate the value of that pharmacy's operating assets in order to determine the price that he or she would be willing to pay. The operating assets consist of inventory, fixtures, and goodwill. Various different methods are currently being used to assess the value of both the tangible and intangible assets of pharmacies. Formal valuations are comprehensive, and may include, for example, physical counts of inventory by independent appraisers, as well as thorough financial analyses and projections. Here, we shall present one of the methods used, which calculates a theoretical or notional value for operating assets based on historical financial data. (Note that our discussion assumes that assets, rather than shares of the corporation, are being purchased – these two alternatives are discussed in the following section.)

Estimating the value of a pharmacy is a specialized area and the services of an accountant experienced in mergers and acquisitions or a business valuator should be engaged. Background in pharmacy valuation should be a prerequisite for the adviser selected. However, the prospective owner should also be able to make informed judgments, and an understanding of the following method, known as the capitalization of earnings method, would allow him or her to do so.

INDICATED EARNINGS

The two major factors involved in determining a reasonable value for any small business are *indicated pre-tax earnings*[2] and the *earnings multiplier*. Indicated earnings are the pre-tax income that a purchaser can expect the pharmacy to achieve after reasonable wages (for both the owner and the staff) and all operating expenses have been paid. To determine indicated earnings, financial statements for the last three to five years of the pharmacy's operations (along with the forecast or budget for next year's expectations) must be reviewed. Expenses should be recalculated to eliminate any charges that would no longer apply under new ownership. Similarly, if the current owner was taking his or her remuneration by dividends rather than salary, a reasonable amount for owner remuneration would have to be added to the expenses. If, after such adjustments are made, the pre-tax earnings show an increase from year to year, and if there are prospects that this trend will continue, then the latest year's adjusted pre-tax earnings may in fact represent the indicated-earnings figure that is being sought.

It might be helpful to consider a hypothetical financial statement for a pharmacy that is being offered for sale, as shown in Figure 4.6. The figure shows the adjustments that have been made and the resulting indicated earnings.

As you can see, the annual net pre-tax income in the original financial statement is $5000. "Wages" and "other" expenses, at 64 percent and 26 percent of gross margin, respectively, appear to be excessive. This would prompt a prospective purchaser to analyze the financial details further. Let us assume that this analysis indicates that the owner took a bonus of $75,000 in excess of a reasonable salary; this would call for an adjustment to reduce the wage expense to $175,000, thus bringing it to a more acceptable 45 percent of gross margin. In addition, it is found that among "other" expenses, there is a $10,000 financing cost and an $8000 auto-

---

[2] Another, more traditional, approach to the capitalization of earnings method uses net or after-tax income in calculating indicated earnings. The use of pre-tax earnings is an alternative approach that is also practised today. Once again, prospective owners should discuss their professional adviser's method of choice in detail and understand all its implications fully.

Figure 4.6
CALCULATION OF INDICATED EARNINGS

	Per Financial Statement		Adjustments	Indicated Earnings	
Sales	$1,300,000		$	$1,300,000	
Gross Margin	390,000	30%†		390,000	
Expenses					
Wages	250,000	64%‡	− 75,000	175,000	45%‡
Occupancy (rent and utilities)	35,000	9%‡		35,000	9%‡
Other	100,000	26%‡	− 18,000	82,000	21%‡
Total Expenses	385,000	99%‡	− 93,000	292,000	75%‡
Net Pre-tax Earnings	$ 5,000	1%‡	+ $93,000	$ 98,000	25%‡

†percentage of total sales
‡percentage of gross margin

mobile expense that will no longer apply once the pharmacy is sold. This results in an $18,000 reduction in "other" expenses, from $100,000 to $82,000, or 21 percent of gross margin. The indicated pre-tax earnings are therefore $98,000, rather than $5000 as suggested by the financial statement.

Although the adjustments in our example lead to improvements in the indicated earnings, this will certainly not always be the case. Also, the need for an adjustment may not always be apparent to one who is inexperienced in accounting procedures; hence, as we suggested earlier, the assistance of a professional accountant is critical.

THE EARNINGS MULTIPLIER

To determine the theoretical value of the operating assets (inventory; fixed assets, excluding property; and goodwill), the capitalization of earnings method multiplies the indicated earnings of the pharmacy by a certain factor, or multiplier, which is related to return on investment (ROI). The earnings multiplier is in fact the reciprocal of the percentage return on investment that the business should be expected to bring to its owner.

The purchaser will be willing to pay, in part, for the security of the business's earning power. The return on investment in small business is expected to be greater than the prime-rate return that would be received on a guaranteed investment with a bank, for the simple reason that the former is not as secure an investment as the latter and the investor expects compensation for taking on the greater risk. At the time of writing, this higher return on small-business investment is commonly estimated to be about 2.5 times (or 250 percent of) the current prime rate. If the prime rate is ten percent, then the suggested return on investment is $10 \times 2.5 = 25$ percent. The reciprocal of 25 percent is $100 \div 25 = 4$, which is our earnings multiplier. Hence, the academic value of the operating assets in our example would be as follows: $98,000 (indicated earnings) $\times$ 4 (earnings multiplier) = $392,000. While we are using the 25 percent ROI for the sake of our example, we must emphasize that it is not an absolute, but a yardstick only. The multiplier used in actual valuations would be adjusted in recognition of various factors, including prospects for growth, efficiency of the business, the state of the economy, competition, and the demand for the particular type of business at the particular time.

What we have described is the basic return on investment expected in a normal small business. A pharmacy, however, is generally a much safer, less risky investment than most small businesses, and the prospect of future profits is more reasonably measurable. Because of this, the anticipated rate of return on investment in a pharmacy need not be as high as it is in a normal small business, as there is less risk of failure for which the investor might deserve compensation. The seller may feel justified in placing a higher value on a pharmacy, and the purchaser must determine whether the particular pharmacy is such a safe risk that it justifies the higher price – by considering profits in the past, the location of the pharmacy, and the measurable prospects for increased sales in the future. The effects on profitability of current legislation in the province and the prevailing provincial drug plan should also be taken into consideration. If future prospects are encouraging, then a reasonable expectation for ROI might be as low as 20 percent. Applying our formula to a 20 percent ROI, we obtain what we shall call a high-value earnings multiplier of $100 \div 20 = 5$, and a high value for the pharmacy of $98,000 \times 5 = \$490,000$. Hence, under normal circumstances, the pharmacy in our example should sell for between $390,000 and $490,000. The notional value of the operating assets would be somewhere in the middle – at approximately $440,000. These calculations are summarized in Figure 4.7.

Let us put this into perspective relative to the actual value of the physical assets of the pharmacy. If the final purchase price is set at, say, $450,000, and the actual worth of the inventory and net fixed assets has been assessed at $200,000 and $30,000, respectively, then the balance of $220,000 is the amount being paid for the intangible asset of goodwill. Some sources suggest that goodwill should be valued at between two and three times the indicated pre-tax earnings. The $220,000 paid for goodwill in our example is 2.25 times the indicated earnings of $98,000. A purchase price of $450,000 is, therefore, probably reasonable.

Figure 4.7
NOTIONAL VALUE OF OPERATING ASSETS

Indicated earnings	$98,000
ROI expected from normal small business	$10\% \times 2.5 = 25\%$
Earnings multiplier	$100 \div 25 = 4$
Value of normal small business	$98,000 \times 4 = \$392,000$
ROI expected from pharmacy with measurable potential for high earning power	20%
High-value multiplier	$100 \div 20 = 5$
High value	$98,000 \times 5 = \$490,000$
Selling price	$390,000 — $490,000

Structuring the Purchase

Once the buyer and seller have agreed to a price for the pharmacy, the purchase must be "structured," which means that the question of purchasing assets versus shares of the corporation must be decided, terms of payment must be negotiated, and various other details of the transaction confirmed.

The income-tax implications in the purchase of any business, including a pharmacy, are extremely important and integral to the decision of whether to purchase the corporation (i.e., its shares) or the assets of the corporation only. Traditionally, the seller wishes to sell shares while the purchaser wishes to purchase assets. The advantage to the seller of selling shares has recently been enhanced in the Income Tax Act, since the seller is now eligible for a capital-gains exemption of up to $500,000 on shares of qualifying small business operations.[3] (Capital gains are gains that result from the disposition of capital property.) However, redundant assets – those that are not essential to operating the pharmacy, such as excess cash in bank accounts, marketable securities, or real estate holdings

---

[3] In order for the shares of the pharmacy to qualify for the $500,000 capital-gains exemption, the business must comply with a number of complex provisions of the recently enacted income-tax legislation, and most notably with the "90 percent rule": at least 90 percent of the fair market value of the underlying corporation must be represented by operating assets (such as accounts receivable, inventory, and fixed assets).

unrelated to the pharmacy – must be removed from the balance sheet before selling the shares of the corporation to any purchaser. Any income or expenses attributable to these redundant assets must also be removed. This can either result in a considerable increase in the seller's personal income tax, possibly offsetting any tax savings afforded by the $500,000 capital-gains exemption, or in increased costs related to professional advice sought in order to minimize any potential problems.

The situation is further complicated, as follows: the purchaser will be at an extreme financial disadvantage when buying shares. First, in certain provinces, 51 percent of the shares must be held by the pharmacist *personally*. The pharmacist will undoubtedly have acquired a debt to purchase those shares, and will be repaying it out of the purchased company's earnings that will be paid to him in the form of salary, bonuses, or dividends. Of course, such funds are then part of the pharmacist's personal income, on which tax must be paid at personal income-tax rates. (In the case of dividends, the pharmacy will have paid tax on the earnings, and the pharmacist will pay tax at personal rates on the portion of income remaining after dividend tax credits are taken into account.) The amount remaining after tax will be used to pay the debt. This may be onerous and costly. If the province allows the creation of a holding company under such circumstances, then purchasing shares is less onerous, but it is still costly. Consider the following[4]: the small-business corporations tax in Ontario, for example, is 22 percent of net profit before income taxes on the first $200,000 of annual taxable income. The dividends paid from the operating company to the holding company would flow tax-free (once earnings have been taxed), and the debt could then be repaid with 78-cent dollars. On the other hand, the top marginal tax rate for individuals (for taxable income greater than $55,000) is 43 percent. So, if the shares (and the debt) are held personally, the purchaser will be paying the debt with 57-cent dollars. (It should be noted, however, that in the latter case, the purchaser would be able to deduct from taxable income the interest costs on funds borrowed to purchase the shares, whereas a holding company would have difficulty obtaining taxable income from which to write off such costs.)

If the pharmacist purchases the assets of the corporation instead of its shares, the newly formed company can write off 75 percent of the goodwill purchased at a rate of seven percent per year on the diminishing balance. For example, 75 percent of the goodwill purchased at $220,000 in our example is $165,000 and the write-off in the first year, at seven

---

[4] This discussion is based on the basic tax rates prevailing in Ontario at the time of writing, not including surtaxes (temporary taxes that provincial and federal governments impose periodically in addition to the basic rates). Readers should recall from the material in Chapter 2 that the small-business tax rate varies from province to province. Also, remember that tax rates are subject to change with each federal budget.

percent, would amount to $11,550. A decreasing annual write-off would then apply until the balance was virtually eliminated.

In addition to the financial problems involved, the other major disadvantage of purchasing the corporation (by buying its shares) is that the purchaser is buying a legal entity. Any problems associated with that entity since the day of incorporation will be inherited by the new owner. This means that the purchaser's lawyer and accountant must be extremely careful in examining the corporate records to be certain that there are no skeletons in the closet. Although the purchase agreement will contain various warranties to guard against such problems, the purchaser should be aware that complications associated with income-tax irregularities or other contingent liabilities could nevertheless surface in the future.

Once the price and structure of the purchase have been determined, the next step is to prepare a simple letter of intent. To save on the costs involved in preparing a major contract, the buyer and seller should be in complete agreement about the basic elements of the purchase, such as price, terms of payment, and structure, before the lawyer is commissioned to draw up a formal purchase agreement. The letter of intent that precedes the formal agreement should include a sentence indicating that the closing will be subject to the purchaser's obtaining the necessary financing to complete the purchase. When both parties have signed the letter of intent, the buyer may proceed with negotiating the necessary financing. This involves the preparation of a business plan, which is outlined in Chapter 5.

Any pharmacist planning to enter into an independent business venture should assemble a reliable management team, including an accountant with proven income-tax expertise, a lawyer, and a knowledgeable banker. The group may be supplemented by a financial consultant, an insurance broker, and, perhaps, a realtor.

BUYING VERSUS LEASING PREMISES

Many pharmacy owners believe that it is important to own the premises in which the pharmacy operates. However, an investment in the premises is not an investment in the pharmacy. As mentioned earlier, a reasonable return on the investment in the operating assets of a pharmacy is 20 to 25 percent. The return (before finance costs) in a real estate property will probably not exceed ten percent.

Pharmacists starting out on their own will normally find that cash is short. The safest approach may be to start as a tenant by taking over the existing lease, rather than to tie up funds in real estate. It is, however, to the buyer's advantage to include an option-to-buy clause in the purchase agreement, or, at least, to ensure a right of first refusal (known as a pre-emptive right). After five years in operation, the new pharmacy owner should be in a better cash position to consider purchasing the premises.

In the case of opening a new pharmacy, once the desired premises have been located, the next step is to have the real estate agent prepare an "offer to lease," which will cover the basic terms that will eventually be included in the actual lease. The key elements to be negotiated include the rent, the definition of the space, any additional costs for common maintenance, insurance, and property taxes, and term and renewal clauses. In some cases, the extra costs we have listed are included within the basic rent, with a proviso that the tenant is responsible for any increases in them, as separate expenses, after the lease is in effect. However, there is something called a "net/net/net" (or "triple net") lease, which makes the tenant responsible for a core rent and, separately, for all other expenses defined in the offer to lease, with the usual exception of major structural repairs. Before an offer to lease is signed, a lawyer should be engaged to review the details and make any necessary changes.

A common mistake made by pharmacists is to lease too much space or agree to a lease that bases rent on a percentage of the pharmacy's sales. Too often that percentage is excessive. Before signing any offer to lease, the pharmacist should determine the proposed pharmacy's estimated sales and gross margin. Occupancy cost, which includes rent, utilities, maintenance, and property taxes, should not exceed ten percent of the gross margin. For example, in Figure 4.6, occupancy cost, at $35,000, is nine percent of the $390,000 gross margin. In an ambitious rental property, the occupancy cost may be 20 percent or more of the gross margin. Under such terms, the pharmacy owner is in effect entering into partnership with the landlord, as the extra ten percent will probably represent close to 50 percent of the anticipated profits of the pharmacy.

CONCLUSION

Pharmacists who plan to own their own businesses must recognize the extent of the financial risks involved and protect themselves by investing the necessary time and energy in planning financial needs and expectations. The practical skills required at the outset of the venture, whether they involve estimating the costs of opening a new pharmacy or evaluating the worth of an existing pharmacy under consideration for purchase, are perhaps the most critical of all. A solid understanding of the basic principles of accounting and a familiarity with financial statements are essential prerequisites that will enable prospective pharmacy owners to apply the tools and methods we have presented in this chapter.

RECOMMENDED READING

Bank of Montreal. *Small Business Problem Solvers.* See especially Problem Solver No. 5, "Making Sense of Terms and Jargon." Available at all branches of the Bank of Montreal.

Bergeron, Piere. *Finance for Non-Financial Managers.* Toronto: Methuen, 1985.

Cook, James T. "Is There a Drug Store in Your Future?" *Canadian Pharmaceutical Journal* 120 (1987), p. 48.

Cunningham, G. *How to Purchase a Pharmacy.* Toronto: The Ontario Pharmacists' Association, 1983.

Gagnon, Jean Paul. "Purchasing and Financing a Community Pharmacy." In *Effective Pharmacy Management.* 4th ed. Kansas City, Missouri: Marion Laboratories, 1987, pp. 65-83.

James, Jack D. *Starting a Successful Business in Canada.* 9th ed. Vancouver: International Self-Counsel Press Ltd., 1986.

"Retail Drug Store Start-Up Financing: Bank Financing Proposal." In *Canadian Small Business Financing and Tax Planning Guide.* Toronto: CCH Canada, Ltd., 1984, pp. 1251-60.

Smith, H.A. *Principles and Methods of Pharmacy Management.* 2nd ed. Philadelphia: Lea & Febiger, 1980, pp. 128-151.

Walgenbach, Paul H.; Hanson, Ernest I.; Dittrich, Norman E.; and Gaber, Brian G. *Principles of Accounting.* 1st Canadian ed. Toronto: Harcourt Brace Jovanovich, 1988.

5

THE BUSINESS PLAN

An understanding of the business plan is critical for all entrepreneurs and owners of small businesses. The business plan is essential both as a necessary document for loan applications and other forms of financing and as a tool for setting, monitoring, and meeting business goals. In a sense, the business plan is a summary of all the pharmacist's knowledge about and plans for the business, whether starting up a new pharmacy or buying an established one. To that extent, the material in this chapter will refer to various aspects of pharmacy operation that are discussed individually and in detail in other chapters of this book. It is meant to provide a framework for your further reading, as well as a source of reference later on.

Setting Personal Goals

The success of any small business depends on planning. Planning starts with knowing what is desired from a business – and from life – and this involves goal setting. It has been documented that the vast majority of people claim to have no specific goals in life. However, those who determine to put their affairs in order are able to achieve important accomplishments for themselves and their families. People who set goals tend to be more successful, suffer less from stress, and work "smarter" rather than harder. Once personal goals have been determined, the short- and long-term planning necessary to achieve them can begin.

If an identified goal is to own a pharmacy, planning must start as soon as possible. Long-term or strategic planning can begin even during a prospective owner's university career. In order to own a pharmacy, a certain amount of seed capital will be required; hence, planning savings from an early date will help ensure that ownership will be possible within five to ten years. It is also important to try to decide at an early stage whether future business goals will conflict with known personal goals. One question to be addressed is how strong is one's need for independence? An entrepreneurial spirit is often characterized by a need to excel and by a desire to achieve through independent effort: it is not necessarily a strictly money-motivated drive. Also, while the career choice of pharmacy ownership certainly suits an entrepreneurial character, it still involves restrictions on independence: the pharmacist-owner is always to some extent dependent on other people, including employees, customers, and suppliers.

Another important question that should be addressed is what level of income will satisfy personal goals? If you would be content with $40,000 to $50,000 annually, then perhaps you need not undertake as ambitious a project as starting up or purchasing a pharmacy, with all its potential for problems. If, however, you aspire to earn $100,000 to $200,000 annually in the next five to ten years, then you should probably pursue the goal of ownership, as it can bear such results.

What type of lifestyle do you prefer? Your personal goals may involve having ample time to spend with family and to pursue hobbies. It is important to recognize that as a pharmacy owner, in the initial years of practice, some sacrifice of such personal goals will be necessary. There would be little point in working the long hours required in the first five years to repay debts incurred in buying a pharmacy if this were to create too serious a conflict with personal goals. Conversely, compromising the success of the new pharmacy business by yielding to strong personal desires could also spell disaster.

Chapter 27 provides a detailed discussion of establishing personal goals. In this chapter, we shall direct our attention to business goals and planning.

Setting Business Goals

Basic business goals are by definition profit oriented. Since the pharmacist's personal income must be paid out of the pharmacy's profit, that profit is closely tied to his or her personal and financial goals. However, the business goals must also include the earning of excess profits, to be reinvested in the pharmacy to repay any debts incurred on purchasing, to subsidize possible expansion, and to finance increasing accounts receivable and inventory. Other expenses, for example, upgrading the dispensary computer or purchasing a point-of-sale computer for the front shop, must also be paid out of the profits.

Although most business-school programs encourage planning for a five-year period, some business people argue that this is quite unrealistic on the grounds that it is too difficult to predict the future with any degree of accuracy. We would maintain, however, that if adequate planning is carried out, a surprising degree of accuracy *can* be achieved. It is imperative that the prospective pharmacy owner set financial goals for the pharmacy at different stages through, for example, the next five years of operation. Such planning will undoubtedly increase the likelihood that the pharmacy will be successful and that the owner will attain the remuneration set out in his or her personal goals.

Developing the Business Plan

The business plan is an essential document and tool for the small-business owner from several perspectives. In order to borrow money from the bank or any other financial institution, it is essential that a business plan be prepared: it is the document that the lender will use to determine if the applicant is worthy of a loan. Even if funds are not being borrowed, however, a business plan, prepared at the outset of the venture and at least once a year thereafter, will help the pharmacy owner focus on and attain personal and business goals.

Our discussion in this chapter assumes planning for an established pharmacy with historical financial records. The prospective owner of a new pharmacy would base a business plan on research and projections from industry averages, as discussed in Chapter 4, and on the results of location analysis, as discussed in Chapter 3.

The business plan itself consists of three sections: a concise narrative report, a financial report, and a set of appendices.

The first section should outline, as clearly as possible, the nature of the operation and the marketing approach that has been planned (Chapter 15 discusses marketing plans in detail). Descriptions of the products and services offered, trends of sales over the years, any new lines of products that are being introduced and why, the market and the target customer groups, competition in the trading area, and advantages of the pharmacy's location should all be included. The report should also specify the legal form of the business and provide information about the pharmacy's owner(s) and/or its management team, highlighting the most positive aspects of their skills and experience. This report should also comment on the pharmacy's organizational structure, current personnel and future staffing needs, and key outside advisers and resources (the pharmacy's accounting and legal firms, for example). Any other general activities of the pharmacy, future directions or expansion plans, and other points of interest should be outlined in the descriptive section of the business plan. Remember that the readers of your business plan are most interested in assessing the operation's potential for success: stress positive points and display your knowledge and organizational skills, but keep the report concise and to-the-point. It must be informative and persuasive, not overburdened with unessential details.

The second section is perhaps the most critical part of the business plan – the numbers that will prove the viability of the operation. It consists of a financial report detailing past operations – specifically, the last annual report of the pharmacy, signed by a chartered accountant – and the latest interim monthly financial statement, together with projected monthly income statements and projected monthly cash-flow statements (also known as "pro-forma" or "forecast" statements) for the following year. A business plan for a new pharmacy would of course include only projected financial statements.

Finally, an apppendix or set of appendices concludes the business plan. Appendices should present information that documents or substantiates your business strategies. They might include a breakdown of sales by product group, as well as some of the key operating ratios of the business (discussed in Chapter 18), to demonstrate to the lender that you are well versed in the financial details of your pharmacy. You should also include a résumé and a personal net-worth statement that lists all personal assets and liabilities. Personal financial-statement forms that are helpful in assessing personal net worth accurately are available at any bank; a sample is shown in Chapter 6 (Figure 6.1). Letters of reference and credit reports might also be useful. Your accountant can help you decide what items to include in this section of your business plan.

The business plan and the financial details it entails are developed on the basis of what is known as an *operational plan*. The balance of this chapter will therefore focus on operational planning, which generates the information that the pharmacy owner will summarize and present in the business plan.

The Operational Plan

As the foundation for the business plan, the operational plan involves gathering, analyzing, and planning action around information that will assist in meeting the pharmacy owner's personal and business goals. This underlying plan revolves around four key questions:

1. How much profit does the pharmacist-owner want to make?
2. What costs will be incurred for salaries, merchandise in the front shop and dispensary, rent, and other expenses?

3. What level of sales will be necessary to cover costs and achieve the desired profit?
4. How much cash or how large a bank loan will be required to finance the pharmacy?

As we saw in Chapter 4, such questions form the basis for estimating the start-up costs for a new pharmacy. As we shall see here, they inform the financial planning process throughout the life of the business as well.

To develop the operational plan for the practice, the pharmacy owner must undertake six essential steps, as follows:

1. *Set goals.* Personal, financial, and business goals should be determined at the outset, as we have discussed so far.
2. *Assemble information.* Adequate information is needed to prepare a realistic operational plan. Much of this information will come from the previous year's monthly financial statements – historical facts about sales, cost of goods sold, and gross margin (by front shop and dispensary) and various detailed expenses for wages, occupancy, and "other" (refer back to Figure 4.1 in Chapter 4 for the list of possible expenses included in this category). In addition, you should gather current-year information by the month. Other information needed to draw up an operational plan includes current events in the pharmacy industry: for example, what effect will the provincial government drug plan have on the future gross margin of your dispensary? If the gross margin of the dispensary is likely to be reduced by two to five percent in the following year as a result of changes in legislation, you should use this information in planning for the following year's operation. If you intend to expand, you should review the labour situation in your area for both the dispensary and the front shop (is there a surplus or scarcity of available pharmacists in the province?; are wages in general staying stable or rising above inflation?), and incorporate the cost of increased labour into your projections.

    Remember that operational planning can be ongoing: it need not wait until the fiscal year-end is approaching.
3. *Analyze sales information.* The entire operational plan revolves around sales projections. Review the sales history of each product line in the front shop to determine upward or downward trends. You must try to forecast what the current trends indicate for the coming year and decide which product groups will increase in sales.
4. *Establish action plans.* Now assess the direction of the pharmacy for the coming year: is growth indicated or rather a possible downturn in sales? Based on general trends among pharmacies in recent years, the likelihood is that sales will increase in both the front shop and dispensary. If, however, there has been a negative shift of the market in your area (involving, for example, numerous job losses due to the

closing of a plant), yours may be one of the few, less fortunate, pharmacies that will experience a downturn in sales. In this case, plans should be made to reduce costs in order to optimize profits. On the other hand, if a significant growth cycle is apparent, you should try to estimate the extent of the growth and the number of additional staff that may be required to provide adequate service for your new customers. A growth cycle could easily be predicted if, for example, a new housing development were being planned in the vicinity of the pharmacy.

5. *Detail the operational plan.* Consider all your operating expenses, including wages, occupancy costs, and general expenses. Personnel requirements must be determined and noted in the plan: list either by name or by position the employees required and their estimated annual incomes and benefits. Occupancy costs should include estimates for rent, utilities, maintenance, and property taxes for the year. All the other expenses should also be estimated. Do not assume that this simply involves calculating set increases over last year's expenses, since factors may become apparent on assembling your information that indicate the need either to increase or decrease certain of these expenses.

6. *Review the plan.* The operational plan for the year should be summarized by listing the *results* of the details in the manner set out in Figure 5.1. This is Operational Plan A. Note that the profit in Operational Plan A is $60,000. If this does not satisfy the personal and business goals you identified in step 1, then you must review all of the details with a sharper pencil.

Operational Plan B (Figure 5.2) sets out the results of this rethinking of the details in your original operational plan. Part of your revised plan may be to reduce the volume of sales of low-profit items, such as tobacco products or paper goods, in the front shop. This may reduce sales by $50,000 per year, with a corresponding $5000 reduction in gross margin. You might also take a harder look at your purchasing of products for the dispensary. Your plan may indicate that you could purchase more wisely and possibly increase the gross margin from 40 percent, as originally estimated, to 42 percent. The overall effect would be a $5000 increase in gross profit.

On reviewing the personnel, you may feel that you can cut back on part-time staff in the front shop because of the reduced sales activity there, and hire pharmacy assistants rather than higher-priced pharmacists for the dispensary. This could result in a reduction in wages of $20,000 per year.

"Other" expenses may include the costs of financing. Part of your plan might involve reducing inventory and extending some of your accounts payable over time in order to first reduce the bank debt and the related cost of financing (interest payments). Cutbacks in some

Figure 5.1
OPERATIONAL PLAN A

	Front Shop	Dispensary	Total
Sales	$600,000	$400,000	$1,000,000
Cost of Goods Sold	450,000	240,000	690,000
Gross Margin	150,000	160,000	310,000
	25%	40%	31%
Wages			140,000
Occupancy			30,000
Other Expenses			80,000
Total Expenses			250,000
Net Profit			$ 60,000

of the minor expenses might also be involved in the $10,000 reduction in "other" expenses.

As you can see from Figures 5.1 and 5.2, if your goal is to make $95,000 in your pharmacy after paying yourself a reasonable wage, you should start by preparing an operational plan and then reworking that plan to achieve the desired result.

Your chartered accountant can review the details of your operational plan to see if it is realistic. If you feel comfortable with the plan, the next step is to prepare your projected monthly income statement.

Figure 5.2
OPERATIONAL PLAN B

	Front Shop	Dispensary	Total
Sales	$550,000	$400,000	$950,000
Cost of Goods Sold	405,000	230,000	635,000
Gross Margin	145,000	170,000	315,000
	26%	42%	33%
Wages			120,000
Occupancy			30,000
Other Expenses			70,000
Total Expenses			220,000
Net Profit			$ 95,000

PROJECTED MONTHLY INCOME STATEMENT

The projected monthly income statement allows you to review or monitor your plan throughout the upcoming year. Preparing this statement should be the task of the pharmacy owner: don't be too quick to delegate it to your accountant or bookkeeper. Although it is generally wise to delegate, keep this particular financial report for yourself, as it is the key to the success of your pharmacy, and provides first-hand details of your financial affairs. Remember, the owner is the chief financial officer of the pharmacy.

Forecasting your monthly income is not as difficult as it may seem. All you need is a sheet of 13-column paper and the figures from your operational plan, together with the details of information assembled by month in the current year. Head each column with the appropriate month of the year and use the last column for the total. Then, in accordance with the operational plan, determine the sales and expenses by month and record them in the appropriate columns. See Figure 5.3. Note that the fiscal year in our example is October 1 through September 30: the pharmacy owner may choose a different 12-month period, but, as you will see in Chapter 6, it is not necessarily advisable to adopt the conventional December 31 year-end.

Figure 5.3
PROJECTED MONTHLY INCOME STATEMENT
(IN THOUSANDS OF DOLLARS)

	(1)	(2)	(3)	(10)	(11)	(12)	
Month	Oct.	Nov.	Dec.	July	Aug.	Sept.	Total
Sales							
Front Shop	40.0	45.0	50.0	35.0	40.0	40.0	500.0
Dispensary	35.0	35.0	40.0	30.0	35.0	35.0	450.0
Total	75.0	80.0	90.0	65.0	75.0	75.0	950.0
Cost of Goods Sold	49.9	53.6	60.2	43.2	49.9	49.9	635.0
Gross Margin	25.1	26.4	29.8	21.8	25.1	25.1	315.0
Expenses							
Wages	10.0	9.5	10.0	9.0	9.5	9.5	120.0
Occupancy	2.5	2.5	2.5	2.5	2.5	2.5	30.0
Other	6.0	6.5	5.5	6.0	5.5	6.5	70.0
Total	18.5	18.5	18.0	17.5	17.5	18.5	220.0
Net Profit for Period	6.6	7.9	11.8	4.3	7.6	6.6	95.0

You will notice on reviewing the sales activity of your pharmacy over the past years that certain months have greater activity than others. For example, November and December will probably indicate higher front-shop sales due to Christmas shopping. Similarly, dispensary sales may be higher in the months just before your senior-citizen clients go down south. Whatever the case may be, you should attempt to take the $950,000 in sales (see Figure 5.2) and spread it across the various months between the front shop and the dispensary. In other words, the forecast monthly income statement represents the pharmacy owner's best estimates, based on experience and previous accounting reports. The more often the pharmacy owner prepares projected income statements, the more accurate they will become and the more informed the owner will be about the operation.

PROJECTED MONTHLY CASH–FLOW STATEMENT

The next step is to consider cash requirements for the pharmacy. The projected monthly income statement is prepared on an accrual-basis. In other words, sales are recorded once the products in the front shop and dispensary are sold, and the corresponding cost of the merchandise sold is recorded at the same time. This obviously does not reflect the actual flow of cash in and out of the pharmacy. For example, prescription sales covered by third-party insurance programs may be recorded in month 5, but the cash may not be collected until month 7. Similarly, drugs sold will be recorded (at cost) as cost of goods sold in month 5, but they may have been purchased in month 2 and paid for only in month 4.

Your operational plan might involve purchasing two new cash registers for about $2500 in the second month and paying for them in the third month. The plan might also include $5000 renovation of the shelving for the reduced inventory, to be incurred in month 1 and paid in month 2. You may be planning to reduce inventory by $24,000 for the year at the rate of about $2000 per month: this will be reflected in a reduced payment for merchandise of $2000 for the previous month.

The question, then, is "How much cash is required to finance my pharmacy?" To answer this, you must prepare a forecast monthly cash-flow statement. This, too, may sound like a lot of detailed paperwork best left to the accountant, but, remember, it's your money and the cash-flow statement is not as difficult to prepare as it may seem. In simple terms, a projected monthly cash-flow statement sets out the estimated amounts of cash receipts and cash disbursements by month for the following year. Again, you will be using a 13-column sheet and heading up the columns with the respective months, leaving the 13th column to represent the total for the year.

Let us consider cash receipts. You must determine when the cash from your projected sales will actually be received. From Figure 5.3, you will notice that in month 1, front-shop sales total $40,000 and dispensary sales total $35,000. Unless you have customer credit accounts, we can assume that the $40,000 is cash received on front-shop sales. If your third-party drug plans represent about 50 percent of your dispensary sales, then we can assume that $17,500 of the $35,000 was received in month 1. If we assume the third-party payments are received within 30 days, then the remaining $17,500 will be received in month 2. The cost of goods sold will no doubt have been expended one, two, or even three months prior to month 1. If you assume that your average payment time to suppliers is 30 days, then the purchases in month 1 will be paid in month 2. In some cases, it is fair to assume that the pharmacy's purchases in month 1 equal its cost of goods sold in the same month. For example, the cost of goods sold in month 1 was $49,900 and purchases are assumed to be the same amount less $2000 for the reduction of inventory. The $47,900 is to be paid in month 2. Expenses for wages, occupancy, and

Figure 5.4
PROJECTED CASH-FLOW STATEMENT
FOR A TWELVE-MONTH PERIOD
(IN THOUSANDS OF DOLLARS)

	(1)	(2)	(3)	(10)	(11)	(12)	
Month	Oct.	Nov.	Dec.	July	Aug.	Sept.	Total
Cash Receipts							
Cash Sales							
Front Shop	40.0	45.0	50.0	35.0	40.0	40.0	500.0
Dispensary	17.5	17.5	20.0	15.0	17.5	17.5	
Accounts Receivable	15.0†	17.5	17.5	20.0	15.0	17.5	445.0
Total	72.5	80.0	87.5	70.0	72.5	75.0	945.0
Cash Disbursements							
Merchandise	45.0†	47.9	51.6	42.0	41.2	47.9	608.1
Wages	10.0	9.5	10.0	9.0	9.5	9.5	120.0
Occupancy Costs	2.5	2.5	2.5	2.5	2.5	2.5	30.0
Other	6.0	6.5	5.5	6.0	5.5	6.5	70.0
Capital Expenditures	—	5.0	2.5	—	—	—	7.5
Depreciation	(.1)	(.2)	(.1)	(.2)	(.1)	(.1)	(1.7)
Total	63.4	71.2	72.0	59.3	58.6	66.3	833.9
Net Change	9.1	8.8	15.5	10.7	13.9	9.7	111.1
Opening Balance	(75.0)						(75.0)
Cash Balance (Deficit)							
Cumulative	(65.9)	(57.1)	(41.6)	12.5	26.4	36.1	36.1

†Previous month

"other" are normally recorded as being paid in the month incurred. So, from Figure 5.4 you will see that the actual cash receipts and disbursements are indeed different from the projected income statement in Figure 5.3.

(*Note*: We have assumed that the accounts receivable for the previous month total $15,000 and accounts payable, $45,000.) Notice the entry for depreciation, wherein an amount is being *deducted* from the cash disbursements (in the projected monthly income statement, depreciation is included within "other" expenses). This is done because depreciation is an expense only in an accounting sense: it is not an actual cash disbursement, and must not be allowed to distort the picture of actual cash flow.

As you can see, our planning has resulted in eliminating the $75,000 bank loan that was outstanding at the beginning of the year and establishing a positive balance of $36,100 at year-end.

MONITORING THE OPERATIONAL PLAN

Think of yourself as an airplane pilot crossing the Pacific, who must not only chart his course (as you do with your forecast monthly income statement) but also get a fix on the location from time to time to ensure that the craft is still on course. In monitoring the operational plan, the latter step is accomplished by preparing monthly financial statements that are compared in detail against the original plan. This makes immediate corrective action possible if you are off course. If you receive annual financial statements only four to six months after year-end and have no monthly reports, you may discover – too late – that you have gone seriously off course. Daily and weekly information serves as an early-warning system to pinpoint problem areas. For example, by accumulating sales on a daily basis, you will know at any point during the month whether you are on target with your monthly forecast. Similarly, your key expense – wages – can be monitored each payday. By maintaining a daily/weekly summary of key areas such as sales, wages, and merchandise purchases, you can monitor your plan and take immediate action to correct any variances even before the current month-end. According to the Seventh Annual Survey of Community Pharmacy Operations for 1986, wages and merchandise account for approximately 89 percent of expenditures. Control these elements, and you have control of the business.

Monitoring the operational plan does not stop here. It is a continuous process of planning, acting, and reviewing. When you review your plan using daily, weekly, and monthly information, you will find that you are frequently at the drawing board revising the plan in light of new information.

It is important to update your present projected monthly income statement for the next twelve months to allow for any changes that might have occurred in the marketplace over the year or any obvious errors in your original plan. Remember, your plan can only be your best "guesstimate"; it is never likely to achieve 100 percent accuracy. Information such as sales and gross margin by product can pinpoint any unprofitable areas and may prompt you to drop certain lines of merchandise in favour of more profitable ones. As chief financial officer, you will not only know what is actually happening in your pharmacy at all times but also be able to influence what takes place in the future.

Summary

Operational planning is an instrumental process by which the pharmacy owner sets out and organizes his or her business goals and undertakes financial projections and tests to determine the optimal approach to realizing those goals. The process involves gathering and analyzing information to formulate a successful strategy. The operational plan is summarized in the business plan, which becomes a critical tool in persuading prospective lenders of the strength of the proposed business venture. It is equally important as a means by which the pharmacy owner stays on course in the successful day-to-day operation of the business.

Recommended Reading

Archer, Maurice, and White, Jerry. *Starting and Managing Your Own Business*. Toronto: Macmillan, 1978.

Bank of Montreal. *Small Business Problem Solvers*. Ten booklets available from Bank of Montreal branches. See especially Problem Solver No. 4, "Developing Your Business Plan" and Problem Solver No. 6, "Cash Flow Planning."

Canadian Federation of Independent Businesses. *A Guide to Small Business Management*. 2nd ed. Toronto: CFIB, Ryerson Polytechnical Institute, 1981.

Federal Business Development Bank. *Do-It-Yourself Business Planning Package, Forecasting and Cash-Flow Budgeting*. Toronto: FBDB, 1983.

Kao, Raymond N.Y. *Small Business Management: A Strategic Emphasis*. 2nd ed. Toronto: Holt, Rinehart and Winston, 1984.

Timmons, Jeffry A. *New Venture Creation: A Guide to Small Business Development*. Homewood, Ill.: Irwin Publishing, 1985.

6

MEETING
CAPITAL NEEDS

Capital Explained

Capital is defined in Webster's New World Dictionary as "wealth (money or property) owned or used in business by a person or corporation; wealth in whatever form, used or capable of being used to produce more wealth." It is a commonplace in business that capital empowers its holder to create, build, expand, and control a business enterprise.

Capital can take many forms, such as cash in a savings account, investments in marketable securities or guaranteed investment certificates, or the capital accumulated in a home (75 percent of the dwelling's market value less any mortgages or other encumbrances).

The total amount of an individual's *equity capital* is in fact his or her *net worth*, which is determined by deducting the value of personal liabilities (or debts) from personal assets. Figure 6.1 presents a standard form used to determine net worth. New pharmacy owners will find that the amount of money required to conduct a business is usually greater than their personal net worth. The difference will be the amount of money that must be borrowed to finance the pharmacy, and is referred to as *debt capital*.

The relationship between equity capital and debt capital is known as *financial leverage*. A relationship acceptable to any financial institution is 50 percent equity and 50 percent debt capital. A basic balance-sheet ratio that bankers consider critical in their assessment of a pharmacy's financial

Figure 6.1
SUMMARY OF PERSONAL/FAMILY NET WORTH

Date _____

Assets   _Debts_

Cash and bank accounts $ Bank debt $

Canada Savings Bonds   Mortgages

Life insurance cash value   Credit card debt

Stocks and bonds   Income tax owing

                                      Life insurance loans

Money owed to you   Other (personal loans)

RRSP

Art, antiques, jewellery

Automobiles

Home

Vacation home

Other property

Furniture

Total $ _Total_ $

   Less debts

Family Net Worth $

Figure 6.2
DEBT-TO-EQUITY RATIO

Formula:	$\dfrac{\text{Total Liabilities}}{\text{Shareholders' Equity}} = \text{Debt-to-Equity Ratio}$	

Example:	Accounts payable	$100,000
	Bank loan – operating	50,000
	Bank loan – term	150,000
	Total Liabilities	$300,000
	Capital stock	$ 10,000
	Loans to the firm from pharmacy owner	
	or shareholders	50,000
	Retained earnings	90,000
	Shareholders' Equity	$150,000
	Debt-to-Equity Ratio	$\dfrac{\$300,000}{\$150,000} = 2{:}1$

statements is the *debt-to-equity ratio*.[1] It is calculated by dividing the pharmacy's total liabilities (accounts payable, bank loans, and so on) by its total owner's or shareholders' equity (loans to the firm made by the pharmacist-owner, retained earnings, and capital stock – in a limited corporation, the total investment made by its shareholders). Referring to Figure 6.2, for example, if the total liabilities are $300,000 and the owner's or shareholders' equity is $150,000, then the debt-to-equity ratio is 2:1. (Ideally, this ratio would be 1:1.) A ratio of 2:1 indicates to any outsider that the pharmacy is levered two to one and that there is a small element of risk for any future creditors. Inadequate equity capital means a higher risk of failure and is a red flag to lending institutions and other creditors. The higher the risk, the greater the difficulty will be in obtaining additional financing or debt capital. Conversely, the more equity capital provided by the pharmacy owner, the less debt will be incurred, and the less debt incurred, the happier the lender will be. A major problem for most entrepreneurs, including pharmacists, is that they tend to operate on a highly leveraged basis and therefore stand the risk of failing in the event of a slight downturn in the business.

There is another type of capital – working capital. Working capital is the value of *current* assets less *current* liabilities. Current assets are the

[1] Financial ratios are discussed in greater detail in Chapter 18. Note also that our discussion in this chapter assumes a corporate form of enterprise.

assets that are expected to be converted to cash within one year. They include cash, accounts receivable, inventory, prepaid expenses, and marketable securities. Current liabilities are liabilities that are expected to be paid within one year. They include bank loans, accounts payable, sales taxes, and the current portion of any long-term debts (to be paid within one year). Another key ratio that bankers use to determine the liquidity of a business is the *current ratio*, which is calculated by dividing the total current assets by the current liabilities. Ideally, this ratio should also be in the area of 2:1, that is, $2 of current assets to $1 of current liabilities, indicating to the prospective lender or creditor that the company is able to pay its current obligations with little difficulty. The validity of this ratio is undermined only if the major part of current assets is represented by slow-moving inventory that is not likely to be sold within one year. Figure 6.3 shows a sample current-ratio calculation.

Debt Capital

As mentioned earlier, the two types of capital available to the prospective pharmacist-owner are debt capital and equity capital. Debt capital is recorded on the balance sheet as a liability and will increase the debt-to-equity ratio and warn the lender of the possibility of a higher risk. Interest, and possibly payments on the principal (on a monthly, quarterly, or annual basis), are payable on debt capital. The interest cost will be recorded as an expense in the income statement and will reduce both profits and owner's or shareholders' equity.

In all probability, the pharmacy owner will sign a personal guarantee

Figure 6.3
CURRENT RATIO

Formula: $$\frac{\text{Current Assets}}{\text{Current Liabilities}} = \text{Current Ratio}$$

Example:

Cash	$ 20,000	Accounts payable	$100,000
Accounts receivable	60,000	Bank loan – operating	50,000
Inventory	260,000	Current portion of	
Prepaid expenses	20,000	long-term bank loan	30,000
Total Current Assets	$360,000	Total Current Liabilities	$180,000

Current Ratio $$\frac{\$360,000}{\$180,000} = 2:1$$

to secure debt capital from the bank and may also be required to provide a collateral mortgage for a specified amount on his or her home. A collateral mortgage is different from a traditional mortgage in that it is used as security for the debt capital. If the pharmacy owner were to sell the home, then the lender who has a claim against it would receive payment of the collateral amount registered.

Equity Capital

Equity capital as opposed to debt capital is money invested in, rather than loaned to, the business. In some provinces, non-pharmacists can own only up to 49 percent of the shares in a pharmacy. So a non-pharmacist investing equity capital in a pharmacy can receive no more than 49 percent of the equity of the pharmacy.

The advantage of equity capital is that the investment will be part of shareholders' equity and will reduce the debt-to-equity ratio. If the debt capital (term loan) in Figure 6.2 were replaced by equity capital, then the debt-to-equity ratio would be 0.5 (see Figure 6.4). In the short run, this would eliminate many of the financial problems that pharmacy owners are likely to confront in the early years of operating the business. The higher the equity capital, the more additional debt capital can be obtained for purposes of expansion or to cover possible losses in the initial years.

That's the advantage of strong equity capital. The disadvantage is that with it, the pharmacy owner necessarily inherits a partner in the person of the investor. This partner will receive his or her share of any

Figure 6.4
ADVANTAGES OF EQUITY CAPITAL

Accounts payable	$100,000
Bank loan – operating	50,000
Total Liabilities	$150,000
Capital stock	$160,000
Advances from shareholders	50,000
Retained earnings	90,000
Total Shareholders' Equity	$300,000
Debt-to-Equity Ratio	$\dfrac{\$150,000}{\$300,000} = 0.5$

dividends issued and of the increased value of the pharmacy as the business grows. Although it is critical initially, after the first few years, the new pharmacist-owner will probably not need this expensive outside financial support. The pharmacist-owner should establish the ground rules of the relationship with investors from the outset. A shareholders' agreement must be prepared. An employment contract must be prepared as well, to set out the terms of reference under which the pharmacist will be working (including hours of work, vacations, holidays, and employee benefits).

SOURCES OF CAPITAL

There are various potential sources of capital. Pharmacists should start by assessing their own net worth. Property or wealth can come in the form of cash, Canada Savings Bonds, guaranteed investment certificates, marketable securities, registered retirement savings plans (RRSP's), and the family home. It makes sense to cash in marketable securities, Canada Savings Bonds, and guaranteed investment certificates and use the money as equity capital. Some "hidden cash" may be found in the home, since it can be mortgaged up to 75 percent of its market value. For example, if the market value of one's house is $100,000 and the current mortgage is $25,000, then an additional $50,000 can be raised either on a conventional mortgage or a collateral mortgage ($25,000 + $50,000 = $75,000, or 75 percent of $100,000). Another source of personal cash is an RRSP. The disadvantage of cashing in an RRSP is that personal income tax must be paid on the amount withdrawn. However, if the pharmacist has a self-administered RRSP, a mortgage can be provided through it. The terms and conditions would have to be competitive with the general market, but the pharmacist would have the option of maintaining an open mortgage, that is, one that can be paid off at the pharmacist's earliest convenience.

Personal sources are the next best source of financing. Funds from family and friends can come in the form of equity capital or debt capital. It is fair to say that many new businesses, including pharmacies, are started with this type of assistance and since, generally speaking, pharmacies are a good investment, many non-pharmacists indeed wish to get involved financially in this industry.

It is also possible that potential employees would wish to invest in the pharmacy. Such an arrangement offers a double benefit: on the one hand, the pharmacist secures adequate equity capital; on the other, the employee will be motivated and will take a greater interest in the pharmacy's operation and profitability. This may improve the productivity of the pharmacy, and, in turn, its long-run profits. However, there is a danger that employee-investors will want to become overinvolved in the day-to-day management of the business. To prevent potential conflicts in this regard, it is essential that a shareholders' agreement be drawn up to define the relationship. As shareholders, such employees must be supplied with the minimum statutory financial information required under the Canada Business Corporations Act (CBCA), which includes annual financial statements and the holding of annual shareholders' meetings within six months of year-end. In fact, providing adequate information about the progress of the company on a current basis can be very effective in motivating employee-investors.

Once adequate equity capital has been obtained, the debt capital required to complete the financing of the pharmacy must be secured. If the pharmacist is purchasing the operating assets for a value of, say, $500,000, adequate equity capital would be in the area of $100,000 to $200,000. The remaining $300,000 to $400,000 must be borrowed from third parties. In many cases, the vendor will allow a reasonable portion of the debt to be repaid over three to five years. Even so, the prospective owner is likely to experience a shortfall of cash. In most cases, equity capital must be supplemented by debt capital – most often obtained from a chartered bank.

Chartered Banks

The Canadian Bankers' Association estimates that roughly 80 percent of all small-business loans are obtained from chartered banks. It is important, then, for the pharmacist to understand what is involved in dealing with bankers.

It might be helpful to start by understanding the banker's point of view. Various North American surveys have shown that bankers consider their small-business customers' major problems to include the following: (1) they are under-capitalized; (2) they have inadequate or unreliable records; (3) they are poor managers; and (4) they know very little about financial management. Bankers also complain that few prospective borrowers come adequately prepared, making it impossible to evaluate the loan application without extensive discussion and requests for more information. Since there is little profit for banks in small loans, bankers cannot afford to devote excessive amounts of their time to them.

The bank's gross margin (the difference between the cost of funds loaned and the interest earned on loans) varies between 2.75 percent and 3.75 percent of the loans outstanding. With a loan of $200,000, this means an average gross margin of $6500 per year (i.e., 3.25 percent of $200,000). This margin shrinks quickly if the banker has to spend time processing incomplete loan applications, upgrading existing loans, or coping with the paperwork involved when cheques are issued that place the loan in an overdraft position. Once write-offs due to uncollectible loans are added to this administrative cost, bankers complain (privately) that they lose money on small-business loans.

The pharmacist will gain a distinct advantage with a banker by presenting financial needs in a finished package. Some bankers will pass up seemingly worthwhile loan applications if they are not presented in a proper manner. It is important to recognize what bankers view as a "good loan." They look for three basic elements: good management, evidence of the pharmacist's financial commitment to the business, and reasonable personal assets to support the loan.

Good management means that the pharmacist has a clear understanding of his financial position and a firm plan for the direction of the business. The primary document that attests to good management is the business plan, which was discussed in Chapter 5. Other basic documents needed are financial statements and weekly and monthly management reports.

To a banker, the pharmacist's equity capital in the business is the true barometer of personal financial commitment. Ideally, the company's current assets (mainly accounts receivable and inventory) should be sufficient to secure the loan up to 75 percent of the value of receivables and 50 percent of the value of inventory. For example, if accounts receivable are valued at $60,000 and inventory at $160,000, then the possible loan is $125,000 ($60,000 × 75% = $45,000 plus $160,000 × 50% = $80,000). The debt-to-equity ratio should be no higher than 2 to 1. Remember, that's the relationship between the cash that others have at risk and the cash that the pharmacist has at risk.

Personal assets, mainly one's home and other hard assets, can be pledged to provide outside support to any bank borrowings.

OPERATING LOAN

When the estimated cash requirements have been determined, it is time to structure the loan. There are two basic types of bank loans – operating loans and term loans. It makes sense to split the requirements between operating and term loans. Knowing the difference can help a pharmacist take better control of the pharmacy finances. An operating loan, sometimes referred to as a demand loan or "line of credit," should be used to finance the current assets (accounts receivable and inventory). It is hence a form of working capital financing. An operating loan varies throughout the year, with the bank extending more or less funding, as the inventory and accounts receivable of the business fluctuate. The bank calculates interest on an average balance of funds loaned throughout the year.

TERM LOAN

The term loan is used primarily to finance the purchase of capital or long-term assets, such as buildings, fixtures, and equipment, whose value will not fluctuate, but will depreciate over time. For these items, it makes sense to borrow on a term basis, with a repayment schedule over three to twelve years (depending on the life of the capital asset). Bankers like term loans because repayment of the principal is built into the financing package; also, the interest on a term loan is often up to one percent higher than on an operating loan. However, some term loans will qualify under the Small Businesses Loans Act (SBLA), whereby the interest rate is pegged at the prime bank rate plus one percent. The SBLA is discussed in greater detail in the following section.

The prospective owner should be aware of certain conditions surrounding term loans. A term loan from a finance company for, say, an automobile, is payable over the term of the loan, as long as the borrower is not in default. But a term loan from a bank, used, for example, to finance the pharmacy's equipment, is tied in to the operating loan and contains an acceleration clause. This means that the term loan is in effect a demand loan, in that the bank can demand its repayment at any time, together with the operating loan, if it sees that serious financial problems are developing.

Most term-loan agreements include several covenants. In some cases, in addition to keeping payments up-to-date, the key balance-sheet ratios must stay in line with the bank's criteria if financing is to continue. The bank reviews the business's total bank borrowings at least once a year and assesses the performance of the pharmacy.

In the case of either the operating or term loan, the bank examines the annual financial statement of the pharmacy, signed by an accountant, which must be submitted to the bank no later than two to three months after year-end, together with the monthly forecast income statements and cash-flow statements for the next fiscal year. Small-business owners are also required to submit monthly inventory certificates (i.e., inventory reports) and monthly aged accounts-receivable trial-balance statements (listings of all unpaid accounts receivable, by customer, which indicate how long each customer's account has been unpaid – whether current over 30 days, over 60 days, or over 90 days).

If the balance sheet has changed or profits have fallen, then the bank may take a hard look at the amount of current borrowings. If there has been a severe deterioration in the business, then the bank may reduce the borrowings or, as a last resort, call in its loans, including the term loan.

Despite such potential complications, it is still wise to structure total borrowings between an operating loan and a term loan. The choice of this approach will not only appeal to the banker, but will also indicate an understanding of bank financing on the part of the pharmacist. Although principal payments have to be made over the term of the loan, this is a small price to pay for a good relationship with a banker; it is also probably the most advantageous method of financing the pharmacy in the long run.

Small Businesses Loans Act

The main source of debt capital is the financial institution and, in particular, the chartered bank. The federal Small Businesses Loans Act (SBLA) essentially allows the small-business owner to borrow funds from a chartered bank at a preferred interest rate of prime plus one percent (normally, interest rates on term loans are higher). This small saving in the initial stages can be significant for a new owner. Under the SBLA, the federal government guarantees to pay the bank 85 percent of any loan losses that might occur, which means that the bank's risk is substantially lower than on a regular loan. SBLA loans are term loans, and repayment terms may be arranged for a period of up to ten years, depending on the type of asset being financed and the borrower's repayment ability.

If such loans are guaranteed, why wouldn't banks approve *all* small-business loans? The chartered bank is expected to treat loan applications under the SBLA according to its normal business practices; in other words, the banker will want to be convinced that the three basic criteria – good management; evidence of the owner's financial commitment to the business; and reasonable assets to support the loan – are being met. In addition, the banker takes into consideration the administrative time involved in overseeing the loan during the term of repayment agreed to with the bank. The bank's annual profit margin may be smaller on an SBLA-guaranteed loan than on a regular loan, and bankers will not be quick to loan money to a pharmacist who cannot demonstrate the ability to make full payments on time or provide the full range of information required by the bank on a regular basis once the loan is obtained.

The loan limit under the SBLA is a maximum of $100,000 to any one borrower, and the funds can only be used to finance up to 80 percent of equipment costs and up to 90 percent of premises and land costs. However, a restriction applies that is especially relevent to pharmacy: while small-business enterprises engaged in retail trade are eligible for loans under the SBLA, the businesses of professions governed by provincial or federal laws are not. Hence, a pharmacy would be eligible for the financing of equipment and premises or land costs, to the limits noted, *only as they relate to the retail front-store operation.* The portion of costs attributable to the dispensary would be ineligible for financing. This clearly makes the benefits of the SBLA program more attractive to owners of retail merchandise-oriented (as opposed to service- or prescription-oriented) pharmacies.

Certain other restrictions apply as well: SBLA loans cannot be obtained to refinance existing debts or to meet working-capital requirements. Finally, in seeking a loan under this program, bear in mind that the banker will be assessing it as carefully as he would any loan application crossing his desk.

Federal Business Development Bank (FBDB)

An alternative source of capital to consider is the Federal Business Development Bank, sometimes referred to as "the lender of last resort" because it is normally approached only after dealings with other financial institutions have met with failure. Unfortunately, if financing cannot be obtained from the chartered banks, the FBDB may not be interested either. However, the FBDB has established what it calls a financial matchmaking program, designed to locate possible partners in business ventures. In addition, under special circumstances the FBDB has been known to provide funds in higher-risk situations, albeit at a higher rate of interest. In other words, the FBDB sponsors several programs that warrant investigation by pharmacists who are just starting out in business.

Leasing

Leasing can be seen as another financing vehicle. Most equipment manufacturers either operate their own leasing companies or are associated with outside finance companies to provide lease financing for equipment, shelving, fixtures, and computers. In many cases, such an arrangement is part of their marketing plan. Although the cost of leasing is slightly higher than bank financing, leasing has the advantage that the interest rate is fixed for the period of the lease, and the pharmacist-owner will know exactly what the fixed payments will be for the term of the lease.

Venture Capital

Venture capital is a viable source of capital only if a new pharmacy venture requires financing well in excess of $500,000 and shows promise of great profits in the future. Venture capitalists would require a percentage of the ownership of the business, an annual return on their investment, and a seat on the board of directors. They would also closely monitor the progress of their pharmacy investment. The right venture capital firm might provide personnel with expertise in the pharmacy area, thereby contributing to the management and ultimate success of the pharmacy operation.

Suppliers

Last but not least, a form of financing is available from suppliers. When suppliers establish terms of payment (i.e., a certain time period within which to pay for purchased products), they are in fact lending money to the pharmacy to buy their products. The usual term of payment is 30 days, although some wholesalers offer only 15 days. Negotiations at the outset can sometimes increase this term to 60 days or 90 days, depending on the supplier. As the pharmacy expands, "dating deals" may be negotiated whereby invoices are issued only 30, 60, or 90 days after the merchandise is received. In such cases, pharmacy owners must calculate the terms under which money will indeed be saved (something we shall discuss in greater detail in Chapter 12). The secret is to have sold the product before it has to be paid for.

Advisers in Financial Matters

Dealing with Your Banker

Surveys conducted in the United States and Canada indicate that, second to the outside accountant, the banker is a small-business owner's most important adviser. As the pharmacy matures, the pharmacist's goals may include expansion and require increased bank borrowings. For this reason, it is important to maintain a good relationship with the banker from the outset and throughout the life of the business. The following guidelines offer some basic advice in this regard:

1. Don't exceed the line of credit.
2. Take the time to bring the banker up to date on the pharmacy's financial condition. Don't hide problems from the banker, but discuss them as they arise, and avoid any breakdown in communications.
3. Monitor the bank position. Keep a daily summary of cheques issued and deposits made, and calculate the bank balance daily. If the line of credit is to be exceeded, pick up the phone and explain the circumstances to the banker before issuing cheques. Although bankers will disapprove of such requests, they are more likely to remain co-operative if they are forewarned and kept abreast of developments.
4. Become thoroughly familiar with the progress of your business by studying financial statements that are prepared on a monthly basis. These statements are extremely important. While they will not guarantee a profitable pharmacy, they will provide a constant measure of the state of the pharmacy's financial health. It is a good idea to send a copy of each monthly statement to the banker, explaining problem areas and the action you are taking to correct them.
5. Ensure that your monthly accounts-receivable lists and inventory certificates are available to the banker as soon as possible after month-end.
6. Take the time to keep the banker abreast of developments in the operation of the pharmacy, especially with regard to any new projects. Invite the banker to visit the pharmacy and meet key personnel.

Keeping the lines of communication open with the banker can reap many benefits, including expert advice based on the banker's experience, that can be most helpful when important decisions are to be made. The banker can be a useful sounding board and should be relied upon as a key source of support in financial management.

Accountants

The most important adviser in matters of securing equity or debt capital among small-business owners – including pharmacists – is the outside accountant. Various North American surveys support this claim. However, incompetency among outside accountants has also been cited as the cause of financial failure among many of the companies that have failed. For owners of pharmacies, the message is clear: the role of the accountant is critical, and it is the owner's responsibility to search out the most reliable and expert accountant possible.

There is a danger that pharmacy owners will be intimidated by their accountants. Without understanding the jargon or the complicated reports that are involved, owners may find themselves getting poor service and paying high fees. It might be useful to view the accountant as simply another major supplier. When ordering merchandise or services for the pharmacy, the pharmacist undoubtedly specifies detailed requirements to do with price, date of delivery, or timing. Dealings with one's accountant should be no different. Before ordering, the pharmacist should determine his or her needs and get some idea of prices involved and of delivery dates. Below is a checklist of the needs that every pharmacy owner should consider. Bear in mind that this is a *minimum* needs list:

1. A monthly financial report, including balance sheet and profit-and-loss statements for the front shop and dispensary, together with a consolidated statement showing expenses as percentages of the gross margin.
2. A monthly sales and cost analysis, by product groupings such as prescription drugs, OTC products, tobacco, and "other" (preferably with a further breakdown of products under the category "other").
3. A monthly inventory analysis by the above-mentioned product groupings.
4. A quarterly review of the financial data with the accountant (one to two hours), to assess the key ratios for expenses, inventory (GMROI), and profitability of the front shop, together with the overall operation of the pharmacy.
5. An annual review of personal and company income tax.
6. Preparation of annual financial statements and personal and company income-tax returns.
7. Ongoing general financial counselling.

The accountant can and should do much more than provide these basic financial services. A competent, professional accounting firm can recommend basic control systems for cash, inventory (specifically in the front shop), accounts payable, and cash disbursements. Beyond this it should be able to provide a full range of advisory services, suggesting what monthly financial information is required as well as providing computerized monthly financial information either through its own computers (or a service bureau) or by showing the pharmacist how to generate this information on in-store systems. Before deciding to relocate to larger premises, take on major new lines, take on a partner, or otherwise reorganize the business, the pharmacist-owner should feel comfortable about calling his or her accountant to discuss the decision. The accountant is an important ally in securing debt capital from the banks, negotiating loan extensions or increases, making decisions about expansion or acquisition, and streamlining operations. But the accounting firm should do even more, specifically in the area of planning. Tax considerations should be an integral part of most of the financial and business decisions that are taken by the pharmacy owner. In later years, the accountant should be able to assist in estate planning. Again, the accountant should be initiating such planning: proper estimates of the value of the business are important in this regard and the accounting firm should be expert in company valuations as well as in matters of income tax.

Another important consideration for the pharmacist-owner is the accountant's bill. Most accountants charge by the hour. Generally speaking, the larger the accounting firm, the higher the rates will be. Rates will vary depending on the experience and position of the accountant assigned. However, hourly rates should not necessarily be the issue for the pharmacist; rather, it is the total fee and the dollars saved as a result of the advice purchased that are important. Some firms will act as the pharmacy's outside "vice-president of finance," on a monthly retainer. The advantage of this system is that the pharmacy will receive the attention necessary to maintain accurate bookkeeping records and control systems, thereby minimizing the overall accounting fee. (Many pharmacist-owners are paying excessive accounting fees simply because their accountants are required to perform mundane duties at year-end in an attempt to clear up the disorder that could have been avoided by a properly trained bookkeeper.) One common error among pharmacy owners is to automatically adopt a December 31 year-end – perhaps the worst date to choose in terms of the cost of accounting services. A good year-end date falls between June and October: accounting fees will be lower during this slower period, and the pharmacy owner will be more likely to obtain the best service at the least cost. Another way to save on accounting fees is to request unaudited instead of audited statements. Because the work involved in audited statements is more comprehensive, bankers will normally require them for companies with borrowings of $500,000 or more. However, in general, unaudited statements will suffice and cost about half the amount. It is of course necessary to determine what your banker requires before making this decision.

Several steps are involved in seeking out the appropriate accounting firm for your pharmacy. The following guidelines will be useful whether investigating firms for the first time or deciding that the services of a current accountant are unsatisfactory:

1. Know what services you need, then collect names of recommended accounting firms from your banker, lawyer, business associates, and your provincial pharmacy association.
2. Telephone at least three of the firms and make an appointment to see the senior partner in his or her office. Take note of the facility, the number of partners, and the quality of staff.
3. Have the senior partner describe the various services offered. Ask to meet the partner involved in tax matters. Discover who is in charge of bookkeeping functions.
4. Explain the nature, frequency, and timing of the services you require. Request an estimate in writing of the annual cost for these services, together with a description of the full range of services to be provided.
5. Do not necessarily select the firm offering the lowest hourly fee. The total estimated charge relative to the quality and range of services offered is more important.

Siecker and Berger discuss some important aspects of the relationship between the pharmacist–owner and the outside accountant in an article published in *American Pharmacy*. The advice they give in the following passage should be heeded by all prospective pharmacy owners:

> A good accountant can save a pharmacy more than the annual cost of accounting services. It is best to look for an accountant with small-business experience. Be careful to ask how recent that experience is, because reporting and tax requirements are continuously changing. Someone with recent experience in community-pharmacy accounting is an even better candidate. There are distinct differences in large and small business accounting, and still finer nuances involved in community-pharmacy operations. The last thing you want is to pay an accountant the going rate for on-the-job training. . . . One-person [accounting] practices pose the special problem of what to do if the accountant dies, disappears, or becomes incapacitated. Other problems can occur with a large accounting firm. You do not want to pay for the services of a senior partner, who turns your work over to a junior associ-

ate. . . . You do not want to educate a new accountant every time you need advice. In today's economy, be careful if the accounting practice is not computerized.[2]

SUMMARY

The reader should now have an appreciation of the relationships between equity and debt capital, the sources to consider for securing capital, and the best methods to use in approaching those sources. Review the Capital Needs Checklist below. Remember that, by using the advice of a banker and a reliable accountant, prospective pharmacist-owners can draw on the available sources of capital to best advantage for the stability and growth of their community-pharmacy practices.

CAPITAL NEEDS CHECKLIST

Key Concepts to Remember:
- Equity capital
- Net worth
- Owner's or shareholders' equity
- Debt capital
- Operating loan
- Term loan
- SBLA
- Financial leverage
- Debt-to-equity ratio
- Working capital
- Current ratio

Sources of Equity Capital:
- Cash in savings accounts
- Investments in marketable securities
- Guaranteed income certificates
- Canada Savings Bonds
- RRSPs
- Capital accumulated in a home
- Investments by friends, family, or employees

---

[2] Bruce R. Siecker and Bruce A. Berger, "Checking up on Your Business Records," *American Pharmacy* NS23, no. 7 (July 1983):42.

Sources of Debt Capital:
- Financial institutions, especially chartered banks
- Federal Business Development Bank (FBDB)
- Lease financing
- Venture capital
- Suppliers

RECOMMENDED READING

Bank of Montreal. *Small Business Problem Solvers.* See especially Problem Solver No. 3, "Sources of Capital."

Federal Business Development Bank. *Minding Your Own Business.* Vol. 1. Toronto: FBDB, 1982.

Olenick, Arnold J. *Managing to Have Profits.* New York: McGraw Hill Book Co., 1989.

Resnick, Paul. *The Small Business Bible.* New York: John Wiley and Sons, 1988.

Timmons, Jeffry A. *New Venture Creation: A Guide to Small Business Development.* 2nd ed. Homewood, Ill.: Irwin Publishing, 1985.

7

REGULATORY AND LEGAL
CONSIDERATIONS

INTRODUCTION

The ownership and operation of pharmacies are provincial matters in Canada and are governed by an established licensing body in each province. In addition, various requirements for the dispensing of prescriptions and the sale of drugs are governed by both federal and provincial legislation.

The ten provincial licensing bodies that regulate the practice of pharmacy and the operation of pharmacies are listed in Table 7.1, along with the short title of the pertinent legislation.

In almost all provinces there is a requirement that a pharmacy be licensed or accredited. The form of authorization varies from province to province: some provinces issue a pharmacy licence, some a pharmacy accreditation, and others a pharmacy permit; but the general requirement is that pharmacies be registered in some fashion with a provincial authority. There is an annual fee for this registration and, in some cases, an initial licensing or accreditation fee as well. There are regulations governing opening, relocating, or changing the ownership of pharmacies, and most provinces require the filing of relevant information either prior to or concurrent with opening, relocation, or change in ownership.

Pharmacies are given a certificate or some other evidence of their compliance with provincial pharmacy laws and are subject to inspection by the provincial pharmacy licensing body. This inspection, normally carried out by representatives of the licensing body, occurs every one to

Table 7.1   PROVINCIAL PHARMACY LICENSING BODIES AND
            PHARMACY ACTS

Province	Licensing Body†	Provincial Act (short title)
Alberta	The Alberta Pharmaceutical Assn.	Pharmaceutical Association Act
British Columbia	The College of Pharmacists of British Columbia	The Pharmacists Act
Manitoba	The Manitoba Pharmaceutical Assn.	The Pharmaceutical Act
New Brunswick	The New Brunswick Pharmaceutical Society	The Pharmacy Act
Newfoundland	The Newfoundland Pharmaceutical Assn.	The Pharmaceutical Association Act
Nova Scotia	The Nova Scotia Pharmaceutical Society	The Nova Scotia Pharmacy Act
Ontario	The Ontario College of Pharmacists	The Health Disciplines Act – Parts I and VI
Prince Edward Island	The Prince Edward Island Pharmacy Board	The Pharmacy Act
Quebec	Ordre des Pharmaciens du Québec	The Pharmacy Act
Saskatchewan	The Saskatchewan Pharmaceutical Assn.	The Pharmacy Act

† Addresses of licensing bodies are listed in the Directory section of this book.

three years. An inspection report is made and, if standards regarding the maintenance and operation of the pharmacy or the dispensing of prescriptions and sale of drugs are not met, various sanctions may be imposed on the pharmacy or on those responsible for its operation. These sanctions range from revoking the licence or certificate of accreditation to imposing such penalties as disciplinary action against the pharmacists involved in the operation of the pharmacy or fines on the persons responsible for its operation.

In addition to being inspected by provincial authorities, pharmacies are visited from time to time by representatives of the federal Bureau of Dangerous Drugs, who review and audit narcotic and controlled drug prescription files and inventories.

OWNERSHIP OF A PHARMACY

There is considerable variation from province to province in the legal requirements for owning pharmacies. Some provinces (Alberta, New Brunswick, Newfoundland, Prince Edward Island) have no restrictions regarding who may own a pharmacy, whereas others limit ownership to pharmacists, a partnership of pharmacists, or a corporation meeting specific legal requirements.

In those provinces where corporations are permitted to operate pharmacies, it is usually required that the majority of directors of the corporation be pharmacists and, in some provinces, there are restrictions regarding the holding of shares. In all cases, regardless of who owns a pharmacy, the laws require that the management and direct superintendence of the pharmacy be carried out by a pharmacist.

OPENING OR CLOSING A PHARMACY

Because all provinces have certain standards for the construction, maintenance, and operation of pharmacies, in almost all cases an inspection is carried out prior to the opening of a new pharmacy to determine if the requirements have been met. In order for proper arrangements to be made, most licensing bodies require that a notice of intention to open be filed before the desired opening date and, in some cases, a floor plan of the pharmacy layout must also be submitted. The timing of the pre-opening inspection is critical since a delay in obtaining a pharmacy licence or accreditation certificate can be a serious inconvenience and can result in a financial loss for the pharmacy operator. Such problems can be avoided by proper planning and by filing notice sufficiently early. Prior notice is also required in certain provinces for the relocation of a pharmacy and, in some cases, for the transfer of ownership of an existing pharmacy.

Therefore, when opening a new pharmacy, relocating a pharmacy, or acquiring an existing pharmacy, it is imperative that the owner carefully examine and adhere to the applicable provincial requirements.

When a pharmacy is sold, a total inventory is always taken to determine the financial aspects of the transaction. In addition, pharmacies are legally required to conduct an audit of their narcotic and controlled drugs, which must be reported to the Bureau of Dangerous Drugs and sometimes to the provincial licensing body. Detailed requirements can be obtained from the Bureau of Dangerous Drugs or the appropriate provincial pharmacy licensing body.

When a pharmacy is closed and ceases to operate, the person responsible for its operation must in all cases notify the provincial licensing body of the date of closure and provide information regarding the proper disposal of all prescription and non-prescription drugs and prescription records. The signs and symbols in and about the premises that identify it as a pharmacy must also be removed. The time period for notifying the licensing body of the closure and other details varies; in some cases (British Columbia and Quebec) it must be done at the closing and, in others, within a stated period of time (usually one to two weeks) after closure.

OPERATING A PHARMACY

In all provinces, there are certain standards set for the maintenance and operation of pharmacies. There is usually a required or recommended list of equipment for the dispensary and of resources for a professional library. Several provinces have particular construction standards and some have requirements regarding the size of the dispensary and dispensing counter.

Constructing a new pharmacy, undertaking renovation, or relocating a pharmacy all require a careful check of the standards set out in the provincial pharmacy legislation as well as in the respective building codes.

Apart from the requirement in some provinces (Newfoundland, New Brunswick, Ontario, Manitoba, Alberta, Saskatchewan, and British Columbia) that the dispensary or dispensing area be of a certain size (see Chapter 9), the main construction requirements govern ease of cleaning, lighting, ventilation, and the availability of facilities related to sanitary considerations.

Equipment requirements include items necessary for the effective operation of the dispensary, such as filing systems for prescriptions; typing equipment (typewriters or computers with printout capability); prescription balances and weights; and glassware and consumable materials, for example, bottles, vials, and labels.

There is considerable variation in the specific library requirements, which are usually set out in regulations or by-laws. However, pharmacy libraries typically contain a current (or recent) edition of a *Compendium of Pharmaceuticals and Specialties*, drug-interaction publications, pharmacology or therapeutics references, provincial and federal legislation applying to pharmacy, a pharmaceutics text, a dispensatory, and a medical dictionary.

The establishment of pharmacies within other larger retail outlets is becoming quite common, and some provinces have special requirements governing this type of arrangement. The main consideration is that no prescriptions are dispensed or drugs sold from the pharmacy outlet when pharmacists are not present. Thus, it is stipulated either that the pharmacy always be open when the other retail aspects of the establishment are operating or, failing this, that some mechanism be employed to close off the pharmacy area when a pharmacist is not present but the premises are open to the public.

All provinces require a pharmacist (or a certified dispenser, in some cases) to be present at all times that the pharmacy is open. Because of the need to attach the responsibility for the operation of a pharmacy to a pharmacist, the various provincial laws require the owner of the pharmacy to designate a person responsible for the management of the pharmacy so far as it concerns the dispensing of prescriptions, sale of drugs, and overseeing of the professional operations. This pharmacy manager (sometimes called the pharmacist-in-charge) has a variety of legal responsibilities and, as the professional in charge of the pharmacy on a day-to-day basis, is responsible for ensuring compliance with pertinent legislation and the professional standards currently accepted in the profession.

Control over the sale of narcotics and controlled drugs is exercised through the federal Narcotic Control Act and the Food and Drugs Act and their respective regulations. Both the Narcotic Regulations and the Food and Drug Regulations (Part G) contain a definition of "pharmacist," which in part reads:

"pharmacist"
(a) means a person who is registered and entitled under the laws of a Province
   (i) to practise pharmacy, and
   (ii) to operate a pharmacy or dispensary and who is operating a pharmacy or dispensary and is practising pharmacy thereunder in that Province.

This part of the definition is used to describe those pharmacists who have the authority to sign for narcotics or controlled drugs when ordered from a licensed dealer. This signing authority, which in some cases is synonymous with the designation "manager," is assigned to a pharmacist

by the owner of the pharmacy or, in the case of hospitals or other institutions, a person representing the institution. A licensed dealer may not supply a narcotic or controlled drug to a pharmacy unless it is signed for by the manager or the person with signing authority either in the form of an original written order or in the form of a receipt if the order is electronic or verbal. It is, therefore, extremely important when opening a new pharmacy, taking over an existing one, or relocating to notify the appropriate agency of the name(s) of the designated person(s) holding this responsibility for the particular location.

In addition to regulations regarding the equipment, library, construction, size, and general maintenance and operation of pharmacies, some provinces have regulations governing the hours of operation. Three provinces (Alberta, New Brunswick, and Newfoundland) have a set minimum number of hours that a pharmacy must be open (30 to 36 hours per week). Other provincial or municipal legislation or by-laws may also have requirements governing hours and holidays.

DISPENSING PRESCRIPTIONS AND THE SALE OF DRUGS

When dispensing prescriptions and selling drugs, pharmacists (and other persons entitled to carry out these functions) are obliged to follow both federal and provincial legislation. In the case of prescription medication, the federal law relates to such things as ordering, records, and prescription and refill requirements for narcotic drugs, controlled drugs, and Schedule F drugs. In addition, the federal legislation establishes requirements for drug identification numbers (DIN) on pharmaceutical products and assigns proprietary registration to certain products under Division 10 of the Food and Drug Regulations. Provincial legislation deals more particularly with the conditions of sale for these products and who may sell them. There is considerable overlap between the various provincial regulations regarding the sale of drugs and the federal legislation. For example, most provinces have their own regulations regarding prescription and other drug records and Alberta, British Columbia, Manitoba, New Brunswick, Ontario, and Saskatchewan each have their own provincial prescription drug schedules in addition to those found in the federal legislation. This overlap can cause confusion at the dispensary level because some prescription drugs will not necessarily bear the prescription symbol (Pr) on the label (as required for federal Schedule F drugs).

While the owner or manager is responsible for the overall operation of a pharmacy, all pharmacists, as independent professionals, must act within their professional competence and are held responsible by the licensing body for their conduct as individuals. As to the dispensing of prescriptions, the sale of drugs, and the professional services associated with these activities, the pharmacy legislation in most provinces permits students under supervision, interns (sometimes under supervision), and pharmacists to carry them out. An additional category, certified clerk or certified dispenser, is designated as permitted to carry out these responsibilities under specified conditions in certain provinces (the Maritimes). Pharmacy assistants or dispensary assistants or technicians are recognized as auxiliary employees in almost all pharmacies in Canada. They are permitted to carry out technical functions and several provinces have published guidelines to assist pharmacists in assigning appropriate tasks to this category of personnel. While such persons are permitted to assist pharmacists in the dispensing function, the pharmacist has the final responsibility for dispensing.

Pharmacists are legal custodians of medications and must exercise this responsibility with due regard for the laws governing the distribution of drugs and the professional responsibilities inherent in this activity. In the case of prescription drugs, it is incumbent on the pharmacist to ensure that the release of the medication is on the order of, and according to the wishes of, a prescriber. Unfortunately, forgeries and false representations to obtain drugs are all too common and special care must be taken by all concerned to combat this problem. Federal legislation (the Narcotic Control Regulations and Food and Drug Regulations) is specific about ensuring that prescriptions are from a bona fide prescriber. Table 7.2 provides a summary of the federal laws governing prescription-drug ordering, records, prescription requirements, and refills. The provincial legislation regarding prescriptions frequently augments the federal legislation and tends to deal with such things as copies of prescriptions, records, labelling, and product selection.

The laws regarding the sale of non-prescription drugs vary considerably from province to province and a detailed description of them is not possible here, but it should be remembered that some provinces (British Columbia, New Brunswick, Ontario, Prince Edward Island, Saskatchewan) have a restricted-access law or policy for certain non-prescription drugs. Such drugs, usually listed in a schedule included in the provincial pharmacy acts (Table 7.1), must be kept in an area of the pharmacy where there is no opportunity for self-selection by the public. Some provinces (British Columbia, New Brunswick, Newfoundland, Quebec, Prince Edward Island, Saskatchewan) have a law or policy regarding a professional-products area in the pharmacy, usually involving the stipulation that non-prescription drugs available to the public on a self-selection basis be located in an area of the pharmacy adjacent to the dispensary. Both policies, restricted access and a professional-products area, are designed to facilitate interaction between the pharmacy professional and the public in the sale of non-prescription drugs.

Another matter related to the sale of non-prescription drugs in pharmacies is the sale, labelling, and record-keeping requirements for poisonous or dangerous substances. Care should be taken to ensure that the

Table 7.2 SUMMARY OF FEDERAL LAWS GOVERNING PRESCRIPTION DRUG ORDERING, RECORDS, PRESCRIPTION REQUIREMENTS, AND REFILLS

Description	Ordering	Purchase Record	Sales Record	Prescription Requirements	Refills
Narcotic Drugs (N) – All straight narcotic drugs – All narcotic drugs for parenteral use. – All narcotic compounds containing more than one narcotic drug. – All narcotic compounds containing less than two other non-narcotic ingredients. – All products containing heroin, hydro-codone, methadone, and oxycodone. – Dextropropoxyphene.	– Written or electronic. – Written orders must be signed by a pharmacist with signing authority. – The receipt for electronic orders must be signed by the pharmacist with signing authority who received the drug and this receipt must be provided to the licensed dealer within five working days.	Purchases must be recorded in Narcotic and Controlled Drug Register or other record maintained for such purposes and be available on the premises.	Prescription on Narcotic and Controlled Drug File plus record of sales in Narcotic and Controlled Drug Register or in a computer from which a printout may be readily obtained on request or be available on the premises. Dextropropoxyphene sales not reportable.	– A written prescription signed by and dated by an authorized prescriber.	– Refills not permitted. – All "reorders" must be new written prescriptions. – Narcotics may be prescribed to be dispensed in divided portions, subject to professional discretion.

Narcotic Preparations (N)				
– All combinations containing only one narcotic drug and two or more non-narcotic medicinal ingredients in a recognized therapeutic dose not intended for parenteral use.	– Verbal, written, or electronic. – Written orders must be signed by a pharmacist with signing authority. – The receipt for verbal or electronic orders must be signed by the pharmacist with signing authority who received the drug and this receipt must be provided to the licensed dealer within five working days.	Prescription on Narcotic and Controlled Drug File. No record of sales in Narcotic and Controlled Drug Register required.	– A written or verbal prescription by an authorized prescriber.	– Refills not permitted. – All "reorders" written or verbal must be new prescriptions. – Narcotics may be prescribed to be dispensed in divided portions, subject to professional discretion.

Description	Ordering	Purchase Record	Sales Record	Prescription Requirements	Refills
Controlled Drugs (C) – All straight controlled drugs. – All combinations containing more than one controlled drug.	– Written or electronic. – Written orders must be signed by a pharmacist with signing authority. – The receipt for electronic orders must be signed by the pharmacist with signing authority who received the drug and this receipt must be provided to the licensed dealer within five working days.		Prescription on Narcotic and Controlled Drug File plus record of sales in Narcotic and Controlled Drug Register or in a computer from which a printout may be readily obtained on request or be available on the premises.		– Refills not permitted if original prescription is verbal. – An original written prescription may be refilled if prescriber has indicated in writing the number of refills and dates for, or intervals between, refills.

Controlled Drug Preparations (C)		
– All combinations containing only one controlled drug and one or more medicinal ingredients in a recognized therapeutic dose.	– Verbal, written, or electronic. – Written orders must be signed by a pharmacist with signing authority. – The receipt for verbal or electronic orders must be signed by the pharmacist with signing authority who received the drug and this receipt must be provided to the licensed dealer within five working days.	Prescription on Narcotic and Controlled Drug File. No record of sales in Narcotic and Controlled Drug Register required.

95

Description	Ordering	Purchase Record	Sales Record	Prescription Requirements	Refills
Controlled Drugs in Schedule to Part G of Regulation (C) – Barbituric acid (except Secobarbital and Pentobarbital), Butorphanol, Chlorphentermine, Diethylpropion, Nalbuphine, Phentermine, Thiobarbituric acid, and their salts and derivatives. – All combinations containing only one controlled drug listed above and one or more medicinal ingredients in a therapeutic dose.	– Verbal, written, or electronic. – Written orders must be signed by a pharmacist with signing authority. – The receipt for electronic orders must be signed by the pharmacist with signing authority who received the drug and this receipt must be provided to the licensed dealer within five working days.	Retain invoices in chronological order for auditing purposes or record purchases in Narcotic and Controlled Drug Register or other record maintained for such purposes.			– An original written or verbal prescription may be refilled if the prescriber has authorized in writing or verbally the number of times and dates for, or intervals between, refills.

Schedule F Drugs (Pr)			
– All drugs listed in Schedule F of Food and Drug Regulations.	– Verbal, written, or electronic.	No record required.	Prescription on regular file.	– An original written or verbal prescription may be refilled if the prescriber has authorized in writing or verbally the number of times it may be refilled.

pharmacy has an adequate supply of these specialized labels, along with properly constituted prescription labels, all bearing the standard information required, including the name and address of the pharmacy. In some provinces, special "poison" registers are required for recording sales of certain non-prescription drugs.

The advertising of professional services is a subject of considerable importance in the operation of a pharmacy. In addition to federal legislation prohibiting false or misleading advertising and imposing certain restrictions on the advertising of narcotic, controlled, and Schedule F drugs, the various provincial bodies frequently exercise control over professional advertising. These controls range from the prohibition of the advertising of certain non-prescription drugs in some provinces to the usual prohibition of the advertising of comparative or superlative professional services. In some provinces, advertising prescription prices and professional fees is prohibited; in others, such advertising is permitted under certain circumstances.

WHERE TO OBTAIN INFORMATION

The licensing of pharmacists and the licensing or accreditation of pharmacies is a provincial matter. Each provincial pharmacy licensing body (see Table 7.1) is responsible for administering the respective provincial pharmacy legislation, and persons contemplating the operation of a pharmacy should, at the earliest opportunity, contact their provincial licensing body for information about the ownership, opening, and closing of pharmacies, as well as their maintenance and operation. Legislation and policies change and it may well be that the documentation you have or the advice you have received is out of date. Most provincial licensing bodies also provide copies of pertinent federal legislation along with the particular provincial act, regulations, and by-laws. In addition, interpretations and policy statements are frequently made available.

The Bureau of Dangerous Drugs (regional or national offices) will provide further information and assistance with respect to laws governing the ordering, record keeping, and sale requirements for narcotic and controlled drugs.

The regulatory checklist on pp. 99-100 will be helpful in obtaining, evaluating, and implementing the legal requirements for the operation of a pharmacy. This list is a guide only and is not intended to be comprehensive. Since legislation varies from province to province and is subject to frequent change, it is imperative to contact the appropriate agency for up-to-date information.

A Regulatory Checklist

1. Has the provincial pharmacy licensing body been contacted?
2. Do you have the pertinent provincial and federal legislation?
3. Does the ownership meet requirements?
4. Have all those involved in ownership and management been advised of their legal responsibilities?
5. Are you involved in:

    (a) an opening of a new pharmacy?
    (b) a relocation?
    (c) a change in ownership?
    (d) a major renovation?

    Have you complied with the pertinent laws for this situation from the following list?

    (a) proper notice
    (b) application submitted
    (c) appropriate documentation provided
    (d) fee paid
    (e) notice given regarding manager or person with signing authority
    (f) arrangements made for an inspection (pre-opening)
    (g) inventory of narcotic and controlled drugs taken and submitted to proper authorities

6. If pharmacy is being closed:

    (a) has notice been given?
    (b) have drugs been disposed of according to law?
    (c) has a closing inventory of drugs been taken?
    (d) have all signs, symbols, etc., of a pharmacy been removed?

7. Is equipment complete?
8. Is library complete?
9. Does construction and layout meet requirements of pharmacy legislation and building code?
10. Do all staff members (managers, other pharmacists, students, interns, certified clerks, pharmacy auxiliary personnel) understand their legal responsibilities?
11. Do hours of operation conform to local requirements?
12. (a) Does the layout meet special requirements regarding restricted access or professional-products area?
    (b) Are drugs appropriately located in these areas?

13. (a) Do pharmacy prescription and other labels meet requirements?
    (b) Have they been ordered?
14. Do the people responsible for advertising understand the rules?
15. Are systems for ordering, dispensing, sale, and record keeping of drugs in place so that staff can meet legal and professional responsibilities?

For Further Reference

Those interested in establishing a pharmacy should consult the pertinent legislation in each province, as identified in Table 7.1 on p. 86. Addresses of the provincial licensing bodies are given in the Directory section of this book.

8

INSURANCE AND THE PHARMACY PRACTICE

INTRODUCTION

The elements of business success can be stated very simply. To succeed, one needs to sell goods and/or services that return more to the provider than it costs to provide them. How much more? That is a question that only the entrepreneur can answer. How successful do you need or want to be? The return on investment – in other words, the reward – depends on the risk and, in business, the greater the risk, the greater is the expectation for a higher return. The risk involved is related to the owner's ability to interpret the needs of the consumer and then to provide the demanded goods and services. Both of these are complex processes, which alone can engage the full-time attention of the businessperson.

However, other risks are also involved in running a business. Some of them are fire, flood, vandalism, disability, and death. Such occurrences can overwhelm even the best-managed business. It is generally accepted that the cost of such risks can be minimized if they are shared, and this concept is realized through insurance. The degree of risk associated with loss by fire or the elements can be greatly reduced by insurance. Insurance is available to protect real estate, salable assets, and receivables; it can even provide for a continuation of income in the event that the business is temporarily closed as a result of fire, damage by the elements, or some form of impact.

ESSENTIAL BUSINESS INSURANCE

Insuring Assets

The major part of a pharmacy owner's investment in a practice is in its fixed assets (land, building, fixtures, and equipment) and its inventory. Each of these assets can be insured for its replacement value by what is known, simply, as "replacement insurance."

If you own the building that houses the pharmacy, replacement insurance is essential. It will provide the full replacement value of the building (i.e., the cost to rebuild, which may be less than the current market value of the building) in the event that it is destroyed – the insured does not have to settle for the depreciated value of the building at the time of the loss. In the normal course of events, a building will depreciate, for accounting purposes, at the rate of five percent per year. After 20 years, it is assumed to have depreciated to a value of zero. However, a loss requires replacement of the building, which, despite depreciation, was adequate for the operation of the business. The accounting principle of "depreciation" assumes (in theory) that a portion of business profits is being put aside annually for the purpose of replacing the building at the end of the 20-year period. This, in fact, is rarely done, and replacement insurance is therefore required to provide the necessary capital in the event of loss.

Inventory is the asset that makes a pharmacy practice viable. An inventory of $100,000 destroyed by fire must be replaced if the pharmacist is to continue in business. Without replacement insurance, the $100,000 would have to be borrowed, placing the pharmacist in an untenable financial situation.

Furniture, fixtures, and equipment are the means by which a pharmacist displays inventory, makes the dispensary efficient, facilitates proper record keeping (in recent times, by computer), and generally enhances the pharmacy's ability to provide a range of services efficiently. In short, the pharmacist would be unable to function without furniture, fixtures, and equipment. How much are these assets worth? A rule of thumb says $15 per square foot, at the very least. Hence, in a pharmacy that occupies 5000 square feet, furniture, fixtures, and equipment will be worth at least $75,000. For accounting purposes, these assets are depreciated at 10 percent per year, so that in ten years, at "book value," they are worth nothing. In reality, however, they are still serving well and, if destroyed, must be replaced. Once again, replacement insurance protects the pharmacist from going into debt to replace assets.

Cash and valuables (bonds and important papers) are similarly insurable and, if lost by fire (or similar fate) or stolen, will be replaced at insured value.

Notwithstanding the above, the pharmacy owner should recognize that while it is hazardous to underinsure, it is also nonsensical and wasteful to overinsure.

SECURITY

Community pharmacies have been increasingly victimized by burglary. "Break and enter" claims (commonly referred to as B & E) have reached an alarming level. The prime targets for theft in pharmacies are narcotic drugs and cigarettes.

Insurance companies now require that pharmacies protect themselves against robbery with adequate security, which implies alarm systems in addition to reliable double locks on front and back entrances. Failure to provide "adequate" security could result in an inability to secure insurance coverage for "all risk." The topic of security in the community pharmacy will be discussed in detail in Chapter 19.

A range of security systems, from the amateurish to the highly sophisticated, is currently available on the market, at prices ranging from $300 into the thousands. There are systems so elaborate that entry through doors, windows, ceilings, or walls will trigger an alarm (by means of infra-red, motion, or heat detectors) that cannot be de-activated because it is linked to the police by a dedicated phone line. The implementation of various security measures has reduced, but not eliminated, the occurrence of burglary among community pharmacies. Your insurance agent should be able to advise you on the type of system that will qualify as "adequate" security from the insurance company's point of view.

Business Interruption Insurance

In the event of fire or other serious disruption caused, for example, by sewer backup, severe hailstorm, or impact by a vehicle, the pharmacy may be unsuitable to render services for periods ranging from a few days to several months. No income will be generated, but interest on loans will accumulate, taxes will continue, and creditors will insist on being paid. How can the pharmacist meet these persisting obligations with no income? The simple answer is found in business interruption insurance. This type of insurance is sometimes based on earned profit, but more often on gross margin. If, for example, annual sales are $1 million and gross margin is 30 percent, the gross margin for the year will be $300,000. The pharmacist agrees with the insurance agent that, even in a major catastrophe, the pharmacy should be able to resume operations in six months or less. Therefore, a business interruption insurance policy valued at half of the annual gross margin – $150,000 – is purchased. This protection will allow the pharmacist, during the period when the pharmacy is closed, to pay:

1. The interest on loans
2. Taxes
3. Debts to creditors
4. His or her own salary.
5. The salaries of key staff members, to prevent them from taking jobs elsewhere.

Failure to secure continuance-of-income insurance is the most common reason why pharmacists who have suffered a major catastrophe to their stores never return to business.

Comprehensive General Liability and Shop Malpractice Insurance

It is important to investigate and understand the nature of the coverage offered under comprehensive general liability and shop malpractice insurance. (Note that the use of the term "commercial general liability" is also gaining favour in the insurance industry today.) Ensure that both the corporation as an entity and all its employees, whether full-time, part-time, or occasional, are covered for legal liability in case of a possible suit. Comprehensive (or commercial) general liability and shop malpractice insurance covers legal liability in cases such as the following:

1. An alleged dispensing error.
2. Alleged misinformation or insufficiency of information: for example, an allegation that a patient became pregnant because *the pharmacist failed to emphasize* that the inert tablets in the birth control prescription were to be taken faithfully for seven days, in addition to the 21 active-ingredient tablets.
3. An incorrect sale: for example, selling oil of wintergreen when castor oil was requested.
4. An allegation of personal injury by a customer while on pharmacy property: for example, a customer trips over an electrical cord, a suspended sign becomes dislodged and hits a customer on the head, a customer slips on an ice patch in the pharmacy's parking lot.
5. Injury to a person by an employee-owned vehicle used on company business.

In other contexts, this type of coverage may be referred to as third-party liability insurance or casualty insurance, which are defined as protection against financial loss arising out of injury to persons or out of damage, loss, or destruction of property caused by negligent, fraudulent, or criminal acts. (The term "casualty insurance" will not normally appear in a "fire and all-risk" certificate of insurance; it is commonly used in automobile insurance contracts and in policies for the types of business where "casualty" damage is likely to occur.)

It should also be noted that in pharmacy, as in other health-related professions, there is ultimately no form of malpractice insurance that can fully protect the practice. Some cases of malpractice may be ruled by professional peers to be so gross as to disqualify the practitioner and thus prevent continuance of the practice.

PURCHASING INSURANCE

All necessary insurance coverage should be purchased on setting up or taking over a practice, when a loss would be particularly distressing. Most pharmacists will need to borrow a considerable amount of money to launch a pharmacy. The lending institution will require a copy of the insurance contract, not only to verify that its investment will be protected, but to ensure that it is named as the first loss payable up to the amount of the loan.

The pharmacy owner should purchase insurance from a reputable firm, whose prices are competitive and which has a proven record of satisfactory claims experience. It is important to locate a firm that will provide advice, premium quotes and comparisons, and, above all, an agent who not only understands pharmacy practice as a business but one you feel you can trust and communicate with. Note that a qualified insurance professional can be either an agent or a broker. An agent is essentially a sales and service representative for a particular insurance company. A broker, on the other hand, is not tied to one company, but acts on a free-lance basis and monitors the policies offered by many companies. In this way, the broker may be able to locate the particular policy that best suits a particular client's needs. Insurance can be a complex subject and the new pharmacy owner cannot expect to be an expert on its various terms, conditions, and costs. The following guidelines will assist the pharmacist in making the proper choice of a reliable insurance firm or broker:

1. *Information*: Ask the agent or broker selected to explain fully the suggested coverage and the company's claims procedures. Be certain that you know what risks are *not* covered in your contract. Too often, policyholders with inadmissible claims find themselves helplessly arguing, "I thought I was covered." For example, the pharmacist should ascertain that the insurance purchased covers any loss of money and securities, whether by theft on the way to the bank or robbery of the pharmacy, where money may have been left, improperly secured, after hours.
2. *Service*: Select an agent or broker who represents a company (or companies) with a proven track record in fair and prompt claims settlement, ready availability of information, and knowledgeability in the full range of adjustment problems that might arise.

3. *Price*: Obtain quotes from several companies, and select not necessarily the lowest, but the one that best addresses your needs and offers the most satisfactory and understandable presentation of the necessary coverage.

You should insist that your agent or broker review your coverage with you annually, at the least. Consider the following example: at a 5 percent annual rate of inflation, a pharmacy's inventory, as listed in the original policy, will have increased in value at least 50 percent in ten years; in addition, the pharmacy may have opted to expand and carry a larger base inventory. In other words, without proper monitoring and discussion, inventory could reach a replacement value of $200,000 during the time that premiums are being paid faithfully on a policy providing protection for only $100,000. Because the owner and insurance agent did not review events as they were unfolding, a claim for $200,000 in the event of loss would not be honoured, since the increased value of the inventory would not be reflected in the policy.

Interprovincial Pharmacy Group Insurance Program

A special insurance plan for community pharmacies is offered through the Interprovincial Pharmacy Group Insurance Program. The plan operates in six provinces: British Columbia, Alberta, Saskatchewan, Manitoba, New Brunswick, and Prince Edward Island, and is sponsored by those provinces' professional pharmacy associations. The insurance agent and pharmacist involved in this plan complete a worksheet, which sets out the basic rates per $1000 of coverage for (1) the building and (2) "other," including inventory, fixtures, the unamortized value of lease improvements, and accounts receivable. The basic rates vary depending on the construction of the building (masonry vs. frame) and the community in which the pharmacy is located. The rates for the building and the assets will differ because, for example, while stock and fixtures might be destroyed in a fire, the building itself could remain essentially unharmed.

The worksheet also sets out a series of rate credits that can result in a substantial reduction from the basic rate (in total, up to 67.5 percent at the time of writing). Credits are given for features that put the pharmacy in a lower-risk category – for example, "less than 5000 square feet," "less than 30 years old," "one storey in height," "concrete floor," "heating standard," "electrical standard." At the time of writing, credit-adjusted rates per $1000 in coverage could range anywhere from approximately $0.04 for the building and $0.06 for assets (masonry building, lowest-risk location, eligible for all credits) to $0.44 for the building and $0.47 for assets (non-masonry building, highest-risk location, eligible for no credits – a case unlikely to occur in actuality as almost all pharmacies would in fact be eligible for at least some of the rate credits).

Finally, a premium is added to the calculated rate according to a "loading" factor. This relates to the quality of security in place in the pharmacy: the lower the level of security, the higher the premium will be.

The insurable values for the building and assets are supplied by the pharmacist and multiplied by the adjusted base rates. The policy also provides for the calculation of business interruption insurance, comprehensive general liability and shop malpractice, and money and securities. The total monthly premium may be paid annually, semi-annually, or quarterly, with no penalty.

The information thus gathered is set out in detail in a Certificate of Insurance, as illustrated on page 108 (reprinted by permission of the Grain Insurance and Guarantee Company, Winnipeg, Manitoba). In addition to the certificate, the policyholder receives a set of "wordings," which specifies exactly what is and what is not insured.

The Interprovincial Pharmacy Group Insurance Program is of interest because its policies are designed specifically to meet the needs of pharmacist-owners. However, various firms across the country offer equally suitable, comprehensive coverages, and pharmacists are encouraged to explore the available options in their areas. Provincial pharmacy associations can generally offer assistance in this regard, sponsoring workshops and other programs on insurance in pharmacy practice.

OTHER INSURANCE APPLICABLE TO BUSINESS

LIFE INSURANCE

Life insurance is relevant in business from a number of perspectives. Consider the following types of insurance and the manner in which they can contribute to success in business.

1. *"Key Person" Life Insurance*: The success of many businesses depends on the leadership of one key person. That person's death may cause a serious financial setback, until such time as a qualified replacement can be found. If the business owns, and is named the beneficiary of, a life insurance policy on the key person, funds will be provided to attract, educate, and train the right candidate to take the place of the deceased. The funds will also keep the business in operation until this occurs, ensuring stability and continuity and protecting the jobs of existing staff members.
2. *Partnership Insurance*: The death of a business partner can result in the withdrawal of his or her investment in the business. The spouse, if any, may not be interested in the continuance of the business, may wish to relocate, or, in any event, liquidate the late partner's share.

CERTIFICATE OF INSURANCE

PHARMACY GROUP INSURANCE PROGRAM
COMMERCIAL STORE PACKAGE

POLICY NUMBER 02
CERTIFICATE OF
INSURANCE NO. _____

THIS PLAN IS SPECIFICALLY DESIGNED
FOR PHARMACIES AND OFFICIALLY
SPONSORED BY

INSURER

Grain Insurance and Guarantee Company

New Brunswick Pharmaceutical Society

INSURED _____

Manitoba Society of Professional Pharmacists' Inc.

_____

Saskatchewan Pharmaceutical Association

_____

Alberta Pharmaceutical Association

Mailing Address _____

British Columbia Pharmacists' Society

_____

Prince Edward Island Pharmaceutical Association

_____

Location _____

_____

POLICY PERIOD: EFFECTIVE 12:01 A.M. STANDARD TIME _____
AT THE ADDRESS OF THE INSURED AND CONTINUOUS UNTIL CANCELLED.

This is to certify that in consideration of the payment of the premium charged the Insured is covered for:

LIMITS

This policy	Section 1	Building(s)	$ _____	STANDARD FORM
contains a clause	Section 2a)	Commercial Property	$ _____	☐ _____
which may limit	Section 2b)	Business Interruption	$ _____	MEMBERS' INITIALS
the amount	Section 3	Comprehensive General Liability & Shop Malpractice		BROAD FORM
payable		Tenants Fire Legal Liability	$ 100,000.00	☐ _____
	Section 4	Money and Securities	$ _____	MEMBERS' INITIALS
		Additional Costume Jewellery and Watches (Section 2a)	$ _____	

LOSS IF ANY PAYABLE TO (mortgage clause overleaf, applicable to mortgages of real property only.)

_____

_____

AUTHORIZED REPRESENTATIVE _____

INTERPROVINCIAL PHARMACY GROUP INSURANCE PROGRAM

DEDUCTIBLE _____

WARRANTED PROTECTION _____

SECTION 1 MAIN BUILDING $ _____

OUTBUILDINGS $ _____

TOTAL $ _____ @ _____ = $ _____

+ 10% $ _____ LIMIT 1

SECTION 2a) COMMERCIAL PROPERTY

AVERAGE MERCHANDISE INVENTORY AT COST $ _____

MAXIMUM INVENTORY SEASONAL INCREASE A _____

FIXTURES REPLACEMENT COST $ _____

LEASE IMPROVEMENTS UNAMORTIZED VALUE $ _____

ACCOUNTS RECEIVABLE $ _____

AMOUNT B $ _____ @ _____ = $ _____

A _____ + B _____ + 10% = $ _____ LIMIT 2a)

SECTION 2b) BUSINESS INTERRUPTION

ANNUAL GROSS SALES	$ _____	Standard Deductible $100.00 Credit For $250.00 Deductible Members' Initials	- $ _____
OTHER INCOME (EG. RENTS) +	$ _____		
COST OF MERCHANDISE SOLD -	$ _____		

_____% (MIN. 25%) x $ _____ @ _____ $ _____

$ _____ + 10% $ _____ LIMIT 2b)

SECTION 3 COMPREHENSIVE GENERAL LIABILITY $ _____ LIMIT 3 $ _____
AND SHOP MALPRACTICE

SECTION 4 MONEY AND SECURITIES _____ _____ X _____ $ _____

ADDITIONAL COSTUME JEWELLERY AND WATCHES $ _____ _____ X $2.00 $ _____

NOTE: THE 100% VALUES DECLARED   MONTHLY PREMIUM $ _____

IN THIS APPLICATION OR AS REVISED   QUARTERLY PREMIUM $ _____

ANNUALLY WILL BE USED IN THE   (ONE TIME ONLY) ENROLLMENT FEE $ _____

SETTLEMENT OF LOSS OR DAMAGE.   MINIMUM DEPOSIT PREMIUM $ _____

DATED _____ SIGNATURE OF APPLICANT _____

Furthermore, the goodwill assets of the partner may be lost. Partnership insurance provides funds to finance reorganization into a new partnership or sole proprietorship.

Partnership insurance usually goes hand-in-hand with a buy–sell agreement. This agreement should be drawn up by a lawyer and provide for the succession of a business in the event of a partner's death. It can specify either a value of the business or a formula to assess the value. This value is then insured by means of a life insurance policy on each partner for the proportion of the business that he or she owns. The surviving partner is the beneficiary of the policy but bound by the buy–sell agreement to transfer the funds to the deceased partner's family in return for their portion of the business. In this way, the business can proceed and money is available to fund the purchase.

3. *Sole Proprietorship Insurance*: A sole proprietor, by insuring his or her own life, is in fact providing the necessary funds for surviving family members to reorganize, carry on, or sell the business in the event of his or her death. If a new manager is secured, money will be available to orient that person and assess his or her value in a "carry-on" decision. Also, creditors could choose to sue the estate of the deceased for any outstanding debts. Without the protection of life insurance, the home and personal assets of the family might have to be sold to meet such claims. This would of course apply to general partnerships as well.

Life insurance has become so sophisticated in recent years that it can virtually be tailored to meet the individual business owner's needs. The policyholder may choose to name several beneficiaries, from family members or the company itself to lending institutions and other parties that may have an interest in the business. Different types of insurance (such as whole-life, term, reducing-term, and endowment insurance) are designed to suit different circumstances and needs: your insurance professional will be able to advise you on the terms and benefits of each. It is also important to explore with your agent or broker the circumstances under which insurance premiums may be tax deductible (caution must be exercised here, since the rules governing tax deductibility of life insurance premiums were, at the time of writing, being challenged before the courts).

AUTOMOBILE INSURANCE

As you are probably aware, automobile insurance is compulsory in Canada. This area of insurance is complex both in its personal and corporate applications and requires the pharmacist's close attention (especially if the pharmacy owns a delivery vehicle). Automobile insurance is not normally part of a "fire and all-risk" insurance package. It is, however, important and should be discussed with an expert in the field.

LONG-TERM DISABILITY

Disability insurance is as important as life insurance. During the course of our working lives, most of us will experience an illness or accident that may keep us out of the workforce for a period of days, months, or years. Statistics show that the average length of disability leave from the workforce ranges from six to eight weeks. Employers generally extend two weeks' pay, meaning that, on average, the disabled employee must locate income for the balance of four to six weeks. In a one-person pharmacy practice, a six-to-eight week disability would involve replacing the owner-manager at a cost of $3000-$4000 per month. The disabled owner's salary would also have to be paid. Can the pharmacy afford to provide for two incomes? In a two-person pharmacy or a partnership, the partner may work overtime for a period of two weeks, but may be unwilling or unable to carry two shifts beyond that period. In this case, the pharmacy would have to provide not two incomes, but three. The solution is personal-income replacement or long-term disability insurance.

This type of insurance is clearly a legitimate store expense. However, if the business pays the premium and deducts it as an expense item, the money received by the beneficiary as income will be taxable. This will also be the case if the employee and employer each pay half the premium. On the other hand, if the employee declares the employer's contribution as income or pays for the entire premium independently, his or her insurance income will not be taxable. In other words, if premiums are paid with after-tax dollars, benefits are received tax free.

As surely as fire insurance protects against loss of property, disability insurance protects against loss of income by providing for its continuance, when the loss is occasioned by illness or accident. As an owner or as an employee, you should not be without it, because to neglect this area of protection is to court financial disaster.

SUMMARY

Insurance can be seen as a process of transferring risk. For a relatively small amount of money, it affords protection from major loss. Insurance is often considered something of a nuisance. This, however, is a misguided view, since insurance is indeed vital to the pharmacist-owner's survival in business.

Find a reliable insurance professional in whom you have confidence. Satisfy yourself that he or she represents a company with a proven record for competitiveness, fairness, and know-how. Review your coverage regularly. Policyholders do not normally find it necessary to change agents or companies if their demands, based on business acumen, are being met to their satisfaction.

RECOMMENDED READING

Catherwood, R.H., ed. *Life Insurance and the Businessman*. Toronto: Maclean-Hunter Ltd., n.d.

Facts of the General Insurance Industry in Canada. 16th ed. Toronto: Insurance Bureau of Canada, 1988.

Snyder, J. Christopher. *It's Your Money*. 6th ed. Toronto: Stoddart Publishing Co. Ltd., 1989.

This Business of Life. Toronto: The Canadian Life and Health Insurance Association [20 Queen St. W., Toronto, Ont. M5H 3S2], n.d.

(Most provincial governments publish consumer guides to insurance; for example, *Insurance. A Basic Guide for Consumers*, Ministry of Consumer and Commercial Relations, Government of Ontario.)

9

PHARMACY DESIGN, FIXTURES, AND EQUIPMENT

INTRODUCTION

Among the responsibilities of the pharmacy owner or manager is the planning of the design and layout of physical facilities for the pharmacy, including its fixtures and equipment. Considerations integral to this undertaking are pharmacy security against theft and /or drug diversion and proper storage conditions for perishable pharmacy items. Security considerations will be discussed in detail in Chapter 19. Here we shall focus on the essential requirements for the physical facilities of a well-operated community pharmacy.

The prospective owner, in developing an operational plan for the pharmacy, will decide on an underlying approach and a set of objectives for the practice. This will entail projecting a desired image for the pharmacy, which will in turn determine the guidelines for its design and layout.

Once such general guidelines have been developed, the new pharmacy owner would be well advised to seek expert assistance in both the design of the pharmacy and the selection of fixtures and equipment. Companies that supply fixtures also generally provide assistance in design and layout. Recently, firms specializing in the design of pharmacy interiors have emerged as well. Some community pharmacies today even seek the services of interior decorators to co-ordinate the decor of their premises.

BASIC PHARMACY DESIGN PARAMETERS

Results of an industry survey conducted in 1987 indicated that the size of the average Canadian pharmacy was just under 4000 square feet.[1] Experts suggest that the ideal shape for any retail outlet is rectangular.

A pharmacy should have an exterior sign or signs clearly identifying it. The entrance to the store should be designed for easy access, presenting no barriers to consumers. Doors that are difficult to open and entrances that are difficult for elderly or disabled people to manoeuvre should be avoided. For example, the use of turnstiles can make entry impossible for the elderly and disabled. During the past several years, many of the larger pharmacies have installed double-door entrances, which have in fact presented a significant obstacle to entry for disabled persons. Exits should also observe the easy-access principle, but they should be well controlled and positioned in such a way that customers must pass through a check-out area to leave the pharmacy. Some pharmacies have more than one customer entrance, but most have only one exit.

The overall decor of the pharmacy should be inviting and tasteful. Perhaps most important, however, is that the store have excellent lighting, which should be "carefully calculated to get the best possible illumination of the product."[2] Good lighting is also valuable to the overall security of the store.

With regard to floor coverings, it should be noted that because carpeting tends to absorb rather than reflect light, it can reduce the lighting level in the store. It is therefore preferable to avoid it, and to maintain clean, polished floors at all times, which will set off the pharmacy's image best. If floor coverings are required, however, they should blend in with the overall decor of the pharmacy, and should be easy to maintain: a commercial grade of carpet is now commonly used.

Aisles should be uncluttered and wide enough both to facilitate traffic flow (especially where shopping baskets and carts are involved) and enhance the consumer's view of the merchandise. The recommended aisle width is six feet.

Signage is extremely important in a pharmacy. All departments should be identified clearly, and particular attention should be given to the prescription department. Whenever possible, the sign identifying your professional department should be visible from any point in the pharmacy. All department signs must be easy to read, durable, and at a height calculated for best visibility by the consumer.

If at all possible, the pharmacy's receiving area should be separate

[1] Vil Meere, "Average ℞ Price Up 10% to $15.45," *Drug Merchandising* (October, 1987), pp. 40-44.

[2] Susan MacLean, "Low-Key Elegance Grabs Customers," *Drug Merchandising* (October 1987), pp. 50-55.

from customer entrances and exits and, for convenience and efficiency, the stockroom should be located near the receiving entrance. The stockroom must be made as secure as possible: any exterior doors and windows should be kept locked at all times, keys should be assigned to only a few selected staff members, and an alarm system should be installed. Stockrooms in contemporary pharmacies are normally small, partly because the current trend is to display as much inventory as possible in the front store and partly because, as rental costs rise, less space is being devoted to non-selling areas. Inventory management is facilitated when stock is concentrated in one area. Other non-selling areas include employee areas, such as staff rooms and washrooms, and while these are likely to be quite small, they should be made as comfortable as possible. It is wise to position these rooms away from the stockroom if possible. It is also important to check building codes to ensure that washroom facilities meet the required standards.

Prescription Department

The Seventh Annual Survey of Community Pharmacy Operations for 1986 found that prescription sales account for 43.2 percent of total sales in the average Canadian pharmacy. (A 1987 survey conducted by *Drug Merchandising* put that figure even higher – at 51.5 percent.[3]) In a store of approximately 4000 square feet, the prescription department would normally occupy approximately 400 square feet, or 10 percent of the total area of the store. The prescription department is most often located at the rear of the pharmacy. It is critical that it be clearly identified and visible from all points in the store.

For many years now, prescription departments in pharmacies have been constructed on platforms raised six inches above the floor. This has afforded pharmacists a good view of both the professional area and the front store, thereby contributing to store security. Recently, however, with the growing emphasis on patient counselling, this design has come to be considered a barrier to effective communication with patients. As a result, some of the newer pharmacies have had their prescription departments constructed at floor level, while others have introduced a step-down area where patients can communicate more easily with the pharmacist. Pharmacy owners who have elected to keep the dispensary at floor level believe that the benefits of direct contact with their patients, at eye level, outweigh the greater security afforded by the raised platform. Some also argue that claims of increased security are exaggerated, since

[3] Vil Meere, "Average R Price Up 10% to $15.45," *Drug Merchandising* (October 1987), pp. 40-44.

dispensary staff seldom have (or take) the time to observe activity in the front store from the higher vantage point. The step-down area would thus seem to be a reasonable compromise.

Pharmacy licensing bodies in each province may have specific requirements pertaining to the size of the prescription department. As noted in Chapter 7, they also stipulate requirements for dispensary equipment. It is essential to check your provincial regulatory agency's requirements in both these areas, and to conform with them.

There are certain design guidelines that contribute to the efficient operation of a dispensary. For example, since pharmacists and other dispensary staff are often required to stand on their feet six to eight hours per shift, their comfort should be considered a design priority. The dispensing counter should be of a height that is comfortable for the dispensary staff who use it – usually, about 36 inches. Each pharmacist should have sufficient space to work: most dispensing counters allow for two pharmacists, with about six to eight feet of counter space for each. Prescription counters should be approximately 24 inches deep, to accommodate computer terminals, keyboards, and printers. (Today, it is not uncommon for each pharmacist to have his or her own computer terminal.) On the whole, the dispensary should be designed for economy of movement, reducing the need for excess steps, hence saving time for the pharmacist.

Storage facilities for products in the prescription department vary among pharmacies, but the most familiar are the white cabinets preferred by many pharmacy owners. They are secure and thus suitable for pharmaceuticals, and are designed for easy cleaning and maintenance. They are also tidy and professional-looking. Bay shelving is another storage facility chosen by many pharmacists. The ends of the bays facing consumers are often attractively finished in woodgrain or decorative colours. Those who prefer bay shelving claim it facilitates inventory monitoring and saves time by eliminating the need to open and close cabinet doors. Since it is exposed to consumers, bay shelving requires more effort in order to keep the shelves and the stock itself clean at all times. Figure 9.1 depicts a prescription-drug cabinet and bay shelving.

Particular attention must be paid to the security of storage areas designated for narcotic and controlled drugs, especially as governed by the applicable legislation (see Chapter 7). The dispensary must also be equipped with a refrigerator for storing insulin, vaccines, injectables, and similar products. Finally, cabinets are needed for containers and labels, and a number of functional designs are currently available.

Housekeeping and lighting are both extremely important in the dispensary. Cluttered, disorganized, and unkempt professional departments not only project a poor image, but can also contribute to confusion, error, and even accidents. Cleanliness and good maintenance will contribute to greater efficiency. Good lighting will improve the department's image and facilitate the pharmacists' work.

Check-out areas are often installed in prescription departments to improve both customer service and store security. These check-outs serve the professional-product areas located near the dispensary as well. In some pharmacies, the owner or manager's office is situated near the prescription department, making it convenient for meetings with medical service representatives, physicians, and others. Finally, for the convenience of customers, a waiting area should be located near the dispensary. It need not be elaborate nor occupy a great deal of space, but should be furnished with at least a few chairs. Some pharmacies display patient-education material in the waiting area.

Each of the provincial licensing authorities has certain requirements regarding the involvement of a pharmacist in the sale of certain non-prescription drugs (for example, Schedule C products in Ontario). Reg-

Figure 9.1.   ℞ DOOR CABINET AND BAY SHELVING

Source: Courtesy of Vic Store Fixtures, Inc.

℞ *Door Cabinet:* Agglomerated board and plywood construction. Sides and front plastic laminate. Interior enamel finish. Silver anodized extruded aluminum door pulls. Cabinet: 6 adjustable steel shelves 8″ depth. Doors: 16 adjustable steel shelves 3″ depth. Standard colour: white.

Bay Type: Entirely detachable. Base, uprights, shelves and plain back, steel construction, baked enamel finish. Available in 48″, 36″, 30″, 24″ length and one section of 12″ used as end section, 84″ high. Standard colour: white.

ulations often require that such products be displayed in an area of the pharmacy where a pharmacist's services are immediately available. You must be sure to consult the pharmacy legislation in your province with regard to such matters.

Other Professional Departments

Since patient counselling has gained in prominence and consumer demand, some provinces have recommended the introduction of private patient-counselling areas. These should be adjacent to the prescription department, but separate from the general waiting area to ensure privacy. In cases where it is impossible to create a separate area, patient counselling may be conducted in the pharmacy owner or manager's office or, where applicable, in the home health-care department's fitting room. The area designated for counselling should be comfortable, well lighted, and well ventilated. It is also a good idea to display health-education literature in this area.

Pharmacies planning a home health-care department should also locate it near or adjacent to the prescription department. If the department will be fitting surgical garments, prostheses, or ostomy supplies, a fitting room must be provided. This room must be large enough to accommodate a fitting table, have proper heating and ventilation, and be completely private. A washroom for the exclusive use of patients should also be available. Like the patient-counselling area, the home health-care department must offer privacy. Like all departments, it should have a clearly visible identifying sign.

THE FRONT STORE

The main objective in the design of the front store is to promote the merchandising goals of the pharmacy owner or manager (see Chapter 15). This involves three essential considerations: a layout that promotes desirable traffic flow, fixtures designed for the optimal display of merchandise, and, of course, attention to adequate security.

Layout and Traffic Flow

The physical layout of the pharmacy plays an important role in the image that is created and in the store's efficiency and sales activity. Traffic flow should be the critical consideration in designing the layout of the front store and dispensary. The main concern of layout design is to activate all areas of the store. Customers who enter the pharmacy should be exposed to as many products as possible while they are there, to encourage impulse purchasing. (It has been estimated that approximately

60 percent of consumers' purchasing decisions are made while they are in the store.[4])

The location of the different departments will determine traffic flow and is hence critical to stimulating sales activity. For example, as we mentioned earlier, the prescription department is normally located at the rear of the pharmacy so that customers will have to pass through a number of other departments and see the range of products offered there before they reach the dispensary. Impulse items (those that the consumer had not planned on purchasing) and seasonal items are usually displayed at the front of the pharmacy, in the high-traffic area of the check-out counter, or near other active service areas. On the other hand, demand items should be located toward the rear of the store or along the centre aisles, drawing consumers further into the pharmacy. Health and beauty aids are frequently found along the wall to the right of the entrance, where consumers tend to be drawn upon entering the store.

In Chapter 15, you will learn how the placement of both demand merchandise and promotional displays can help to achieve sales objectives. The layout of the pharmacy should take advantage of the sales potential inherent in displaying associated items in proximity to one another – baby gift items near infant products, gift items near greeting cards, oral hygiene products near dental products, and so on. It is sometimes helpful to visit a number of pharmacies, observe the layout of departments and promotional displays, and draw on what you have seen as an aid to planning your own store (a basic layout is shown in Figure 9.2). Discuss your plan with the company you have engaged to design your pharmacy and supply fixtures. Wholesale drug companies and suppliers of store fixtures will often provide pharmacists with customized traffic-flow analyses of their stores. The results of such studies will supply the information necessary to decide on a design or determine whether an existing layout requires improvement. Whatever layout is finally agreed upon, it will be necessary to assess its effectiveness over time. One of the tasks of management is to evaluate and re-evaluate decisions taken, and be prepared to make changes when they are required.

Merchandise Display and Fixtures

Merchandise in the pharmacy should always be attractively displayed within clearly identified departments. As shown in Figure 9.2, wall cases may line the perimeter of the store. Such fixtures are normally 6 feet high and often have a lighted canopy above to heighten the effect of displayed products and enhance the overall decor of the store. In the remainder of the floor area, merchandise is displayed on gondolas (free-

[4] A. Archambault and H. Segal, *Merchandising. Pharmacy Management Program, Module 3* (Kirkland, Que,: Nordic Laboratories Inc., n.d.), pp. 1,3.

Figure 9.2. STORE LAYOUT, TRAFFIC FLOW, AND FIXTURES

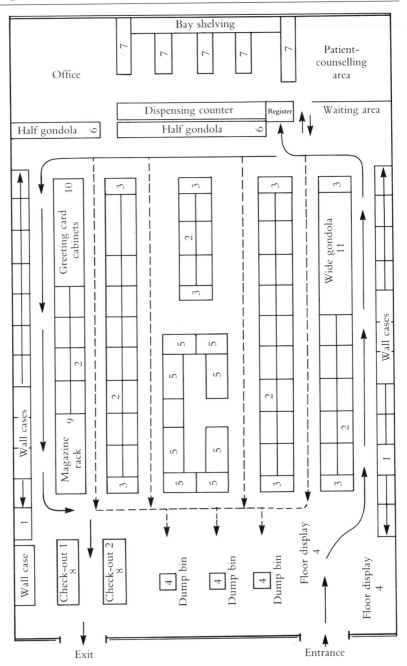

Note: Floor area is 4000 square feet (50' × 80'). Scale: 1 cm = 4 ft.

standing fixtures that hold shelving), which should be positioned to create six-foot aisles. Both wall cases and gondolas are normally constructed of metal, with adjustable shelving. Gondolas typically run parallel to the wall cases and perpendicular to the dispensary. In recent years, gondolas have more frequently been set up to extend without interruption from the check-out area at the front of the store to the prescription department at the rear. This arrangement exposes customers to a wide range of merchandise as they travel from the entrance to the rear of the store. The resulting alignment also improves control over the store by giving personnel a better view of customer movement. While opinions on this point differ, some experts recommend that gondolas not exceed a height of four feet, since anything taller impedes visibility. A clear view across aisles not only helps customers to locate the items they are looking for, but also exposes them to a wider range of products; for staff, it facilitates monitoring customer movement and thereby improves store security. Promotional displays are often situated at the ends of the gondolas.

The display of paper products, in particular disposable diapers, had posed a problem until relatively recently, when manufacturers increased the width of shelving in gondolas to 24 inches or more. This has proved useful for the display of infant formula as well, and indeed many products

---

Key

Note: Solid and broken arrows represent probable routes of traffic flow.

Wall cases: may be fitted with shelving and / or peg board or slat wall.

1. Wall cases: may be fitted with shelving and / or peg board or slat wall.
2. Gondolas: as above.
3. End displays: may be fitted with pegged or clip strips or slat-wall backing. Merchandise may also simply be stacked.
4. Floor displays or dump bins: normally used to display promotional items. Floor stands may also be supplied by manufacturers.
5. Showcases: usually contain cosmetic items or high-ticket items.
6. Half gondolas or 4-ft.-high wall cases: normally used in front of the dispensary.
7. Bay shelving: used in the dispensary for pharmaceuticals.
8. Check-out counters: two are shown here, but there may be more as necessary.
9. Magazine rack: may replace gondolas in location near check-out-counters.
10. Greeting card cabinets: usually located to the rear of the store and may replace gondolas.
11. Wide gondolas (4 ft.): often used for paper products in oversized packages (eg., disposable diapers) infant formula in cases.

Each department would have proper signage and lighted canopies would be placed over all wall cases.

can now be stocked in greater depth on the shelves, alleviating the problem of reduced storage space in contemporary stores.

In addition to wall cases and gondolas, display cases are used, particularly for high-ticket items, such as cosmetics, clocks, or cameras. Cosmetics departments often consist of a square arrangement of display cases, frequently in the centre of the front store. These are referred to as service areas in that a cosmetician is normally present to serve customers. Cosmetics departments tend to be distinctively identified and are usually equipped with their own cash register.

Suppliers will often provide display stands for their products, some designed for temporary and others for more permanent use. It is up to the pharmacy owner's discretion whether or not to use them in the store. While some of the temporary stands are ideal for special promotions of particular products, care should be taken to integrate them properly with the pharmacy's other promotional displays and to avoid cluttering the aisles. With the more permanent types of suppliers' displays, consideration should be given to their suitability for use in the store: they should blend in well with the other fixtures and the general decor.

The use of pegboard, a hard backing with movable hooks, has been popular in pharmacies for several years now. It is inserted into sections of wall cases or gondolas, to display items such as carded cosmetics, blister-packed hair-care items, first-aid supplies, or school supplies. More recently, however, slat wall has been gaining in popularity among pharmacies. A slat wall, as the name suggests, is a slatted or grooved backing that can be fitted with either shelves or rows of hooks. Slat walls can be very attractive and are perhaps even better suited than pegboard to the display of blister-packaged products.

Some recent innovations in display techniques and fixtures deserve attention. Among them are so-called profit panels, which hook into the ends of gondolas and can periodically be moved to different positions in the store. They are made of pegboard and can be used for products such as notions and baby toys. Profit panels should not be installed in areas where they could obstruct traffic flow. A display device called a clip strip is also currently on the market. As the name suggests, it facilitates the display of packages that can be held by a clip. This device resembles a potato chip stand, except that it is a free-standing single strip.

The sale of pantyhose in pharmacies can be reasonably high, and consists mostly of impulse purchases. For some time, pantyhose were displayed on revolving wire racks. Recently, Lucite-faced pull-out trays that will fit into gondola or wall-case sections have improved the appearance of pantyhose displays.

Other innovations include a convenient gravity-feed display case for trial sizes of products. It is made of transparent acrylic and allows the customer to select the product(s) desired. Attractive new designs of upright refrigerated cabinets are now available for soft drinks and ice cream or other food products. Some pharmacies use sloped shelves in wall cases and gondolas as a new technique. This gives the appearance of greater depth with a minimum of inventory. Products displayed on sloped shelving are easier to see, particularly if they are contained in a flat type of packaging.

GREETING CARDS AND STATIONERY

Another department for which special fixtures are required is the greeting card section. Greeting card cabinets are normally provided by the suppliers, with whom payment arrangements may be negotiated. The location of this department is important and will depend on whether cards are a demand item or an impulse item in the particular store. If there are no specialty stores in the area that carry them, greeting cards are more likely to be a demand item in the pharmacy and can be located toward the rear of the store (near the post office substation, where applicable). Greeting cards and gift wrap generally have a relatively high gross margin but a low turnover rate, so their profitability should be carefully assessed to determine the appropriate amount of space that should be allocated to them. (As you will see in Chapter 15, space allocation is determined by a product group's profitability per square foot.) Recent improvements in available display fixtures for stationery products include separators for paper products and specially designed stands for bristol board and wrapping paper.

MAGAZINES

Fixtures for magazines may either be obtained from the magazine dealer or custom built. New designs have been developed to display magazines in a more orderly fashion. Pharmacies that sell paperback books often display them on revolving wire racks. Again, attention to space allocation is important, since magazines bear a low gross margin but tend to have a relatively high turnover. Magazines are often a source of security problems and should therefore be located near a check-out counter or service area.

Check-out Counters

Check-out counters are located near the store exit. Large independent pharmacies typically have at least two cash registers in the check-out area. Impulse items are best located at or near the check-out counters.

When selecting a cash register today, the pharmacy owner should consider computerization of the front store with a point-of-sale system. (Point-of-sale systems are described in greater detail in Chapters 11 and 20). Such systems involve equipping check-out counters with product-scanning capabilities or having cash registers adapted for use with hand-held scanners. Point-of-sale systems are becoming more affordable for the average pharmacy and offer great promise of improved profitability. Prospective pharmacy owners or managers, in planning their operations, should view them as a valuable investment.

Post Office Substations

Some pharmacies provide post office substation services, which can generate considerable traffic. They are generally located in the rear of the pharmacy. Care should be taken to prevent post office line-ups from impeding traffic flow in adjacent areas. Post offices must be equipped with a safe to protect the substantial amounts of cash and inventory that they often handle.

FIXTURE SUPPLIERS

There are a number of suppliers offering fixtures for sale or lease to community pharmacies. They are usually listed in professional publications or can be reached through wholesale drug companies. When deciding on a supplier, pharmacy owners and managers should observe the following guidelines:

1. Choose one who can supply all or most of your fixtures.
2. Be familiar with the services they offer. Do they provide traffic-flow analysis? Do they offer layout and design services? Do they offer both leasing and purchase arrangements?
3. Seek proposals from more than one supplier.
4. Discuss the subject with local wholesalers.
5. Seek references and advice from other pharmacy owners.

Fixtures and Equipment Checklist

Fixtures (Front Store)
Gondolas
Wall cases
Display cases
Display bins
Greeting card fixtures
Magazine racks

Signage
Department identification signs
Promotional signs

Prescription-department identification

Furniture and Office Equipment
Furniture as needed for patient-counselling area, waiting area, fitting room, and office.
Adding machine or calculator
Filing cabinet
Bookcase
Typewriter/computer

Dispensary
Dispensing-container fixture
Dispensing counter
Pharmaceutical equipment (check provincial regulations)
Refrigerator
Dispensary cabinets or shelving
Dispensary computer
Patient-record system
Electronic pill counter
Typewriter/computer

Narcotic cabinet or safe
Sink unit

Check-Out Areas
Check-out counters
Cash registers (terminals)
Scanners
Pricing equipment

Stockroom
Stockroom shelving
Safe

RECOMMENDED READING:

Davidson, W.R.; Sweeney, D.J.; and Stampfl, R.W. *Retailing Management.* 6th ed. New York: John Wiley & Sons, 1988.

Effective Pharmacy Management. 4th ed. Kansas City, Mo.: Marion Laboratories, Inc., 1987.

Merchandising. Guide to Good Pharmacy Management. Vaudreuil, Que.: Hoffman–La Roche Ltd., 1978.

Smith, Harry A. *Principles and Methods of Pharmacy Management.* 3rd ed. Philadelphia: Lea & Febiger, 1986.

10

HUMAN RESOURCES

INTRODUCTION

Human resources management is an area that many pharmacists tended to neglect in the past. Today, more pharmacy owners are recognizing the need to invest time and energy in this most crucial – and costly ⊣ aspect of their business. The impact of human resources on the image of a pharmacy is even more significant with consumers' growing interest in personal contact, particularly in the area of professional services. Various studies[1] have shown that a consumer's choice of pharmacy is strongly influenced by the quality of service offered, be it in the dispensary or other specialized areas of the store, such as cosmetics or natural products.

Pharmacy owners must also recognize the importance of their financial investment in human resources. Hiring a pharmacist today involves an investment of approximately $250,000 over the next five years, and perhaps $100,000 for a pharmacy assistant. It therefore makes sense to invest wisely by spending as much time and effort as necessary to locate the best people for the positions. Unfortunately, some pharmacy owners spend more time shopping for a computer system – a significantly smaller

---

[1] For example, Canadian Pharmaceutical Association/The Upjohn Company of Canada, *What Your Customers Think of You*, 1982; Ordre des pharmaciens du Québec, *Enquête sur la perception du pharmacien*, 1981, and *Le pharmacien et le public*, 1988; C. Laurier, "Les comportements de pratique des pharmaciens Québécois," PhD dissertation, University of Montreal, 1987; J.-Y. Le Louarn, "Enquête sur les effectifs en pharmacie," *Québec Pharmacie* 34 (May 1987): 252A–H; and (June 1987): 305–312.

investment – than they do in assessing their staff requirements and hiring the right employees.

The proper selection of staff is important from other perspectives as well. New employees must be considered in light of their compatibility with the existing team of pharmacy personnel. If such criteria are ignored, the friendly atmosphere that is necessary for the successful operation of the pharmacy may be jeopardized, leading to morale problems and possible resignations by existing staff. Similarly, since pharmacy staff interact with outside suppliers and prescribers, the choice of personnel can affect the nature of the pharmacy's critical business and professional relationships.

Managing human resources is more difficult than managing the material resources of a business. Although the human element can create unique problems for management, it can also bring tremendous benefits if managed properly. A computer will only do what it is told; it is predictable, but will not go beyond its capabilities. On the other hand, people can, in times of need, surpass their apparent capabilities. By respecting human elements and trying to understand the needs of staff members, pharmacy managers can increase productivity while at the same time providing staff with greater job satisfaction.

There is no universal prescription for the successful management of human resources, partly because every relationship with staff members is in some way unique and partly because the size and nature of the pharmacy will demand a particular policy and approach to communications with staff. This chapter presents some basic guidelines that prospective pharmacy owners and managers can adapt to their particular situations.

STAFFING REQUIREMENTS

The obvious objective in assessing staff requirements is to relate the number of personnel employed to the amount of work that has to be done. This is relatively straightforward in an established store with accumulated information about workload cycles, but more difficult in the case of a new pharmacy, where projections must be made with regard to the distribution of work and the situation constantly monitored for necessary adjustments in staff levels.

Three steps are involved in the assessment of staff requirements: job analysis, position description, and detailed job description.

1. Job analysis is a concise and factual study of the pharmacy's staffing needs. The scope of each job must be delineated, anticipated problems outlined, and the hierarchy of positions established. A thorough job analysis will encompass all areas of the work to be done and will alert the pharmacy owner to any grey areas or duplication of functions. In

the longer run, it will determine the responsibilities of each employee and help prevent potential interpersonal conflicts.

2. The position description outlines the main components of each position. A good position description should be relatively short (no more than two pages), providing a general description of the job, the nature and the scope of the position, the main areas of responsibility, the positions which the incumbent will supervise, and those to which he or she will be accountable. (Two sample position descriptions appear in the appendix to this chapter.) Whenever possible, it is advisable to evaluate how much time is to be spent on each of the activities listed. In creating the position description, the employer should also consider the qualifications that will be required of the incumbent, in terms of educational level, type of degree (where applicable), length and nature of experience, and special skills.

3. The detailed job description should (1) list, in order of importance, all the tasks to be accomplished and (2) describe each in detail. This is useful in establishing the priorities of job functions within each position.

Properly done, job analysis, position description, and detailed job description, together with subsequent study of the combined information, should result in a reasonably accurate assessment of staffing needs.

To ensure that all tasks will be accomplished by the optimal number of people, it is still necessary to estimate the actual volume of work in the pharmacy. In a larger store with a greater volume of work, it may be necessary to hire two or three employees to fill the same position. The daily and hourly fluctuations in workload must also be considered. In some pharmacies, weekdays might be much busier than weekends, and fewer employees would be required on a Sunday than on a Thursday or Friday. A store that fills 150 prescriptions in a day would normally require only one pharmacist; if, however, those 150 prescriptions occur in a four-hour span, one pharmacist will clearly be unable to cope with the rate of work. Or, if a pharmacy dispenses 400 prescriptions per day, with a rush hour between 4 p.m. and 6 p.m., a bottleneck situation will develop if only one pharmacist is on duty during that period, even if additional dispensary assistants are employed. A second pharmacist added during those hours would double productivity, thereby increasing customer satisfaction. This solution may not even involve a greater cost for the pharmacy owner, because the second pharmacist's salary can be paid out of the savings from one less pharmacy assistant and the elimination of overtime payments to the initial pharmacist. Changes in patterns of work flow are always possible, and it is advisable to monitor operations regularly in order to react to them promptly.

The pharmacy owner or manager will of course be concerned with the financial capacity of the pharmacy to support its payroll. The literature suggests that total salary expenses (including the owner's) should not exceed 12 to 15 percent of sales.[2] However, this percentage may increase over the next few years as a result of the shortage of pharmacists in some provinces. Pharmacy owners must keep abreast of provincial salary-to-sales ratios for pharmacies of comparable size (which are published in the professional literature) and compare the ratios for their own operations. With properly planned staffing, a pharmacy should compare favourably against provincial industry averages.

Finally, it is important to check the local by-laws governing hours of store operation on weekends and holidays, which will vary from city to city.

STAFFING THE DISPENSARY

If volume of business is high, a pharmacy will employ other staff in addition to at least one pharmacist in the dispensary. Some provincial regulations dictate the ratio of pharmacy assistants to each pharmacist (for example, "one on one plus one," that is, one pharmacist to two assistants, two pharmacists to three assistants, and so on); other provinces set no limits on the number of assistants that a pharmacist may supervise. All provinces require that each prescription is filled under the authority of a pharmacist, and, as discussed earlier, caution must be exercised to avoid overworking the pharmacist or creating backlogs. It is wise to investigate the possibility of automating the pharmacy's dispensing operations, as you will learn in Chapter 22.

STAFFING SPECIALIZED AREAS

Some specialized areas of a pharmacy, such as the cosmetics department and the home health-care department, will require specialized personnel. Depending on the particular pharmacy, these staff members may not need to be on duty at all times during store hours. The cosmetician may only be needed in the latter part of the day if that is when potential consumers of cosmetics tend to shop. Knowing the shopping habits of the pharmacy's clientele is essential to the proper planning of staffing requirements in specialized service areas.

OTHER PERSONNEL

The pharmacy owner must assemble a support staff of salesclerks, cashiers, stock clerks, and receivers. Some of the support-staff members may

[2]G. Cunningham, "Independents' Sales Up, but Profit Deteriorating," *Drug Merchandising* (October 1987): 47; Pfizer Canada, "La Gestion du Personnel," *La Bonne Formule* no. 1; H. Segal, *Annual Survey of Community Pharmacy Operations*, 1985, 1986.

be hired on a full-time basis, while others will be part time or temporary employees. Some pharmacies have chosen to employ only part-time support staff, because this allows for readily available replacement personnel and greater flexibility during holidays or in the event of illness among staff members. The drawbacks to such an arrangement are that (1) customers are less able to develop the sort of personal relationship with employees that can create loyalty to the pharmacy and (2) part-time staff are unlikely to learn as much or develop skills as thoroughly as full-time staff. The pharmacy owner must arrive at an arrangement that both enhances customer satisfaction and ensures the availability of backup staff. Part-time staff are most commonly used during rush-hour periods, while temporary replacements are generally used during vacation times and exceptionally busy seasonal periods. Students, and preferably pharmacy students, are a good source of part-time and temporary staff, especially since pharmacies often experience staffing shortages during the summer months. Pharmacy students are a valuable investment as well: upon graduation, they may return as replacement pharmacists, already familiar with the methods of the pharmacy.

It is important to avoid overstaffing, since it is not only financially burdensome but can also have a negative effect on customer service and on the pharmacy's image. Employees who are not fully occupied will naturally tend to socialize with other employees, thereby distracting them from their work. This can create motivational problems among the busier employees in addition to jeopardizing ideal service levels to customers.

Conversely, if the pharmacy is understaffed, service problems will arise because personnel are overworked and service is slower. Employee dissatisfaction is likely to develop, and possibly result in a high turnover of staff. This can lead to a poor reputation for the pharmacy as an employer, cause frustration among the store's customers, and prevent the development of a team spirit among the employees.

Managerial Staff and the Principle of Delegation

In a large operation, it is impossible for the pharmacy owner to supervise all the employees directly. An organizational structure must therefore be established that will allow for the delegation of certain supervisory responsibilities (see Chapter 13 for details of managers' responsibilities). Depending on the size of the pharmacy, this structure might include a store manager; an assistant manager; a head cashier (if there is a team of cashiers); and a head cosmetician (if there is a team of cosmeticians). This is a crucial phase in the growth of an organization and demands that the pharmacy owner learn to delegate responsibility effectively, moving from the role of the entrepreneur who handles all problems to that of the manager who supervises, controls, and motivates a management team. While all this may seem obvious, it is frequently a major source of difficulty for pharmacy owners, who find that they are unable to "let go."

The principle of delegation consists of three components: responsibility, authority, and accountability. If, for instance, you own two pharmacies, each of the managers that you employ should be fully responsible for the operation of his or her store and must be given the requisite authority to do so. At the same time, both managers will be accountable to you for the decisions they make and for the consequences of those decisions. The same principles would apply within each store, where, for example, the manager might assign direct responsibility for three employees to an assistant manager. The three employees might include a stock clerk responsible for receiving, a store clerk responsible for price ticketing, and a head cashier who in turn supervised three other cashiers. Each employee in this chain of responsibility would be accountable to his or her direct supervisor (in this example, head cashier, assistant manager, and manager). All organizational structures are based on the principles of delegation.

Failure to observe these principles will result in a loss of your own and your staff's time, as well as a potential loss of money. It will also create dissatisfaction among the people promoted to positions of responsibility and confusion among the rest of the staff.

RECRUITING STAFF

Once staff-requirement assessment is complete, the pharmacy owner will know exactly what positions are to be filled and how many employees hired. The first principle of effective recruiting is to hire the candidate best qualified for the job available. Before exploring the process that will best enable the pharmacy owner to realize that principle, however, we must stress the importance of avoiding any sort of discrimination in hiring. It is illegal for an employer to refuse to hire a person on the basis of race, sex, or religion. Before engaging in active recruiting, the pharmacy owner or manager should become familiar with the Canadian Human Rights Commission's published guidelines and the pertinent provincial labour legislation. Observing the tenets of these documents will not only protect the owner as an employer, they will also help to increase managerial effectiveness in the task of recruitment.

Seeking Job Candidates

PHARMACISTS

The first eligibility requirement for new pharmacists is, of course, that they be licensed in the province where the hiring pharmacy is located.

Other qualifications may also be specified: knowledge of more than one language might be required if the pharmacy is located in an ethnic area; knowledge of the pharmacy's computer system may be essential; or the flexibility to work evenings and weekends could be a prerequisite.

The recruitment of a pharmacist can be approached in several ways. An advertisement in a daily newspaper is an option, but perhaps not the most cost-effective one, since the circulation of the paper is not restricted to pharmacists. The more productive option is to run the ad in a national trade journal, such as *Drug Merchandising* or the *Canadian Pharmaceutical Journal*, as well as in a regional journal or newsletter. A drawback here is that the ad may not appear for six to eight weeks after submission. Hence, this is not the ideal approach if the new pharmacist is needed in a hurry.

Another approach is to seek assistance from pharmacy faculties, professional associations, and provincial licensing bodies, which sometimes have placement agencies and keep a record of graduating or unemployed pharmacists. Such referral services can be very helpful and are a reliable source of information.

A pharmacy owner may not wish to have the pharmacy's needs known by competitors, especially if, for some reason, a high turnover of staff has been experienced. This is an understandable concern, since the pharmacy community might speculate that working conditions are not satisfactory in the pharmacy, and this could indeed make the recruiting process more difficult. To avoid the problem, it is advisable to use a post office box or reference number in the advertisement, and thereby remain anonymous. With the scarcity of pharmacists in some provinces today, it is not uncommon for pharmacy owners to try to lure staff away from competitors. This practice should be discouraged, however, in part because the pharmacist hired this way may be receptive to yet another, slightly higher outside financial offer, and could therefore be a poor risk, and partly because a price war could result among pharmacy employers, leading to tensions within the professional community.

Other approaches include using the services of a professional placement agency and seeking recommendations from colleagues and current staff members.

MANAGEMENT STAFF

If the pharmacy is large enough to warrant hiring management staff, candidates must be evaluated carefully for their potential to meet the demands of the position description. The recruiting process is similar to that used for locating pharmacists, with the exception that, because this is not a closed professional community, the daily newspaper is the best advertising vehicle. The ad should appear in the career section (*not* the classified ads), since the appropriate potential candidates – those who consider themselves professional people planning to make a career with an organization rather than only to fill a job – will be more inclined to look there. Group advertising (for example, seeking a pharmacist, cosmetician, head cashier, and supervisors through a single ad) should be avoided when seeking management personnel.

OTHER STAFF

In the case of support staff, an anonymous ad in a district newspaper is probably the most efficient approach. Candidates should be advised to send their résumés or applications to a post office box number. Support staff should be recruited from the local area in order to avoid travelling problems during the winter season. It is quite likely that there will be store customers among the candidates for support-staff positions: these situations should be handled with diplomacy and tact if the applicant is not qualified or suitable for the position.

OUTSIDE AGENCIES

As mentioned earlier, the pharmacy owner might choose to use the services of a private agency or a government service, such as Employment and Immigration Canada, for assistance in fulfilling staffing requirements. All agencies, whether private or public, screen candidates and send only those who are considered qualified for the job. It is important to select a reliable agency, supply them with the position description for the job opening, and explain as precisely as possible the kind of employee being sought. The agency will then arrive at a short list of candidates from which the employer can select. Agency candidates are normally "guaranteed," meaning that if they do not perform to the employer's satisfaction within a specified probationary period, the agency will locate a replacement at no extra charge. Private agencies can be expensive and should probably be used only if the pharmacy owner is unskilled as a recruiter and interviewer or simply cannot spare the requisite time. To avoid agency candidates altogether, it is wise to specify "personal applications only" in the advertisement for the job.

To summarize, the recruiting process is not dissimilar to advertising. The product advertised is the job opportunity, which should be made attractive to its target market, and the message is directed to that target population by the most economical and productive means.

Evaluating Applications

Applications from potential candidates will begin to arrive soon after ads have been placed. Depending on the level of candidate being sought, a certain quality in the presentation of the résumé or application form can be expected. Applying for employment should be one of the most important things a person does, and this should be reflected in a job application. The pharmacy owner should screen candidates on the basis of their applications. It is possible to perceive a great deal about an applicant's character and attitude to the job from his or her résumé and covering letter and to eliminate the applications that do not reflect sufficient care, interest, and effort. It is quite appropriate to adopt a selective attitude from the outset: if an application is full of spelling errors, it is fair to assume that the applicant would bring the same carelessness to the job.

The résumé will describe an applicant's career evolution. For a senior position, the pharmacy owner would look for indications of progress and commitment in the candidate's achievements of the past years. The applicant's stability as an employee will be reflected in the absence of erratic employment patterns. Someone who changes positions regularly every six months, and has done so for several years, may be incapable of staying in the same place for a long period of time. Any employer who has invested time and money in the search for an appropriate candidate should certainly be wary of one who could leave the organization in six months' time.

The receipt of all résumés or applications should be acknowledged by letter, even if the applicant is not selected for an interview.

The Interview

The interview is the next stage in the selection process. If at all possible, the pharmacy manager should try to interview several candidates – ideally between five and ten, since the interview process is invariably based on a comparison of applicants. Fewer than five candidates may not afford a broad enough view of what the market has to offer. If the preselection of applications has been successful, everyone interviewed will be essentially qualified for the position offered. The interview process should occur within a limited time frame: if it is spread over too long a period, the candidates seen initially may recede from memory by the time the last interviews are conducted, giving the later candidates an unfair advantage. Ideally, the interview process should take place over a period of one week.

The interview itself is perhaps analogous to precontract negotiations. The interviewer is attempting to determine whether this is the candidate best qualified for the job and someone who will contribute to the value of the organization; at the same time, the interviewer must ascertain whether the candidate understands exactly what is being offered and will be happy in the position. If either side in the "negotiation" is not satisfied, the relationship is not likely to survive over time. It is therefore important that all the rules of the game are clear for both parties at the time of the interview. This is not an easy process, since the two people involved in the interview are usually strangers and the interviewer must try to establish a climate conducive to communication. To facilitate the process, the interview should be conducted in a relaxed atmosphere and without interruptions. Most pharmacies do not have an area appropriate for conducting interviews; if this is the case, it would be advisable to rent or borrow an office somewhere outside the pharmacy.

The opening conversation should be aimed at establishing a rapport between the two parties. The pharmacy owner should start by asking candidates how they see the position offered, to ensure that they do not have an unrealistic idea of the nature of the job. If a candidate seems to be knowledgeable about the position, it is likely that he or she has done some research to become familiar with the pharmacy – a positive sign, indicating a high level of interest. The next step would be to clearly establish what the job entails and what is expected of the candidate. At this point, some candidates may decide that the job is not exactly what they are looking for – a disappointing development, but one best discovered at the interview stage.

Once both parties are clear on the position, the interviewer should work through the résumé or application form with the candidate. Query the applicant about empty periods evident in the résumé and discuss the general trend of his or her career. Try to pose open-ended questions that require some explanation by the candidate; avoid leading questions, such as "We have an elderly population; do you like to work with older people?", to which the candidate can simply answer yes. Avoid any questions that can easily be answered yes or no; instead, ask questions starting with *why* or *how*. If it seems that the candidate is avoiding certain topics or being indirect or that more information relating to the topic under discussion would be desirable, do not hesitate to remain silent after the candidate has finished answering. In an effort to end the slightly uncomfortable silence, the candidate may spontaneously provide some information that could be very interesting to the interviewer.

The pharmacy owner in the role of interviewer should be aware of a phenomenon known as the "halo effect." Every person is influenced by a particular personality or physical trait, an attitude factor, or a style of clothing that can cause them to react more favourably toward another person. As an interviewer, you must be aware of your own bias and of the type of candidate that is likely to make a stronger impression on you, so that your decision is not swayed by the halo effect. This is a bias that has no relevance to the position; it simply hides other factors that may be of much greater importance.

The interviewer's role is to orient discussion and draw out answers, encouraging the person being interviewed to do most of the talking. If the interview is conducted properly, you will find out if the candidate is capable of following a logical train of thought and expressing himself clearly and easily. This may be a feature you are looking for in a pharmacist who will have to communicate effectively in counselling patients. Other aspects that will be of interest to the pharmacy owner, depending on the size of the company, are the candidate's future career plans and ambitions. If an employee is being sought for a large organization, it would be important to discover whether the person has the potential to move up in the organization and possibly occupy managerial positions.

The interviewer is best advised, even when very favourably impressed with a candidate, to avoid making premature promises, either about a job offer or possible promotion within a short time. Without having seen the person at work any such suggestion is out of place; furthermore, the employee will be dissatisfied and lose trust in an employer who has made false promises.

If the individual's personality and career progression are appropriate for the job, their technical competence must then be determined. The criteria for this will differ with the type of position being filled. Where possible, try to give candidates an aptitude test or place them in a situation where you can see them perform. It is also important to consider whether the candidate will fit in well with the other employees and with your customers. A candidate with the necessary technical skills may have a way of communicating that you can predict will antagonize your customers. If this is the case, and if you feel that the candidate cannot change, he or she is probably not the best person for the job.

The questions asked in an interview must be related to the job exclusively. The personal life of the candidate, including age, marital status, or number of children, is in no way related to the job and cannot be a subject for questioning. However, the candidate's outside interests may be explored during the interview. What candidates do in their spare time may have some relevance to the business and may also give some indication of their capacity to work in a team, if not of their potential for leadership.

Do not hesitate to ask for references. Since references provided by the candidate will most likely be positive, you must try to ascertain their credibility and, if need be, contact other people that may know the applicant. It is advisable to make the employment of a candidate conditional to the verification of references. The length of a candidate's working life should be taken into consideration: a new graduate will obviously not be able to supply as many references as a person with ten years' work experience.

Coming out of the interview, the pharmacy owner should know whether the candidate has the requisite technical competence, whether he or she will be compatible with the clientele and with other employees, and also whether there is some potential for moving up in the organization. The candidate should know exactly what the job entails, what kind of organization he or she is joining, and have a good idea of the working conditions.

Toward the end of the interview, questions of salary, work schedule, and benefits should be discussed. The salary range and work schedule might be raised initially to ensure that the candidate's expectations are not too divergent from your offer; otherwise, the interview itself might be a waste of time for both parties. Caution should be exercised in this, however, because if your offer is much higher than what the candidate expects, he or she might be tempted to exaggerate about aptitudes and competence in an attempt to impress you – not because the position is of interest, but because of the salary. The best policy is to ask candidates what their salary expectations are, and proceed (or not) from there.

The salary policy and benefits package of the organization should always be explained clearly. The candidate should understand that employees have the opportunity to move up in salary within a given range for the particular position. This information should be restated and confirmed upon hiring.

Once the position has been filled, it is important that all the other candidates interviewed be notified in writing as soon as possible that they have not been selected. A brief letter, thanking the candidate for meeting with you and advising with regret that the position has been filled, is sufficient. Lengthy and non-essential explanations should be avoided. However, thorough notes on the candidates, based on the interviews, should be kept in a file for future reference – you may want to return to these candidates when a new opening arises.

Finally, it is important to note that an employee file must be created for each new employee. The file must be kept updated through the course of the individual's employment with the pharmacy. It should contain all relevant personal information about the employee, a copy of his or her résumé or application, and copies of the applicable position description and the detailed job description. Salary, salary range, and benefits must also be recorded. Over time, each of the employee's performance evaluations will be entered into the file. Attendance records, payroll records, and insurance-benefit claims forms should similarly be included.

Orientation and Training

It is recommended that the pharmacy owner meet once more with the newly hired employee before he or she begins work to review the position description and detailed job description, as well as compensation and work policies. Most positions have a probationary period of sixty to ninety days during which the performance of the employee is assessed. Several meetings should be held to discuss the employee's progress during that period. If problems are apparent, the employee should be warned, and given an opportunity to improve. During the probationary period, benefits such as group insurance coverage do not usually apply. At the end of the probationary period, a meeting should take place with the employee to review his or her work; if it has been satisfactory and both parties are in agreement, a permanent offer of employment should be made.

On the first day of the probationary period, the pharmacy manager or an immediate supervisor should give the newcomer an orientation tour of the store to meet fellow employees and learn who does what and where everything is located. Give the new employee a copy of the pharmacy's policy and procedures manual (or training manual, if one exists), and review it together a few days later. Smaller organizations may not have printed and bound manuals; in that case, a senior employee should be appointed to train the newcomer and explain store policies. In the initial period, it is important that the new employee know whom to approach with questions or when facing a problem situation.

STAFF MOTIVATION

Once you have hired your team, it is up to you, the manager, to keep them motivated. A highly motivated staff will be dedicated to your organization and to your customers. Furthermore, it will help to prevent human-resource problems in the future.

Much has been written on motivation, but Maslow's "hierarchy of needs" theory continues to dominate the field.[3] Maslow suggests that every person has five basic levels of needs, ordered from lowest to highest as follows: physiological, safety and security, social, esteem, and self-actualization needs. The theory holds that only upon satisfying one level of need can people move on to satisfy the next. Hence, if a primary level is not being satisfied, people will revert back to that level, then work their way up again. For instance, if one of your employees is highly motivated and works on satisfying self-esteem needs, but in the process a physiological need ceases to be satisfied, he will revert to the satisfaction of that need before pursuing his search for self-esteem.

Another theory of motivation has been developed by Frederick Herzberg, who conducted an extensive survey of what satisfies and motivates employees.[4] He concluded that only factors directly related to the content of the job can increase motivation by being satisfied. They include the work itself, responsibility, achievement, chances of advancement, recognition for achievement, and so on. On the other hand, factors not directly related to the job, such as company policies, working conditions, salaries, interpersonal relations, and so on, will not effectively motivate employees. Although these external factors can be a source of dissatisfaction, leading to problems such as high staff turnover, satisfying them

---

[3] A. Maslow, "A Theory of Human Motivation," *Psychological Review* 50 (1943): 370–96.
[4] F. Herzberg, *Work and the Nature of Man* (Cleveland: The World Publishing Company, 1966).

will not serve to motivate an employee. Herzberg's theory also holds that, overall, the duration of an employee's positive response is more prolonged when a motivating factor is satisfied than when one of the external factors is satisfied.

We shall now return to Maslow's hierarchy of needs theory, and explore some of its implications in the context of the workplace.

PHYSIOLOGICAL NEEDS

This is the most basic level, representing the need for warmth, nourishment, and rest. This level is therefore satisfied through good working conditions. The pharmacy must be properly lit, well ventilated, and adequately heated or cooled. Employees must have reasonable breaks during the day (for coffee and lunch), as well as an area in which they can relax during break periods. Work schedules can also affect the satisfaction of employees' physiological needs. When possible, it is wise to be flexible, accommodating employees' stated preferences for working on a particular day rather than another because of family obligations or other important factors in their lives. In general, try to make work schedules meet employees' needs as closely as possible, while being fair to the overall employee population. This area should be given serious thought, especially since recent surveys have shown that dissatisfaction among pharmacists stems largely from the working conditions imposed on them.[5] Never forget that the market is competitive and that your employees will certainly consider working for different employers if they offer better working conditions, that is, if they are more respectful of their employees' physiological needs.

SAFETY AND SECURITY NEEDS

Especially at the beginning of their employment, employees will experience a measure of uncertainty, not knowing exactly what is expected of them and being unfamiliar with the overall functioning of the store. New employees should be introduced to representatives of the different departments to give them a sense of what the team, as a whole, is doing. After the orientation period, the new employee will need frequent feedback, either from the pharmacy owner or manager or an immediate supervisor, depending on the size of the store. This will not only ensure the level of contact necessary for management to gain a reasonably accurate idea of the new employee's progress, but will also tell the employee whether he or she is progressing in the right direction. An absence of

---

[5]C. Laurier, "Les comportements de pratique des pharmaciens Québecois," PhD dissertation, University of Montreal, 1987; J.-Y. Le Louarn, "Enquête sur les effectifs en pharmacie," Québec Pharmacie 34 (mai 1987): 252A–H; and (juin 1987): 305–312.

feedback could lead to a feeling of insecurity and consequently to a lessening of initiative, as the employee tries to avoid making mistakes and works defensively rather than confidently, in the interest of the operation. This need for security is also satisfied through work performance reviews at regular intervals after the orientation period.

SOCIAL NEEDS

Every employee wants to become part of the group. It is up to the pharmacy owner or manager to ensure that new employees are encouraged to participate in employee activities. Department or general staff meetings should be held at fairly regular intervals. Such meetings will develop a team spirit by allowing employees to express themselves and including them in plans for the pharmacy. Employees may be encouraged in this way to offer suggestions for improving the efficiency and productivity of the operation. Various employee get-togethers will also ease the integration of new staff; the pharmacy owner does not necessarily have to subsidize such events, but should encourage, facilitate, and participate in them.

ESTEEM NEEDS

If the first three levels of needs are satisfied, employees will become interested in addressing the higher levels, through recognition by the group as leaders or experts in their particular areas. The manager must attempt to identify the emergence of these ego needs in individuals and facilitate their satisfaction. The employees that seek recognition by their peers are the potential future managers of the store and the people who can be relied on to advance the interests of the organization. Recognition can come in various forms: responsibilities might be increased as a consequence of excellent performance; the employee might be given an opportunity to address a particular topic before the other employees at a staff meeting; an employee-of-the-month award might be introduced; bonuses based on achievement or a speedier progression on the salary scale could be considered. Smaller operations may not be able to extend as many opportunities for recognition; nonetheless, the pharmacy owner must find ways to let employees know that their efforts and expertise are recognized and appreciated.

SELF-ACTUALIZATION NEEDS

This is the highest level of needs, wherein employees will strive toward greater accomplishment and responsibility in their work because it gives them personal satisfaction. At this level, employees work for the benefit of self-fulfillment and it is at this level that the best results are achieved.

Do not forget, however, that if store policies or working conditions act to reduce the satisfaction derived in one of the lower-level needs, even the achiever will revert to a preoccupation with satisfying that lower level. It is thus important to constantly monitor the satisfaction of all the five levels of needs among pharmacy staff.

Under ideal conditions, the first three levels will be satisfied for the employee group as a whole. The pharmacy owner will also have given those employees that have the potential a chance to position themselves at higher levels of motivation. Their leadership will help to draw the rest of the staff in the right direction.

PERFORMANCE REVIEW

It is essential that, at least annually, the pharmacy owner/manager and the supervisors of departments conduct performance reviews with each of the employees for whom they are responsible. Performance reviews can be scheduled for the anniversary date of the person's employment or at the same time of the year for all the employees. (When salary reviews are also involved, the latter option will simplify accounting procedures, but it may place too great a burden on the pharmacy's cash flow and the owner's time.) Evaluation criteria should be known to the employee and pertinent to the job. Figure 10.1 lists the various criteria for evaluation. It can be very productive to have employees evaluate their own performance and to base the discussion on a comparison of their perceptions and those of the supervisor or manager.

Whenever possible, performance evaluation should be based on the achievement of mutually agreed-upon objectives. (This approach is known as "management by objectives.") It is thus essential for the objectives to be discussed, understood, and mutually accepted by the employer and employee. Objectives should be quantifiable and not left open to interpretation. For instance, increasing sales is not a quantifiable objective, but increasing sales by five percent over last year is easily measured. Make sure that the method you use is compatible with the employee's level of responsibility, and always apply the same method. Agreed-upon objectives should be recorded; one copy is given to the employee and one is kept in his or her employee file.

Like the hiring interview, the performance review should be conducted without interruption in a relaxed atmosphere. To overcome certain psychological barriers, it is also wise in the case of the performance review to sit next to the employee rather than behind a desk. Employees tend to approach evaluations with some apprehension, especially the first time, fearing that their work will be criticized. The manager should try to dispel such fears by explaining that the exercise has a constructive

Figure 10.1.   CRITERIA FOR EMPLOYEE EVALUATION

Work-Related:
Theoretical knowledge
Practical knowledge
Quantity of work
Quality of work

Employee-Related:
Attitude
Initiative
Autonomy
Punctuality
Dress

Social:
Relationship with other employees
Co-operation

Growth:
Potential
Ambition

---

purpose: to examine the employee's strong features as well as the areas of their work that may require improvement. Clarity and directness are important: employees should leave the review knowing exactly what they are good at and what they must work on during the forthcoming period. Always relate the evaluation to the employee's position and job descriptions, be as specific and as quantitative as possible, and provide some tangible objectives that the employee should try to achieve by specified target dates – this makes it much easier for employees to monitor their own progress. Under no circumstances should comparisons be drawn between one employee and another: they are irrelevant and decidedly unproductive. For most employees, the performance evaluation can take place during any time of the day or week. If, however, your evaluation is somewhat negative or you suspect that an employee may react to the review in a negative way, schedule the review early in the week and at the beginning of the employee's shift. That way, if the employee does not respond well to what you have said or feels discouraged, there is time left in the day to follow up – either to encourage the employee or clarify any points that may continue to cause concern.

The performance review also provides a good opportunity to assess your employee's level of satisfaction in his or her work as well as to explore his or her potential for increased responsibility.

SALARY POLICIES

The performance evaluation can be used as a guide to determine employees' salary progression. While performance reviews can be undertaken several times a year, salaries are usually adjusted annually, with the possible exception of new employees' salaries, which may be adjusted after a three-month probationary period, with a performance and/or salary review, during the initial year of employment.

A sound salary policy is based strictly on the employee's performance in the job. Whenever an increase is given, it should be related to an improvement in performance. Too often, salaries are increased on the basis of personality rather than merit and achievement, and it is important that owners and managers adhere carefully to a merit-increase policy.

Salary policy should respect internal equilibrium and external equilibrium. Internal equilibrium means that, within a given organization, two people doing equivalent jobs should be able to earn the same amount of money. External equilibrium means paying a fair market value for the services your employees provide. Overpayment is an unnecessary cost to your operation; underpayment will, sooner or later, result in high staff turnover.

Ideally, every job in the pharmacy will have a dollar value, which should be revised annually according to market conditions and, of course, the pharmacy's ability to pay. The factors that influence a job's value include cost of living and the supply and demand for the particular service at the particular time. Employees believe wage increases to be related primarily to the cost of living, but this principle does not necessarily hold, since some jobs increase in value faster than the cost of living, while others may not increase at all. (As a job becomes obsolete, its value declines; in such cases, the job is normally eliminated and the employee moved to a different position.) In pharmacy, the effects of technology in recent years illustrate these principles: with the impact of computerization on pharmacy management, jobs that require related skills have rapidly outpaced others in their rate of increase in value.

The value of a position should be a target for the employee to reach within a certain period of time. New employees should be hired at 80 – 90 percent of the value of the job, allowing them to acquire experience and expertise over the course of several years before they can qualify for a salary that represents the full value of the job. The level at which an employee is hired is related to previous experience in a similar job and to the person's technical abilities. Hiring at more than 90 percent of the value of the job will create a problem in the next year, since the new employee will presumably have made some progress, but there will be no room in the pay scale to reward them. The steps of progression over time between the hiring point and the target point should be determined in advance so that all employees could theoretically progress at the same rate. Adjustments can be made more frequently in the case of employees who show a higher-than-average potential.

The performance of employees is said to follow a bell distribution curve. You can expect approximately two-thirds of your employees, after a reasonable period of time, to perform within the target zone. In some cases, however, employees will be unable to reach this level and, if their performance cannot be improved, the manager must face the possibility of terminating their employment. Conversely, the performance of especially high achievers must be recognized in monetary terms: the manager might allow their salaries to exceed the top of the range by up to 10 – 12 percent. Anything more than this would wreak havoc with the pharmacy's pay scales and is probably a sign that the employee has outgrown the position. Whenever possible, it is best to relocate these high achievers in more senior positions that allow them greater self-fulfillment.

Contrary to popular belief, salary adjustments and higher salaries are not a source of motivation. Referring back to Herzberg's theory of motivation, salary falls into the group of factors not directly related to the job – an increase will provide satisfaction for a relatively short duration, but will not effectively motivate the employee.

Benefits and Incentives

Many community pharmacies today are in a position to provide employees with a full benefits package. Among the benefits most often included are life insurance, disability insurance, a drug plan, a dental plan, and an optical plan. More and more pharmacies are also offering retirement plans for their full-time employees. The range of positions and salary levels in the pharmacy should be considered in establishing a benefits policy. Benefits for managerial staff are usually different from those offered to clerical staff. Information on the kind of compensation and benefits offered to different classes of employees is available from management firms or business consultants. It is also advisable to monitor market trends in order to position your firm in relation to the competition.

Incentive policies should aim at rewarding excellence according to the basic principles of management by objectives, as outlined in our discussion of the performance review. A bonus plan to reward employees who significantly surpass the expectations of their jobs is a valuable incentive. (It is worth mentioning as well that bonuses have the added advantage for employers of not raising the salary base or increasing cumulative salary paid.) The criteria employed, however, must be clearly understood by management and staff and must be objectively quantifiable. Subjective interpretation may lead to more dissatisfaction than positive incentive among personnel. A bonus plan for pharmacists could, for example, recognize achievement in terms of the profitability of the dispensary (not in terms of sales, as this could involve a conflict of interest) or involvement in continuing education, professional conferences, or other professional commitments outside the pharmacy.

SUPERVISION, DISCIPLINE, AND DISMISSAL

Managing human resources will always involve certain unique difficulties, and communication is the key to minimizing the occurrence of such difficulties. Your management staff should be seen not as a disciplinary team but as a supportive resource for employees, assisting them in their efforts to become more proficient in their work. Educate your managers to be consistent in the decisions they make and to avoid showing favouritism. Your management team must understand the need to be approachable enough for employees to seek their help if they have a problem, but distant enough that their authority is not undermined.

There will unfortunately be cases where the pharmacy owner or manager must take disciplinary action against an employee, which may result in termination of employment. This involves the possibility of legal consequences against which the pharmacy should protect itself. It is important to anticipate such potential problems and react immediately rather than wait until the problem is critical. If a supervisor encounters difficulty with an employee, the first step is to communicate verbally with the person to establish a mutual understanding of the situation and to suggest corrective measures. A target date for resolving the identified problem should be set and monitored closely. If the supervisor cannot detect any improvement in the situation by that date, a second meeting is necessary wherein the details of the problem are recorded and the expectations of management are clearly documented in writing. The employee must at this point be made to understand that failure to resolve the problem – again, within a specified period of time – could result in the termination of his or her employment. The employee should acknowledge receipt of this performance-evaluation update in writing. All documentation of such proceedings, from the outset, should be kept in the employee's file.

If an employee must be let go, the separation should be effective immediately. Most of the staff in a pharmacy is in direct contact with customers, and a disgruntled employee might well be tempted to vent resentful feelings on customers or suppliers. If possible, try to sustain good relations with the terminated employee. Explain that although his or her relationship with your organization has not been successful, another company that functions differently in terms of work and requirements may well be interested in the employee's services. The pharmacy owner or manager must not lose sight of the human element involved in such situations, and must try to make this difficult transition as smooth as possible for the employee by exercising tact, discretion, and a supportive attitude.

CONCLUSION

Effective human resources management is an integral aspect of effective business management. Pharmacy owners will improve the productivity and profitability of their operations by recognizing the importance of accurately assessing their staffing requirements, hiring the right candidate for the job, and effectively motivating their staff members. Consistent and progressive policies in the areas of performance evaluation, salary policy, and staff supervision will create a positive image for the pharmacy as an employer and attract valuable additions to its staff. It is perhaps most important to remember that, simply, a high level of job satisfaction among the employees will result in a high quality of service to the pharmacy's customers.

APPENDIX: SAMPLE POSITION DESCRIPTIONS

POSITION DESCRIPTION (1)[6]

Position: Pharmacist – Corporate Store
Location: Corporate Store
Incumbent: (name)
Reports to: Head Pharmacist
Date: September 27, 1987

GENERAL ACCOUNTABILITY
This position is accountable to the Head Pharmacist and to the Manager [of the individual corporate store] for co-ordinating the dispensary, dispensing medication, providing health information, and for prompt and courteous customer service.

STRUCTURE
This position is one of approximately three reporting to the Head Pharmacist, including two Pharmacists and one Assistant Pharmacist.

There is one position reporting to the incumbent: Pharmacy Assistant.

NATURE AND SCOPE
As Pharmacist, the incumbent is responsible for assisting in the supervision and co-ordination of the daily operations of the dispensary.

[6]For a list of the full range of possible duties and responsibilities assigned to staff pharmacists, as well as to head pharmacists, see Chapter 13.

He/she is accountable for ensuring the provision of prompt and courteous customer service and for efficient management of all customer complaints and requests. The incumbent ensures the cleanliness of the dispensary and the appropriate appearance of all dispensary employees. He/she is responsible for properly precounting and preparing for dispensing all commonly requested medications.

In addition, the incumbent is responsible for filling prescriptions. The incumbent receives prescriptions over the telephone, calls physicians to verify prescriptions, and arranges prescription back-orders. The incumbent serves all in-store customers before filling called-in prescriptions and instructs all patients in the proper ways of using their medication. He/she creates computer files for all new patients and completes all submitted health-insurance forms. Furthermore, the incumbent is responsible for conducting pregnancy tests and for discreetly communicating their results.

In addition, where applicable, the incumbent is responsible for:
– assisting the Head Pharmacist in effectively scheduling all dispensary employees;
– assisting in the training of all new dispensary employees.

Finally, before leaving each day, the incumbent is responsible for ensuring the cleanliness of the dispensary and the proper placement of all pharmaceutical products. Furthermore, he/she is accountable for informing the incoming Pharmacist of any remaining tasks to ensure their prompt completion.

WORKING CONDITIONS
Corporate store. Incumbent stands for a large part of the day.

SUPERVISOR: _____   DATE: _____
PHARMACIST: _____   DATE: _____

POSITION DESCRIPTION (2)
Position: Pharmacy Assistant
Location: Franchise Store
Incumbent: (name)
Reports to: Head Pharmacist – Franchise Store, and
                    Pharmacist – Franchise Store
Date: September 27, 1987

GENERAL ACCOUNTABILITY
This position is accountable to the Head Pharmacist and the Pharmacist [of an individual franchise store] for efficiently dispensing medication

(under the supervision of a Pharmacist), for providing prompt and courteous customer service, and for assisting in the maintenance of the dispensary.

STRUCTURE
This position is one of approximately two reporting to the Head Pharmacist – Franchise Store. The other is one Pharmacist.

This position is the only position reporting to the Pharmacist – Franchise Store.

There are no positions reporting to the incumbent.

NATURE AND SCOPE
Members of the dispensary are responsible for filling prescriptions and for providing prompt and courteous customer service.

As Pharmacy Assistant, the incumbent is responsible for assisting the Head Pharmacist in the maintenance of the dispensary. He/she is accountable for providing prompt and courteous customer service and for efficiently managing all customer complaints and requests. The incumbent is responsible for maintaining the cleanliness of the dispensary, precounting and placing all commonly requested medications (under the supervision of the Pharmacist), answering the telephone, as well as maintaining all prophylactic displays and the store's lost and found box.

In addition, the incumbent is responsible for:
- filling prescriptions, under the supervision of the Pharmacist;
- assisting the Head Pharmacist in controlling and monitoring dispensary and non-prescription drug inventory levels;
- assisting the Head Pharmacist in training all new dispensary employees.

Finally, before leaving each day, the incumbent is responsible for ensuring the cleanliness of the dispensary and the proper placement of all pharmaceutical products.

WORKING CONDITIONS
Franchise store environment. Incumbent stands for a large part of the day.

RECOMMENDED READING

Drucker, P. F. *The Practice of Management*. New York: Harper and Brothers, 1954.

Effective Pharmacy Management. 4th ed. Kansas City, Mo.: Marion Laboratories Inc., 1987.

Herzberg, F. *Work and the Nature of Man*. Cleveland: The World Publishing Company, 1966.

―――. "One More Time: How Do You Motivate Employees?" *Harvard Business Review* 46 (Jan.–Feb. 1968): 53-62.

Langevin, J. L., et al. *La direction participative par objectifs*. Quebec City: Presses de l'Université Laval, 1976.

Lau, J. B. *Behaviour in Organizations*. Homewood, Ill.: Richard D. Irwin, 1975.

McCormick, W., and Segal, H.J. *Personnel Management*. Toronto: Ontario College of Pharmacists, Continuing Education 80–81, 1980. (Two booklets: (1) *Staffing and Delegation*; (2) *Motivation, Evaluation, and Compensation*.)

McGregor, D. *The Human Side of Enterprise*. New York: McGraw-Hill, 1965.

Maslow, A. *Motivation and Personality*. 2nd ed. New York: Harper and Brothers, 1970.

11

INVENTORY CONTROL

INTRODUCTION

Not only the success but the very survival of a community pharmacy can depend on the skill with which its inventory is managed. Inventory represents approximately 50 to 55 percent of the average Canadian pharmacy's total assets,[1] and is consequently one of the major investments to be made and managed by the pharmacy owner or manager. A typical Canadian pharmacy in 1986 spent approximately $920,000 annually in purchases, and maintained an average inventory valued at approximately $206,000.[2] The strength of the pharmacy's sales and profits will hinge on proper planning and control of inventory.

The primary aim of good inventory management is to minimize the investment in inventory while maximizing sales and profit. To achieve this balance, the pharmacy owner must essentially learn to meet – rather than to exceed or frustrate – the demands of the pharmacy's clientele for products, and to do so without unnecessary expenditure; in other words, to avoid both overstocking and understocking. The former results in funds (that could otherwise be usefully invested) being tied up in stock

[1] The Seventh Annual Survey of Community Pharmacy Operations puts this figure at 54.6 percent for 1985 and 50 percent for 1986.

[2] Seventh Annual Survey of Community Pharmacy Operations. A 1987 *Drug Merchandising* survey put this figure at $208,000 ("Drug Merchandising Survey for Canadian Pharmacies," *Drug Merchandising* [October 1987], pp.40-44).

that sits on the shelf and generates no return for the business. The latter has possibly even graver consequences: customers will quickly lose faith in a store that cannot supply desired goods. It is perhaps not surprising that, according to Dun and Bradstreet, ten percent of all business failures in the United States are attributable in some part to inventory-related problems. To achieve the proper selection of merchandise, in adequate quantities and at the appropriate times, pharmacies employ various systems of inventory control, some of which we shall explore in this chapter.

First, however, it must be stressed that the prerequisite for the success of any of the existing methods of inventory management is sound financial record keeping. The pharmacy owner should review complete financial statements on a monthly basis. With accurate and current data in hand, pharmacy owners can promptly identify problems associated with inventory and take action to correct them.

TERMINOLOGY

Before proceeding to our discussion of specific methods of inventory control, it would be useful to define some of the terminology integral to that discussion. The following terms and concepts[3] are essential to the understanding of inventory control in any retail venture.

Inventory Control. The monitoring of stock on hand and sales patterns to facilitate purchasing the types and quantities of products that will generate sales and profits.

Methods of Inventory Control. Methods or systems employed to control inventory and facilitate the sort of purchasing that minimizes costs and investment while maintaining levels of merchandise adequate to meet consumer demand. Inventory-control methods, of which there are several and which can be quite simple or highly sophisticated, fall into two basic categories: dollar control and unit control. Most pharmacies use some combination of dollar- and unit-control systems to achieve appropriate quantities and quality in their product mix. Inventory control systems can be manual or electronic.

Dollar Control. Any approach to controlling inventory that focusses on the amount of money invested in inventory rather than on the number of units or the particular products involved. While dollar control is useful for monitoring expenditures against planned purchasing budgets, it does not ensure a proper product mix. Dollar-control systems include the

---

[3] The definitions given in this section are adapted from *Effective Pharmacy Management*, 3rd ed. (Kansas City, Mo.: Marion Laboratories, Inc., 1986) and from "Merchandise Control for Retailers," FBDB *Management Clinic* (Montreal: Federal Business Development Bank, 1982).

open-to-buy budget method, merchandise budgets, and the economic order quantity (EOQ) method.

Unit Control. Any approach to controlling inventory that focusses on the number of units of particular products carried in inventory. It monitors quantities of products received and sold, as well as their rate of sale. Examples of the unit-control approach include visual systems, systematic wantbook methods, periodic systems, and perpetual systems.

Stock-Keeping Unit (SKU). The smallest distinguishable unit in a product category.

Beginning Inventory. The total inventory on hand at the start of a specified period.

Ending Inventory. The total inventory on hand at the close of a specified period.

Average Inventory. The amount calculated when the beginning inventory and ending inventory are added together and divided by two (assuming that only two physical counts of inventory are involved, one at the beginning and one at the end of a given period).

Reorder Point. The minimum level to which the quantity of a product in stock is permitted to drop before it is reordered. The reorder point should be set taking into account the product's rate of sale and the time required for delivery of the merchandise. It represents the minimum quantity of a product that should be in stock at all times to meet consumer demand.

Physical Count. The exercise of physically counting and costing each item in the inventory. The results are compared with the book value of inventory (a record of the inventory value that *should* be on hand), and shrinkage is calculated. Physical counts are conducted on a periodic basis, usually annually but sometimes on a quarterly or even monthly basis. Physical counts are required at year-end for tax purposes and are usually performed by pharmacy staff, although companies that specialize in taking physical inventories are sometimes hired.

Shrinkage. The variance between the book value of the inventory and the physical count. Factors contributing to shrinkage include customer theft; employee pilferage; errors in shipping and receiving, bookkeeping, invoicing, and pricing; deterioration and breakage; misplacement of merchandise; and failure to record stock placement.

Procurement Costs. The costs associated with obtaining merchandise. They include the cost of checking inventory, purchasing, receiving and checking the merchandise, marking and stocking the merchandise, and paying the accounts.

Carrying Costs (also called *holding costs* or *maintenance costs*). The costs associated with holding products in inventory. They include: interest on loans; losses due to obsolescence of unsold stock; depreciation; loss through theft; deterioration or damage; and storage and handling costs, including insurance and tax, rent, labour, and utilities. Carrying costs can also include the opportunity cost of having funds invested in unsold stock.

Cost of Goods Sold (COGS). The cost of merchandise sold to customers during a specified period, usually one year. It is calculated by adding the net cost of purchases during the period to the beginning inventory, and deducting the ending inventory. For example, if (a) beginning inventory is $200,000, (b) $1 million is spent on merchandise for sale during the year, and (c) the ending inventory is $250,000, then the COGS will be $950,000.

Gross Margin (or *Gross Profit*). You will recall that gross margin is the difference between sales and cost of goods sold. With regard to pricing, the term is used in reference to the percentage by which the selling price exceeds the cost price. It is computed by subtracting the cost price from the selling price, and dividing by the *selling price*. For example, $1.50 (retail) − $1 (cost) = $0.50 ÷ $1.50 = 0.33 or 33%. In this context, gross margin can also be referred to as a "markup on retail." (Gross margin pricing will be discussed in greater detail in Chapter 16.)

Markup on Cost. The amount that is added to the cost price to arrive at a selling price; this amount is expressed as *a percentage of the cost price*. It is calculated by subtracting the cost price from the selling price, and dividing by the *cost price*. For example, $1.50 (retail) − $1 (cost) = $0.50 ÷ $1 = 0.50 or 50%.

Turnover Rate (TOR). The number of times during any period, usually one year, that the inventory is bought and sold. It is calculated by dividing the cost of goods sold by the average inventory at cost for that period.

Gross Margin Return on Inventory Investment (GMROI). A ratio that is calculated as follows: (Gross margin $ ÷ Average inventory at cost) × 100. The calculation of GMROI is a method used to assess the effectiveness of inventory management by determining the productivity of the inventory, i.e., the gross–margin dollars that are generated by each dollar invested in inventory.

As noted in our list of definitions, inventory may be controlled either by dollar-control or unit-control systems, or, more typically, by some mixture of the two. We shall now examine several systems under each category, moving from the simplest manual systems, generally employed by smaller pharmacies, to the more complex – often computerized – systems suitable for larger pharmacies with higher sales volume.

Unit-Control Systems

Visual System

This method of inventory control consists simply of examining the merchandise on the shelves and reordering if it is below a desired level or out of stock. Order quantities are determined largely by intuition: the pharmacy manager estimates an amount, based on experience, that will satisfy consumer demand. The visual method is inexpensive to operate and simple to conduct, but, to be effective, must be performed frequently and should be used only in low-volume situations. This method clearly involves a high risk of error, and it can be difficult to control. A "want-book" is often used to keep a simple record of items to be reordered.

Systematic Wantbook Inventory Control

This method is essentially a more systematic version of the visual method, employing wantbooks by product classification or by each supplier that sells directly to the pharmacy. Generally, minimum and maximum order quantities are noted for each product: the minimum serves as a reorder point; the maximum prevents overstocking. Similar notation may also appear on shelf labels to assist in checking inventory. Frequent review of wantbooks by management can help to make this system more reliable and more sensitive to fluctuations in product movement.

Periodic Inventory-Control System

The periodic method involves monitoring sales of products over specific time periods, as well as conducting periodic physical counts of products on the shelves. This approach to inventory management is also known as the stock-record card system, as a stock-record card for each product is commonly used to record the number of units on hand, sold, and on order within a given period. The card also bears supplier information (name, address, salesperson's name, terms of payment, supplier's special offers) and product information (format, size, cost, retail price, minimum/maximum order quantities). Figure 11.1 shows two typical stock-record cards. The clear advantage of the periodic system, when properly maintained, is to show, for example, monthly opening and closing inventories and rates of sale for particular products, thereby allowing the pharmacist-manager to identify shrinkage (and possibly some of its causes, depending on the extent of detail recorded) as well as to analyze sales in different time periods to determine patterns and adjust ordering habits accordingly. This is the most accurate of the *manual* unit-control systems, especially if order periods are shortened so that purchasing decisions are made more frequently.

Figure 11.1 TWO SAMPLE STOCK-RECORD CARDS

Manufacturer's Name				Address							
Salesman's Name				Address			Phone				
Discount Terms	2%, 30 days, 10th of Mo. (Books close on 12th)*										

Item	Size	Cost	Retail Price	Min/Max	Deal Periods		1/11	2/11	3/11	4/11	5/11	6/11
Antacid Brand Q Liquid-Plain	15 oz.	8.52	11.95	$1/2$ doz./ 2 doz.		S.O.H.	5	4	1			
						ORDER	12	12	18			
						SOLD	13	15				
Antacid Brand Q Liquid-Plain	12 oz.	5.32	7.45	$1/2$ doz./ 2 doz.	Nov. 1 doz. + 2 free	S.O.H.						
						ORDER						
						SOLD						
Antacid Brand Q Liquid-Plain	5 oz.	3.16	4.45	1 doz./ 3 doz.		S.O.H.						
						ORDER						
						SOLD						

Manufacturer's Name				Address								
Salesman's Name				Address			Phone					
Discount Terms	2%, 30 days, 10th of Mo. (Books close on 12th)*											

Item	Size	Cost	Retail Price	Min/Max	Deal Periods	Quantity Savings	1/11	2/11	3/11	4/11	5/11	6/11
Antacid Brand Q Liquid-Plain	15 oz.	8.52	11.95	$1/2$ doz./ 2 doz.		beginning inventory	5 / 12	4 / 12	1 / 18			
Antacid Brand Q Liquid-Plain	12 oz.	5.32	7.45	$1/2$ doz./ 2 doz.	Nov. 1 doz. + 2 free	quantity ordered						
Antacid Brand Q Liquid-Plain	5 oz.	3.16	4.45	1 doz./ 3 doz.								

*"2%, 30 days, 10th of Mo." means that a two percent discount will be given if the invoice is paid no later than the 10th of the month that falls after 30 days from the invoice date; in other words, within (30 + 10) 40 days of the invoice date.

Source: Adapted from "Inventory Control Guide to Good Pharmacy Management" (Vaudreuil, Que.: Hoffman – La Roche, Inc., 1978).

Perpetual System

This type of system records sales *as they occur*, continually calculating increases in inventory as products are received into stock and reductions as products are sold. It is the most accurate and effective of all inventory-control systems, but only when it is computerized. Performed manually, perpetual systems are the most time consuming and costly to operate, requiring constant maintenance to be kept current (Figure 11.2 shows a manual perpetual inventory-control record). Rendered much simpler, more accurate, and more effective through automation, perpetual systems are now gaining wide acceptance. A computer running a perpetual inventory-control program is able to generate data at any time on the units-on-hand and sales activity of any product that has been entered into the system.

Figure 11.2   SAMPLE OF A PERPETUAL STOCK CARD

Manufacturer: A & B Manufacturing Co.   Salesman: W. Jones

Address: 23 First Street

Product: Hair Dryer   Unit Cost: $11.50   Retail Price: $22.99

In Stock		Re-Order Time	Terms
Minimum	Maximum	7–10 days	2/10 net 30 (books
3	12		close on 10th)

Date	Received	Sold	Balance
			5
3 Jan.	5	2	8
5 Jan.		2	6
7 Jan.		1	5
7 Jan. One returned damaged			
10 Jan.		2	3
10 Jan. P.O. #1234 issued			
17 Jan.	6		9
18 Jan. Cheque #0456 issued against Invoice #2678			
19 Jan. Damaged hair dryer returned via salesman. Credit note to follow.			
20 Jan.		2	7

Source: Courtesy of H.J. Segal

In recent years, computers have played a significant role in inventory control and have improved the profitability of pharmacies both in the dispensary and in the front store. Initially, the emphasis in automated systems for pharmacies was on the dispensary, where computers programmed for perpetual inventory control were able to generate information in several extremely useful ways, and to perform additional functions as well:

1. Provide information on the categories and quantities of drugs dispensed during specified periods.
2. Provide data on the categories of drugs *not* dispensed during specified periods.
3. Provide current data on dollars invested in dispensary inventory by selected periods or "year-to-date."
4. Notify pharmacists of quantities of products on hand to enable them to reorder; also, if invoices are entered when a new stock of drugs comes into the dispensary, the computer tracks increases in stock-on-hand.
5. In the most sophisticated systems, the computer automatically generates orders when stock levels fall to previously established reorder points, and adjusts those reorder points automatically in response to fluctuations in sales patterns.

POINT-OF-SALE SYSTEMS

More recently, pharmacies have started to use what are known as point-of-sale (POS) systems to provide efficient inventory control of merchandise in the front store. These systems have the ability to track inventory from the time it is received to the time it is sold. Once item files are built and order levels established, the system can generate purchase orders at the appropriate times, its accounting functions can create all the necessary records, and, when the ordered merchandise is received, can add it to the inventory and even generate price stickers and shelf labels. Among the reports that a POS system can produce are daily transaction reports, regular gross margin reports, product movement by department, purchasing reports, and GMROI by product or department. In fact, reports can be customized as required; for example, turnover rates can be plotted and new product lines evaluated. It is said that such systems, if properly designed, can reduce inventories by ten percent or more. This is perhaps not surprising when one considers the vast increase in control that is afforded by such a system.

Much of the merchandise carried in pharmacies today bears a Universal Product Code (UPC) identification, as shown in Figure 11.3, which makes it possible to scan products on scanning counters or with hand-held scanners, and thereby register in the system all necessary product

Figure 11.3.   SAMPLE UNIVERSAL PRODUCT CODE

information and appropriate prices. (Cash registers – in fact, terminals – are specially equipped.) In addition, companies offering point-of-sale systems have developed assigned product codes for items that do not yet bear UPCs; they also supply labels bearing assigned UPCs for shelves and for products. Some suppliers provide the purchaser with an item file of up to 30,000 items of merchandise, all priced. The purchaser may have to customize this file to ensure that the prices are appropriate for his or her store. Also, data on existing inventory and minimum stock levels must be entered. If desired markup information is entered, the system will provide the appropriate retail prices. POS systems thus feature the capability to search prices and can be programmed to (1) bring discounted prices into effect on specified dates for purposes of sales or special offers; (2) resume regular pricing on a preprogrammed selected date; and (3) generate new price stickers and shelf labels.

The principal advantage of point-of-sale systems is that they provide more accurate information more promptly. Overstocks and out-of-stock situations can be reduced through early detection: fewer sales are lost, turnover increases, and profitability increases. All this contributes to improving the pharmacy's cash position as well. It has been suggested that, with the aid of a POS system, the 65 percent of products that yield only five percent of sales can virtually be eliminated, or at least dramatically reduced. POS systems also help to control procurement costs in that they reduce the labour costs associated with order generation as well as with price marking and price changing. Finally, the carrying costs of inventory will be reduced proportionally to the reduced stock. The system allows discrepancies between inventory levels in the computer and physical inventory levels to be detected more promptly, and hence affords greater control over shrinkage, waste, and damaged goods.

At the time of writing, the cost of POS systems ranged between approximately $20,000 and $100,000 (or more), depending on the equipment, the number of lanes requiring scanning capability, the inclusion of integrated accounting systems, and so on. Prices will likely decline as the systems become more widely available – and their popularity is gaining rapidly. It would appear that, as an investment in the practice, a POS system could bring a very high return.

DOLLAR-CONTROL SYSTEMS

Open-to-Buy (OTB) Budget Method

As we mentioned earlier, dollar-control systems are concerned with controlling the money invested in inventory rather than the actual items in stock, their balance and assortment. The open-to-buy budget method is based on establishing overall monthly purchase budgets in advance, monitoring actual sales and purchases during each month, and adjusting the purchase budget for the following month to compensate for documented overspending or underspending and sales declines or increases in the previous month. This method protects the pharmacy, on a monthly basis, from either exceeding or falling too far below its intended inventory investment for the year. However, it does not address understocking or overstocking of particular products, and, where this does occur, permits the problem to continue. Used in conjunction with an item-specific, unit-control system such as the periodic method, it ensures a more balanced and accurate overview of the inventory situation. The OTB method may be applied by section, by department, or to the entire store.

The estimated or "unadjusted" purchase budget for each month is in fact an estimate of cost of goods sold for that month. To arrive at this estimate, sales are projected for the month and the anticipated gross margin deducted. In some systems, the sales figure is simply taken from the same month last year, and an average gross margin percentage – for the sake of this discussion, let us say 40 percent – is deducted. At the end of the month, actual sales are recorded, together with actual purchases. Variances between the estimated and actual sales figures and between the purchase budget and actual purchases are the factors that will determine the adjustment to each following month's purchase budget.

Table 11.1 shows a completed annual open-to-buy budget chart. Refer to the chart as you read the following steps involved in the method:[4]

[4]This discussion is adapted from A. Archambault and H. Segal, *Inventory Management. Pharmacy Management Program, Module 1* (Kirkland, Que.: Nordic Laboratories Inc., n.d.), pp. 9-10.

Table 11.1. SAMPLE OPEN-TO-BUY BUDGET CHART
(This example is based on an estimated gross margin of 40%)

Month	Estimated Sales	Unadj. Purch. Budget (Est. COGS)	Adjusted Purchase Budget	Adjustments	Actual Sales	Actual Purchases	Cumulative Change in Inventory
Jan.	$21,000	$12,600	$12,600	not available	$20,000	$14,000	+ $2,000
Feb.	18,000	10,800	8,800	− $2,000†	17,500	9,300	+ 800
Mar.	19,000	11,400	10,600	− 800‡			
—	—	—					
—	—	—					
—	—	—					
—	—	—					
—	—	—					
—	—	—					
—	—	—					
—	—	—					
Dec.	20,000	12,000					

† − $ 1,000 × 0.6 = − $ 600
$12,600 − $14,000 = − 1,400
− $2,000

‡ − $500 × 0.6 = − $300
$8,800 − $9,300 = − 500
− $800

Source: B. McCormick and H.J. Segal, Systems Management Program: Inventory Control. Ontario College of Pharmacists, Toronto, p. 9.

1. At the beginning of the year, a chart is set up with column headings similar to those in our sample and with a row for each month. Estimated sales for each month are entered in column 1 and the corresponding cost-of-goods-sold figures in column 2, to represent the unadjusted purchase budget.
2. At the end of January, that month's actual sales and purchases are entered in columns 6 and 7, respectively. (Note that no adjustments can be made to the purchase budget in the first month of implementing this system.)
3. The February purchase budget must be adjusted to reflect activity in January. In this case, $1400 more merchandise was purchased than had been allowed for in the purchase budget. Also, January's purchase budget was based on estimated sales of $21,000; actual sales that month were $1000 less. At cost (60 percent of $1000), this means that $600 less merchandise was sold than anticipated. The net result is that inventory went up by $2000 ($600 + $1400) in January (see column 8). February's purchase budget must therefore be *reduced* by $2000 (as entered under February, columns 4 and 5 in the chart) to bring inventory back to its original level.
4. At the end of February, actual sales and purchases are entered and adjustments calculated for March. The process continues in the same way each month throughout the year, with purchase budgets being changed each month to compensate for actual events of the previous month that affected inventory. Work through the remainder of our sample chart to familiarize yourself with the process.

In addition to revising monthly purchase budgets, the open-to-buy budget method involves tracking actual orders placed to keep an eye on the balances left to spend during the month on merchandise purchases. See Table 11.2, which depicts this sort of open-to-buy worksheet, using our figures from Table 11.1.

Our sample describes a situation wherein the inventory is maintained at the same level as it was at the end of the previous year. If the pharmacist-owner planned to reduce the pharmacy's investment in inventory during the year, the monthly adjustments could be reduced by a desired average percentage.

Economic Order Quantity

The economic order quantity (EOQ) method, as its name suggests, seeks to minimize inventory investment by determining the most economical quantities to be ordered and the frequency with which these orders should be placed. Unlike the methods discussed thus far, the calculation of the EOQ takes into consideration the effects of the value of an order (and

frequency of ordering) on the two sets of costs associated with purchasing
– *procurement costs* and *carrying costs* (see definitions on pp. 153-54). The
EOQ is in fact the dollar volume of purchases or level of inventory at
which *combined* procurement and carrying costs are lowest. Although
this method is not commonly used by community pharmacies, the principles on which it is based are important and worthy of consideration
by the pharmacist-owner or manager.

A procurement cost is incurred with each order placed; hence, to keep
procurement costs down, orders should ideally be made larger (i.e., of
a higher dollar volume) and placed infrequently. Carrying costs, on the
other hand, increase with the value of the inventory, and can hence be
minimized by placing smaller orders more frequently. This inverse relationship, depicted graphically in Figure 11.4, finds a balance at a particular size of order at which procurement costs are (theoretically) equal
to carrying costs (practically, it is the point at which the two sets of costs
are closest to one another). This is the economic order quantity, in that
it results in the lowest combined cost.

Figure 11.4.   BEHAVIOUR OF PROCUREMENT AND CARRYING COSTS
WITH CHANGES IN ORDER SIZE

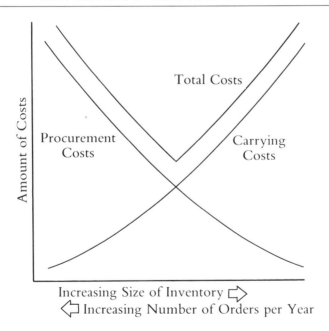

Source: Effective Pharmacy Management, 2nd ed. (Kansas City, Mo.: Marion Laboratories,
Inc., 1983), p. 216.

Table 11.2 OPEN-TO-BUY WORKSHEET

Month	Jan		Feb		March		April		May		June	
Planned purchases	25,00		12,500		35,00		27,50		12,50		6,250	
Order No / Supplier	Amount	Bal	Amount	Bal	Amount	Bal	Amount	Bal	Amount	Bal	Amount	Bal
Dec. adj.	3,100	22,00										
1491 Blain Co.	3,000	19,000	4,000	8,500	3,000	22,00						
1492 Acme Macrame	5,000	14,000	2,000	6,500								
1493 Hobby Crafts	2,000	12,000	2,000	4,500								
1494 Models Ltd	1,000	11,000										
1495 Blain Co.	4,000	7,000										
1496 Acme Macrame	2,000	5,000	2,000	2,500	1,000	2,000						
Jan adj.	500	—	(500)	7,500								
1497 Hobby Crafts			2,000	5,500	3,000	18,000						
1498 Blain Co.			6,000	(500)	5,000	13,000						
Feb. adj.			500	—								
1499 Acme Macrame				500	12,500	2,000	10,500	5,000	22,500	500	7,500	
1500 Models Ltd						3,000	7,500	3,000	19,500	5,000	2,500	
(1499) Mfr order cancelled									(5,000)	7,500		
1501 Blain Co.						4,000	3,500	5,000	14,500			
1502 Hobby Crafts						3,500	—	3,000	11,500			
April adj.							11,500	—	(11,500)	14,000		
1503 Acme Macrame								3,000	16,000	3,000	3,250	

Source: As adapted from *Minding Your Own Business*, vol. 2 (Montreal: Federal Business Development Bank, 1980), p. 94.

Table 11.3 illustrates this relationship between the value of orders and total cost. Our example assumes a procurement cost of $3 per order and a carrying cost of 20 percent of the average inventory value (beginning inventory plus ending inventory divided by two). The cost of the product in the example is $720 for a full year's supply, and, assuming depletion of the order at the end of the period, average inventory is calculated as ($720 − 0) ÷ 2 = $360 on a one-time order. As you can see, total costs are minimized at five orders per year.

The EOQ method is best suited to high-volume products that incur high procurement and carrying costs; it is not useful with seasonal merchandise, nor with items that demand particular reorder cycles by virtue of limited shelf life or for other reasons. Similarly, the results of EOQ calculations must be weighted against outside factors such as suppliers' terms of payment, order cycles, and available volume discounts, and order quantities must be modified as necessary to obtain optimal returns on investment in inventory.

Table 11.3. VALUE OF ORDERS AND TOTAL COST

No. of orders per year	1	2	3	4	5	6	7	8
Value of order	$720	$360	$240	$180	$144	$120	$102.85	$90
Procurement costs	3	6	9	12	15	18	21	24
Ave. active inventory	360	180	120	90	72	60	51.43	45
Carrying costs (20%)	72	36	24	18	14.40	12	10.29	9
Total cost	75	42	33	30	29.40	30	31.29	33

Source: Adapted from B. McCormick and H.J. Segal, *Systems Management: Inventory Control*, Ontario College of Pharmacists, Toronto.

ASSESSING THE EFFECTIVENESS OF INVENTORY CONTROL

An examination of the various inventory-control systems available is necessary to decide which ones are best for your practice. But it is important to recognize that not every product in a pharmacy needs to be formally controlled. There is a guideline known as Pareto's Law, which holds that 20 percent of all products stocked generates 80 percent of total dollar sales, 15 percent of inventory generates another 15 percent of sales, and the remaining 65 percent of the stock generates only 5 percent of sales. Identifying the products that produce the greatest percentage of revenues and managing them properly is therefore extremely important; conversely, undue attention to the 65 percent of inventory that generates minimal revenues could be potentially disastrous.

One important measure of how well or how poorly inventory is being managed is the turnover rate. This is a ratio calculated by dividing the cost of goods sold by the average inventory at cost. For example, if the annual cost of goods sold is $800,000 and the average inventory at cost is $200,000, then the turnover rate is 4; that is, merchandise has been ordered and sold four times in the course of a year. When the turnover rate is too high, the level of inventory is likely to be too low and out-of-stock situations frequent; when it is too low, inventory levels are probably excessive, tying up funds that could be used more profitably otherwise and leading to lower profits. The appropriateness of a pharmacy's turnover rate may be judged against past performance or against industry standards. It is reported that the average turnover rate among Canadian pharmacies is currently about 4.

Another measure of the efficiency of inventory control is the gross margin return on inventory investment (GMROI), which is calculated by dividing the annual gross margin by the average inventory at cost, and multiplying by 100. According to the Seventh Annual Survey of Community Pharmacy Operations, the average Canadian pharmacy in 1986 had a gross margin of approximately $387,051 and an average inventory of $205,733, giving a GMROI of 188 percent, that is, a gross margin of $1.88 for every dollar invested in inventory. Some authorities claim that pharmacies should be able to achieve a GMROI of 150–300 percent.[5]

Good pharmacy management can contribute to both increasing the gross margin and reducing inventory, thereby improving the GMROI. Since the goal of 150–300 percent represents an overall GMROI, it is important to consider the performance of each of the pharmacy's departments to ensure that the overall objective is reached. For example, tobacco products may bear a low gross margin but, since their turnover rate is high, their average inventory will also be low, producing a good GMROI. Both greeting cards and cosmetics may have relatively high gross margins (approximately 50 and 40 percent, respectively) but also relatively high average inventories, producing poor GMROIs. The dispensary typically has a good gross margin (approximately 40 percent on average) and a low average inventory, producing a very good GMROI. It follows that, if the percentage of prescription sales (and sales of other product groups yielding high GMROIs) is high relative to total sales, it will be easier to achieve the desired GMROI for the pharmacy as a whole. In other words, pharmacy managers should regularly monitor the effect on overall GMROI of the varying contributions by the different departments, striving to increase the sales of those departments that yield a higher individual GMROI so that they will represent a greater percentage of the pharmacy's total sales.

PURCHASING

Purchasing, that is, the activity of replenishing stock and introducing new products in the store, is closely related to inventory control and management. Products to be purchased must be selected on the basis of a number of criteria, from customer demand for the product, its turnover rate and profitability, and associated carrying costs, to its suitability for the store's merchandise mix. We have described the dangers of both under- and overstocking; we shall now outline some of the choices facing the pharmacist-owner in the process of investing inventory dollars wisely.

[5] Graham Cunningham, "Lessons in 'Just-in-Time' Inventory Replenishment," *Drug Merchandising* 66, no. 4 (April 1985): 43–44.

Purchasing Decisions

There are a number of factors that a pharmacy owner or manager must consider when making purchasing decisions. One decision that can be complex – and that should not be based solely on price – is whether to purchase through a wholesaler or directly from the manufacturer. When a product is available from either source, the manufacturer's price will generally be lower. This, however, is only one factor, which should be considered along with the following:

1. payment terms (including incentives for prompt payment or dating, credit terms, and penalties for late payment);
2. minimum-order requirements (do you have to order more than you can sell in a reasonable period?);
3. order cycle or time for delivery (that is, the lag time between order placement and actual delivery);
4. the pharmacy's cash flow;
5. the overall objectives of the pharmacy;
6. the supplier's policy on returned goods;
7. the range of services offered by the supplier and how well they meet the pharmacy's needs;
8. the effects of suppliers' incentive plans on the pharmacy's purchasing plans.

In addition, all purchasing decisions must of course relate to the identified needs of the pharmacy's customers and the inventory-control systems used by the pharmacy.

In the dispensary, many products are supplied by pharmaceutical manufacturers, whose prices are generally better than those of the wholesaler. (This is because wholesalers' prices include the cost of the functions they perform as middlemen, including consolidation of purchasing from several manufacturers, storing merchandise, and various other services.) Drug manufacturers also offer prompt delivery, and their minimum-order requirements, unlike those of non-drug product manufacturers, are sufficiently low that pharmacies are not forced to purchase excessive quantities in order to meet them. In addition, the manufacturers extend good payment terms and favourable returns policies. These features have made the decision regarding pharmaceutical suppliers relatively straight-forward. In recent years, however, some wholesalers have become more aggressive and are attempting to compete, even on price, with manu-facturers. They are offering discounted prices on pharmaceuticals pur-chased in quantity, as well as further discounts when predetermined annual purchasing levels are reached. In addition, they may offer extended payment terms, personal servicing of the pharmacy's account by their customer-service representatives, and same- or next-day delivery. These changes in the wholesaler's approach have given the pharmacy owner a wider range of options in his or her choice of supplier – and by doing so, have introduced a wider range of factors to consider in making that choice.

Suppliers

WHOLESALERS

Full-service wholesale suppliers offer a wide range of services, which include:

1. same- or next-day delivery;
2. customer pick-up counters for emergency orders;
3. a wide assortment of products from various manufacturers;
4. regular visits by customer-service representatives;
5. store-planning services, including traffic-flow analysis;
6. convenient payment terms and reasonable returns policies;
7. co-operative advertising and promotional programs;
8. lower rates on charge cards (because of negotiated lower administrative fees);
9. inventory-control services;
10. marketing and merchandising information and assistance;
11. incentive programs providing additional discounts on volume purchases.

For low-volume pharmacies, wholesalers represent a "one-stop" shopping opportunity. Through some of their programs, they also represent an opportunity for these pharmacies to compete (to some extent, at least) with larger pharmacies. Wholesalers meet the smaller pharmacy's needs with respect to inventory control and cash flow as well. For larger pharmacies, they represent an attractive supplier alternative to manufacturers, especially since they have recently improved their approach to the servicing of larger accounts.

MANUFACTURERS

The role of manufacturers in the pharmaceutical industry and the pharmacy profession involves more than offering good prices on drug products to pharmacies. Through their medical service representatives, the innovative companies provide invaluable drug-information services. In addition, they are strong supporters of continuing-education programs in pharmacy and contribute, in both time and money, to the advancement of the health professions, as well as to the research and development of new drugs.

As suppliers, pharmaceutical manufacturers offer pharmacists the opportunity to "prestock" newly released prescription and non-prescription drugs. This means that the manufacturer and the pharmacy owner/manager have an understanding that a specified quantity of a new drug product will be shipped to the pharmacy automatically upon its release. Should physicians fail to prescribe the new product with any frequency, the pharmacy is free to return the stock to the manufacturer. On the other hand, prestocking ensures that the pharmacy will not have out-of-stock situations when physicians begin to prescribe the new product (or, in the case of non-prescription drugs, when customers begin to request it). Prestocking also gives the pharmacist time to assess the demand for the product and plan purchasing for the future.

As mentioned earlier, manufacturers of both drug and non-drug products can generally offer lower prices than wholesalers, and many pharmacies prefer to purchase directly from manufacturers for this reason. Some manufacturers, however, impose minimum-order quantity requirements that make them unattractive to the smaller pharmacy, which, in many cases, would have to risk overstocking in order to meet the requirements. Furthermore, the pharmacy that purchases at lower prices from manufacturers is in fact choosing to undertake on its own certain services that are otherwise provided by the middleman. Absorbing these functions involves a cost to the pharmacy, which the owner or manager must recognize and assess.

Terms of Payment, Dating, and Quantity-Purchase Deals

As part of their marketing approach, both manufacturers and wholesalers may offer a special payment provision known as "dating," which in this context refers to the practice of extending payment terms for 30, 60, or 90 days or permitting the splitting of payments over that period of time. Dating deals are normally arranged on large-quantity purchases. Also, the supplier is likely to be most flexible about extending terms of payment with a long-standing and reliable customer who directs a significant portion of the pharmacy's business to him. (This is one reason why it is wise to develop a strong relationship with only a small number of suitable suppliers, rather than to spread the pharmacy's business too thinly among many sources of supply.) The secret to success with dating deals is to ensure that purchases are confined to quantities that can be sold by the time payment is due. Note that this is where inventory-control data is invaluable.

Some suppliers offer payment terms such as "2%/10 days," meaning simply that if the order is paid within 10 days after the invoice date, a two percent discount will be deducted from the amount invoiced. Some argue that such opportunities for cash discounts should always be taken (even if funds must be borrowed for the purpose) because over the year the total discount could amount to as much as 36 percent. This argument is in fact flawed, however, since cash-discount savings must be assessed in light of prevailing interest rates, and, at the time of writing, it is indeed more advantageous to opt for extended terms of payment than to earn a two percent discount through early payment. The advantages to be gained in this way will be outlined in Chapter 12, in the context of good cash management in pharmacy practice (see pp. 182-83). It should be noted, finally, that some suppliers are now charging a monthly interest of 1.5 percent or more on overdue accounts.

There are a number of suppliers who also offer quantity-purchase "deals" or discounts. These deals, offered on large-quantity purchases, are often designed to introduce a new product or encourage the pharmacy to select a particular brand of product. The deals may take the form of offering "free goods," promotional allowances, co-operative advertising allowances, or extra discounts and premiums. Promotional allowances are in fact payments to the purchaser, which are intended to be used in association with the promotion of the particular product. Similarly, co-operative advertising allowances are allowances or payments toward the advertising of the product. In the case of non-prescription drug products, the supplier may support the offer with a backup media promotion as a further inducement for the customer to purchase in quantity. The decision to purchase on deal or in larger-than-normal quantities must be based on cash-flow and inventory-control considerations. Some pharmacies adhere strictly to established policies requiring that products purchased have a proven specified turnover rate or that they carry a dating advantage, so that they are sold by the time they must be paid for. Others will only take quantity deals on a consignment basis and still others insist that products gain customer acceptance before they will buy in quantity. In general, while buying certain products in bulk can lower unit cost and help increase gross margins, it may also result in excess inventory levels, decreased gross margins, and too much money invested in inventory. Therefore, each individual pharmacy must carefully assess its ability to sell off the merchandise before engaging in large-quantity purchasing. Such an assessment is of course made easier with the help of a computer to provide timely information on the movement of products.

It should be noted here that point-of-sale systems are immensely helpful with regard to capitalizing on discounts and, generally, adhering to suppliers' terms of payment. The system stores information on when accounts are due for payment, ensuring that the pharmacy will take advantage of discounts where applicable. (It will even generate the cheques for payment.) The supplier files also contain relevant information on minimum-order requirements, prices, and other pertinent supplier information.

Central Purchasing and Co-operatives

In some chain pharmacies, much of the purchasing is done by a central office, in consultation with the managers of the chain's affiliated stores. Senior management in such situations believe that cost savings are made with this method and that better control of inventory is achieved. Merchandise is either distributed directly to the respective units of the chain (a system known as "drop shipment") or delivered to a central warehouse, from which it is redistributed to each unit. In these instances, the chain adopts some of the functions of a wholesaler.

To gain the advantages that come with large-quantity purchasing, a number of independent pharmacies will often combine to form a voluntary purchasing or buying group (examples include Pharmasave and Value Drug Mart). The resulting savings are shared among group members, helping them to compete with larger pharmacies or to increase their profitability (or both). In some cases, each member of a co-operative group will purchase specific products, so that no single member is unduly burdened by the process. These informal groups meet frequently, usually monthly, to plan purchases.

Receiving, Marking, Stocking

The responsibility for receiving merchandise in a pharmacy should be assigned to one staff member. That person must ensure that all merchandise received agrees with the purchase order and is accurately reflected in the invoice, and that it is in good condition, suitable for sale. Errors in back orders or quantities received, and any damaged merchandise, must be reported immediately, following store policies and procedures. Items received but not invoiced, or invoiced but not received, must also be reported and a record kept in order to maintain proper inventory control and, where appropriate, for re-order purposes. Some pharmacies have specific receiving hours to ensure that staff is available to receive merchandise in accordance with established policies. Most stores have specific policies with regard to certain categories of merchandise, such as narcotics, high-ticket items, or perishable products.

Prior to the placement of merchandise on the shelves or in the stockroom, products must be priced correctly, employing the appropriate markups. Careful attention should be paid to avoid error in these procedures. In some stores, pricing methods may involve marking the cost of the item, in code, on the price sticker, in addition to the retail price. The date of receipt of the merchandise may also be indicated on the ticket, in code. Pharmacies with POS systems must follow specific procedures for the use of the system with regard to pricing.

The importance of issuing a purchase order with each order placed cannot be overemphasized. Purchase orders should be prepared consistently and according to specific guidelines, identifying the supplier correctly and listing the products ordered, the sizes and quantities of each, the unit costs, and the total value of the order. The P.O. is not only necessary for inventory control and bookkeeping purposes, but also helps to reduce errors in receiving procedures and can be used for pricing by staff. As mentioned earlier, POS systems have the capability of generating purchase orders and purchase reports – another invaluable aid.

Those responsible for placing merchandise on the shelves should ensure that stock is rotated properly, moving existing stock to the front of the shelves and new stock toward the back. Care must also be taken to see that each product is placed in its designated position on the appropriate shelf, in accordance with the store's merchandising plan, or "planogram." The latter will be discussed in detail in Chapter 15.

Purchasing Policies

Based on the choices and approaches taken in all these facets of purchasing activity, the pharmacy owner should develop a set of purchasing policies for the store. Chapter 14 discusses the development of various store policies, including purchasing policies, in greater detail.

SOME GENERAL GUIDELINES

When planning inventory management for your pharmacy, it is useful to start by establishing the goals you wish to achieve. Those goals might be formulated as follows:

1. Reduce the average inventory by a certain percentage or dollar value while maintaining or increasing sales.
2. Increase turnover rate by maintaining present inventory levels and increasing sales, or by reducing inventory levels and maintaining (or increasing) sales.
3. Increase GMROI by increasing turnover rate while maintaining gross margins. A reduction in gross margin would require a higher turnover rate to maintain a desirable GMROI.

Regardless of the particular inventory-control methods you select to achieve your goals, there are a number of general principles that should always be observed:

1. Monitor sales, purchases, and cost of goods sold continually.
2. Watch for shrinkage, determine its causes, and take steps to reduce it; implement or reinforce measures to reduce theft and pilferage.
3. Control the receipt of merchandise carefully. Ensure that all mer-

chandise for which you are charged is received and put in its proper place.

4. Implement measures designed to reduce error, particularly with respect to pricing; allocate responsibilities related to inventory control to reliable, responsible, and competent personnel.
5. Control spoilage and obsolescence by ensuring that merchandise is stored properly and that stock is rotated and by watching the movement of products in order to clear slow-moving products promptly rather than allowing them to inflate inventory.
6. Streamline assortments, eliminating slow-selling sizes or multiple brands.
7. Study peaks and valleys of demand and keep stocks in correct proportion to sales; implement a control system to report out-of-stock situations immediately; monitor back orders regularly.
8. When overstocks or low turnover conditions exist, improve merchandise displays; where possible, return items to suppliers (in multiple-store situations, redistribute merchandise); employ markdowns and sales to cut losses due to overstocking.
9. Test products before buying in depth.
10. Avoid buying products that exceed your usual price lines.
11. If at all possible, establish more efficient inventory-control systems by means of automation.
12. Learn about the terms of sale and services offered by a range of suppliers, then select the ones that will be most beneficial and best suited to your particular practice.

Summary

Inventory is the largest single investment of the community-pharmacy practice. Mismanaged, it can become the greatest liability of the business, tying up funds that could be invested to upgrade or expand the business and incurring excess insurance, interest, rent, and labour costs. Properly managed, it can be the pharmacy's strongest asset, ensuring the profitability and future income of the operation.

Inventory-Control Checklist

1. Learn and understand the terminology of inventory management.
2. Become familiar with the various inventory-control systems:
   Unit-control systems:
   1. Visual systems
   2. Systematic wantbook method
   3. Periodic systems

    4. Perpetual systems
Dollar-control systems:
    1. Open-to-buy budget
    2. Economic order quantity (EOQ)
3. Watch for developments in and affordability of computer systems in inventory control for the dispensary and the front store (POS systems).
4. Understand gross margin and turnover rate and their importance to profitability.
5. Know the factors to consider when choosing suppliers.
6. Know the factors to consider in making decisions about bulk buying.
7. Be familiar with the benefits of good inventory management.

RECOMMENDED READING

Archambault, A., and Segal, H. *Inventory Management. Pharmacy Management Program, Module 1.* Kirkland, Que.: Nordic Laboratories Inc., n.d.

—. *Purchasing Management. Pharmacy Management Program, Module 2.* Kirkland Que.: Nordic Laboratories Inc., n.d.

Berger, B.A. "Gross Margin Return on Investment." *American Pharmacy* NS26, no. 8 (August 1986): 567.

Cunningham, Graham. "Turn on to Turnover." *The Magazine That's All About Small Business* (May/June 1983), p. 56.

Effective Pharmacy Management. 4th ed. Kansas City, Mo.: Marion Laboratories, Inc., 1987.

Federal Business Development Bank. "Merchandise Control for Retailers." FBDB Management Clinic. Montreal, FBDB, 1982.

—. *Minding Your Own Business.* Vol. 2. Montreal: FBDB, 1980.

Inventory Control. Guide to Good Pharmacy Management. Vaudreuil, Que.: Hoffman-La Roche, Inc., 1978.

Israel, Florence. "Your Guide to Scanners." *Drug Merchandising* (June 1985), pp. 33–37.

Management Handbook for Pharmacy Practitioners: A Practical Guide for Community Pharmacists. Chapel Hill, N.C.: Health Sciences Consortium, Inc. and The Upjohn Company, 1982.

Royal Bank of Canada. *Your Business Matters: A Guide for Independent Business.* See booklet no. 7, "Planning and Budgeting."

Smith, H.A. *Principles and Methods of Pharmacy Management.* 3rd ed. Philadelphia: Lea & Febiger, 1986.

Tharp, C.P. and Lecca, P.J. *Pharmacy Management for Students and Practitioners.* 2nd ed. St. Louis, Mo.: C.V. Mosby Co., 1979.

Tyrus, Reiman. "Automating the Front Store." *Drug Merchandising* (June 1985), pp. 29–32.

12

FINANCIAL MANAGEMENT

INTRODUCTION

In-store financial management can be expressed in another way – *cash management*. An expression common among small-business owners, including pharmacists starting up their own practices, is "I have cash-flow problems." In some cases, this is the result of inadequate debt or equity capital; usually, however, cash-flow problems are the result of poor cash management.

What, then, is cash management? Put simply, cash management means freeing up funds for operating purposes by minimizing assets and maximizing liabilities – specifically, accounts payable. Although it may sound paradoxical, the lower the value of the assets (accounts receivable, inventory, and non-current or fixed assets) involved in operating the pharmacy and the higher the accounts payable, the more cash there will be at the owner's disposal. Similarly, increasing owner's or shareholders' equity will increase available funds.

In Figure 12.1, for example, Column 1 presents data from a hypothetical year-end balance sheet, in which the bank loan is $80,000. Column 2 shows the resulting bank position when inventory is reduced by $40,000, from $170,000 to $130,000. Assuming that no other items on the balance sheet change, the bank loan is reduced from $80,000 to $40,000. In other words, if inventory is minimized, a smaller bank loan will be needed, and the cash position will improve.

175

Figure 12.1   MINIMIZE ASSETS – MAXIMIZE LIABILITIES

	(1)	(2)	(3)	(4)
	Actual Year End	Decrease Inventory	Increase Accounts Payable	Increase Shareholders' Equity
Assets				
Accounts receivable	$ 40,000	$ 40,000	$ 40,000	$ 40,000
Inventory	170,000	130,000	170,000	170,000
Fixed assets – net	30,000	30,000	30,000	30,000
	$240,000	$200,000	$240,000	$240,000
Liabilities and Shareholders' Equity				
Accounts payable	$ 60,000	$ 60,000	$ 80,000	$ 60,000
Shareholders' equity	100,000	100,000	100,000	130,000
	160,000	160,000	180,000	190,000
Bank Loan	$ 80,000	$ 40,000	$ 60,000	$ 50,000

Column 3 reflects a reduction in the bank loan resulting from an increase in accounts payable of $20,000, from $60,000 to $80,000. By delaying payment to suppliers, the pharmacy has more cash at its disposal, and its bank position can be decreased from $80,000 to $60,000.

In Column 4, the result of increasing shareholders' equity from $100,000 to $130,000 (by improving profits) is to reduce the bank loan from $80,000 to $50,000.

Thus, as strange as it might seem, cash management aims to minimize assets and maximize liabilities.

Many pharmacists, on reviewing their annual financial statements, find themselves wondering, "Where did all the money go?" The data in Figures 12.2 and 12.3 may help to explain this. The pharmacist in this example had after-tax earnings of $60,000 (see Figure 12.2). On reviewing the income statement, the pharmacist's spouse suggested that they use some of the $60,000 to finance a well-earned trip to Europe, trade in the old car for a new one, and make several minor improvements to their home. However, on reviewing the balance sheet, they were appalled to find not only that there was no money in the bank, but that they *owed* the bank $30,000. Their plans for a better lifestyle were put on hold.

To understand how this can happen, let us refer to the balance sheet in Figure 12.3. Notice that there has been a $100,000 increase in total assets from last year (i.e., $30,000 more cash is tied up in accounts receivable, $50,000 more in inventory; and $20,000 more in fixed assets. This increase has been partially offset by increases in accounts payable

Figure 12.2 "WHERE DID ALL THE MONEY GO?"
INCOME STATEMENT

	This Year		Last Year	
	(dollars)	(percent-ages)	(dollars)	(percent-ages)
Sales				
– Dispensary	$ 800,000		$ 700,000	
– Front Shop	400,000		300,000	
Total Sales	1,200,000		1,000,000	
Cost of Goods Sold	750,000		600,000	
Gross Margin				
– Dispensary	360,000	45%†	315,000	45%†
– Front Shop	90,000	23%†	85,000	28%†
Total Gross Margin	450,000	37%†	400,000	40%†
Expenses				
Wages	200,000	44%‡	180,000	45%‡
Occupancy	50,000	11%‡	50,000	12%‡
Other	120,000	27%‡	110,000	28%‡
Total Expenses	370,000	82%‡	340,000	85%‡
Net Income (or profit)				
before Taxes	80,000		60,000	
Taxes	20,000		15,000	
Net Income	$ 60,000		$ 45,000	

† percentage of corresponding sales
‡ percentage of gross margin

Figure 12.3 "WHERE DID ALL THE MONEY GO?" BALANCE SHEET

	This Year	Last Year	– Cash – Increase (+) Decrease (–)
Accounts receivable	$ 70,000	$ 40,000	$– 30,000
Inventory	220,000	170,000	– 50,000
Non-current (fixed) assets	50,000	30,000	– 20,000
Total Operating Costs	340,000	240,000	– 100,000
Accounts payable	70,000	60,000	+ 10,000
Shareholders' equity	240,000	180,000	+ 60,000
	310,000	240,000	+ 70,000
Bank Loan	$ 30,000	$ ——	$+ 30,000

and in shareholders' equity of $10,000 and $60,000, respectively, for a total of $70,000. The resulting bank position is therefore $30,000 worse. In simple terms, the pharmacist has used $90,000 more cash ($100,000 assets less $10,000 accounts payable) to finance the operation of the pharmacy.

Basing our discussion on the case described above, we shall now explore the means by which assets may be minimized and liabilities and shareholders' equity increased to best advantage for cash management in a community pharmacy practice.

How Assets Are Minimized

Accounts Receivable: Credit Policy

The first question to address is how the pharmacist-owner can minimize accounts receivable. (Omar Khayyam put it simply: "Ah, take the cash, and let the credit go." This may be a word to the wise.) Although pharmacist-owners cannot avoid third-party accounts receivable, they can neither afford to extend the courtesy of credit to their cash customers – the equivalent, in effect, of providing them with interest-free loans. With annual interest rates in the area of, say, 12 percent, the cost to the pharmacist is about one percent for 30 days on unpaid accounts receivable.

The best approach is to accept only cash or credit cards to improve the cash position. Major credit cards are now a way of life, and they simplify the situation for both pharmacist-owners and their customers. Pharmacists can avoid the burden of bookkeeping chores and the potential bad debts that come with personal credit accounts, and customers do not need to prepare a separate cheque each month. The new owner of an older, established pharmacy with a tradition of extending credit to customers may certainly find it difficult to introduce this new policy. But times have changed, and, at least in a start-up situation, the pharmacy owner should make it a policy at the outset not to establish personal credit accounts.

Among pharmacies where charge accounts are still prevalent, the major cause of high accounts receivable is poor credit control. This would include poor credit policy, poor bookkeeping, and inadequate collection procedures. Poor credit control means higher costs, potential losses due to bad debts, and potential loss of credibility with the pharmacy's banker.

The first step where charge customers are involved is to establish a credit policy for them. This credit policy should include terms of payment ("due on receipt of statement," "due in 15 days," etc.), credit limits (rate customers on their financial stability, establish credit limits, and review them on a regular basis); and requirements for new customers (credit application forms, bank references). Viewing customer charge accounts as interest-free loans, the pharmacy owner must judge whether the customer is worthy of this trust.

A simple bookkeeping system must be implemented to maintain a daily record of sales, cash receipts, and accounts receivable. To speed up payments, month-end customer statements must be sent no later than the first week of the following month. An open file system of outstanding accounts-receivable invoices is usually adequate and saves many hours of mundane recording in ledger books.

An aged accounts-receivable trial balance must be prepared at the end of each month, immediately after month-end. This document, listing each customer, the amount owed, and the month in which the charge was incurred, is required for two reasons: the banker must receive a copy and the pharmacist relies on it as the main follow-up tool for credit control. Payments must be recorded in the normal manner in the bookkeeping system, but notation should also be made on the accounts-receivable trial balance for a daily update on who still owes how much. As an internal control, only one employee in the pharmacy should be given access to and responsibility for the receivables file, under the supervision of the pharmacy owner.

The third aspect of credit control is the collection procedure, which requires both diplomacy and firmness on the part of the pharmacist. Any customer who fails to pay in accordance with the credit policy – say, by the 15th of the following month – should automatically receive a telephone call no later than the 25th of the month as a reminder. On a designated morning each week, the staff member responsible for accounts receivable should review the updated accounts-receivable trial balance and phone delinquent customers whose accounts remain unpaid. It is important to get a commitment and to record the date of the proposed payment on the customer's record sheet. If payment has not been received by the commitment date, the customer should be called again and another commitment date determined and recorded on the collection record. If payment is still not received by the third commitment date, the owner should telephone the customer. Should this action fail, a firm demand letter specifying a deadline for payment must be sent. If this final attempt proves ineffectual, as a last resort issue a writ in a small claims court – a simple, if expensive, approach, but very effective.

Again, pharmacies should limit accounts receivable to third parties. In such cases, the required documentation should be prepared promptly and appropriate reports filed with third parties at the earliest possible time. The new pharmacy owner would be well advised to purchase or lease a dispensary computer to transmit billing electronically to the key third party. This will speed up payment and reduce accounts receivable on third-party plans significantly, and ultimately result in the desired improvement in bank position.

Figure 12.4   GROSS MARGIN RETURN ON INVENTORY INVESTMENT

Formula:
$$\frac{\text{Annual gross margin} \times 100}{\text{Inventory}}$$

Example:

	Last Year	This Year
Annual gross margin	$400,000	$450,000
Inventory	$170,000	$220,000
GMROI	$\dfrac{\$400,000 \times 100}{\$170,000} = 235\%$	$\dfrac{\$450,000 \times 100}{\$220,000} = 205\%$

Inventory

From Figure 12.2, we can determine that the inventory turnover rate of the pharmacy in our example has decreased from 3.5 last year to 3.4 this year. (Recall that turnover rate is calculated by dividing the cost of goods sold by inventory; hence, in our example for this year, $750,000 [COGS] ÷ 220,000 [inventory] = 3.4 TOR). But the inventory turnover rate is not, in fact, the most useful measure for our purposes: the real barometer of effective inventory management is the gross margin return on inventory investment (GMROI). Recall that GMROI is calculated by dividing the annual gross margin by the inventory and multiplying by 100. Figure 12.4 shows GMROI calculations using the financial details from Figure 12.2. As you can see, the GMROI last year was 235 percent and is shown to have deteriorated to 205 percent this year. This means that for every dollar invested in inventory last year, the pharmacy received $2.35 in annual gross margin; this year, it receives only $2.05. A good yardstick is 300 percent GMROI, or $3.00 of annual gross margin per $1.00 of inventory. According to the Seventh Annual Survey of Community Pharmacy Operations, the average GMROI among surveyed Canadian pharmacies for the years 1985 and 1986 was 186 and 188 percent, respectively. If, for example, the 1985 GMROI had been 300 percent, then the reported average inventory of $194,262 would have been reduced by $73,776 to $120,486 – a reduction of about 38 percent.

In our example, if the GMROI for this year were 300 percent, then the inventory would be $150,000 ($450,000 gross margin divided by 3) as opposed to $220,000. This would represent a reduction of $70,000 and would improve the bank position by $70,000, bringing it to a positive balance of $40,000. Although some might suggest that a target GMROI of 300 percent is too aggressive, the fact is that well-managed pharmacies with active front shops are indeed maintaining a GMROI of 300 percent or more. However, if an effort were made to meet the target even half way, the improvement in the bank position would be $35,000, resulting in a $5000 positive bank balance. How, then, would the owner go about increasing the pharmacy's GMROI?

Although inventory control was discussed in detail in Chapter 11, some of the points bear repeating here. There is no real secret to controlling inventory. Pareto's law holds the key – that 80 percent of sales and profits are derived from 20 percent of the products stocked – and all that remains is to determine *which* products comprise that 20 percent. Pharmacist-owners are currently doing this in two ways: (1) by manually recording and tracking sales, inventory, and gross margin by *product grouping* (for example, non-prescription drug products, cosmetics, health and beauty aids, photography, greeting cards, and paper goods); and (2) by implementing a point-of-sale (POS) computer system that will automatically provide data on sales, stock, and gross margins for every individual product sold. This modern technology is becoming more readily available to pharmacies.

The grouping approach involves determining the product groups that you wish to control. By each product group, record purchases at cost, then deduct sales at estimated cost to arrive at the book value of inventory by product grouping each month. Estimated cost is calculated by multiplying each respective product group's sales by a cost factor, i.e., a percentage of the retail price, which should be determined from time to time during the year by comparing revenues to invoiced costs for the different groups. For example, under normal circumstances, non-prescription drug products will have a cost factor of, say, 60 percent of the retail price. If, however, the pharmacy sells high volume at a low margin, this cost factor could be as high as 80 percent of the retail price. The cost factor should be determined for each product group when the system is implemented to pinpoint the groups that are not providing a reasonable return. Now the pharmacist can act on Pareto's Law by zeroing in to reduce that part of the pharmacy's inventory that represents 80 percent of the volume but only 20 percent of the sales and profit. The importance of taking advantage of the inventory, planning, and control systems outlined in Chapter 11 should now be clear in light of the dramatic effects that minimizing inventory can have on the pharmacy's profitability and cash flow.

Non-Current or Fixed Assets

The other major category under total assets is non-current or fixed assets. In our example in Figure 12.3, let us assume that the pharmacist increased this year's fixed assets by purchasing a $20,000 delivery vehicle. Further analysis might have shown that it would have been more prudent to lease the vehicle and conserve the cash, or, on the other hand, to sub-contract delivery to a delivery service and thereby save on costs such as employing a driver, maintaining and repairing a vehicle, depreciation, and interest on a bank loan. This would not only have improved the cash position, but increased net profit as well.

How Accounts Payable Are Maximized

The higher the accounts payable, the better the cash position will be. This is not a suggestion to increase purchasing arbitrarily, but to understand the financial wisdom of delaying payment on purchases as long as reasonably possible. In Figure 12.3, accounts payable have increased from $60,000 to $70,000. On the surface, that's good, since an increase in liabilities means an improvement in the cash position. But, as you can see in Figure 12.2, with the increased sales activity this year over last year, the cost of goods sold also rose (by $150,000), and this increase is reflected in the accounts payable. In order to determine if there has been a real increase in the accounts payable, it is necessary to calculate and compare this year and last year's average period of time taken to pay for purchases – otherwise known as the number of days of accounts payable outstanding, or the "average payable period." This is done by dividing the accounts payable by the cost of goods sold, then multiplying by 365 days. Figure 12.5 sets out these calculations, which show 34 days this

Figure 12.5 NUMBER OF DAYS OF ACCOUNTS PAYABLE
(Average Payable Period)

Formula: $\dfrac{\text{Accounts payable}}{\text{Cost of goods sold}} \times 365$

Example:

	Last Year	This Year
Accounts payable	$ 60,000	$ 70,000
Cost of goods sold	$600,000	$750,000
Number of days of accounts payable	$\dfrac{\$60,000}{\$600,000} \times 365 = 36.5$ days	$\dfrac{\$70,000}{\$750,000} \times 365 = 34$ days

year and 36.5 days last year. Had the 36.5-day term prevailed through this year, the accounts payable would have been $75,000 ([36.5 ÷ 365] × $750,000) – a $15,000 increase over last year. So although the accounts payable have increased by $10,000 in our example for this year, this sum actually reflects only the increase in purchases – and this is poor cash management.

As we discussed in Chapter 6, suppliers can represent a major source of capital for financing the pharmacy operation. The pharmacy owner should take the time and effort to negotiate advantageous terms with suppliers, wherein payment can be delayed as long as possible. As we suggested in Chapter 11, such dating deals can be very attractive if properly managed. For example, if a supplier requires payment on a $10,000 purchase in 90 days, the pharmacist should estimate potential sales of the purchased product within that time period. If the shipment can be sold in under or close to 90 days, the dating deal is a good one. If not, the pharmacist should try to have the terms extended to 120 days – or purchase less inventory.

If the pharmacy is being financed with debt capital, it does not usually make sense to take advantage of cash discounts of, say, "2%/10" (that is, a two percent discount if payment is made within ten days of the invoice date). If the annual interest cost on debt capital is 14 percent, for example, then the interest per day is 0.038 percent. By delaying payment for an average of 70 days after receipt of the goods, the pharmacy owner can save the interest on 60 days, which would amount to 2.30 percent – more than the supplier's discount. The advantage to the pharmacist-owner is that he can reduce his bank loan during that time. The best approach is to delay the average payment 70 days, then pay on the 25th day of the second month following the date of purchase. For example, month one will average 15 days; month two, 30 days; and month three, 25 days, for a total of 70 days. If it is possible to prolong the payment beyond that time without alienating the supplier, the pharmacist-owner should do so: this is part of good cash management and effective financing of the pharmacy operation.

INCREASING SHAREHOLDERS' EQUITY

A fundamental aspect of cash management involves increasing the owner's or shareholders' equity (which is on the liability side of the balance sheet) by increasing the profits in the income statement. This is done by monitoring operating expenses on a regular basis.

As a minimum target, pharmacies should have a net income before taxes of 25 percent of the gross margin. Reasonable yardsticks for operating expenses as a percentage of gross margin are as follows: wages, 45 percent; occupancy, 10 percent; and "other," 20 percent, for a total of 75 percent. These should be considered maximum allowable percentages. In our example in Figure 12.2, the operating expenses for this year are 82 percent, the main culprit being "other" expenses. If we were to trim these expenses down to 75 percent of gross margin, they would amount to $337,000 – a reduction of $33,000, which would be added to net income. This represents a 41 percent improvement in net income or profit ($33,000 ÷ 80,000 × 100). According to the Seventh Annual Survey of Community Pharmacy Operations for 1986, the average net operating income before taxes among Canadian pharmacies was $72,957 or 19 percent of gross margin. Given the actual 1986 data, some might suggest that our proposed targets are too aggressive. Nonetheless, there are also many pharmacies in Canada earning net incomes well above our target of 25 percent of gross margin, and they are doing so primarily because they are well managed. Their owners are able to make good decisions because they insist on having adequate, up-to-date information. In many cases, pharmacy owners are working with insufficient information. Although some may have a "nose for business" that allows them to monitor inventory and operating expenses using informal methods, most pharmacists starting out in their own practices would be well advised to take the sure, safe approach and develop systems that will provide the information necessary to make sound business decisions. The next section sets out some of the details of such essential financial-management information.

FINANCIAL-MANAGEMENT TOOLS

In the average Canadian pharmacy, the front shop generates approximately 60 percent of total sales and the dispensary, 40 percent. The gross margin is significantly higher on dispensary sales than on front-shop sales. Also, the personnel working in the two areas are quite different: a qualified pharmacist and trained assistants work in the dispensary, while the front shop is normally handled by sales clerks and cashiers. In fact, the average Canadian pharmacy owner manages two distinct businesses. Therefore, financial reporting in a pharmacy should reflect the activity of the two businesses separately, as well as the consolidated outcome of both.

Financial Reporting

In order to properly monitor the financial activity of a full-service pharmacy, the owner will require the following reports on a monthly basis. (A sample of each of the reports listed appears in the appendix to this chapter, identified here by the appropriate figure number.)

Fig. 12A.1. Balance sheet, providing details of:
a. current assets
b. non-current or fixed assets
c. other assets
d. current liabilities
e. long-term liabilities
f. owner's or shareholders' equity

Fig. 12A.2. Consolidated statement of income, setting out:
a. sales
b. cost of goods sold
c. gross margin
d. expenses in the following key areas:
    i. wages (including employee benefits)
    ii. occupancy cost (rent, utilities, repairs, property taxes)
    iii. other expenses

Fig. 12A.3. Statement of income for the front shop (listing the same details as the consolidated statement)

Fig. 12A.4. Statement of income for the dispensary (listing the same details as the consolidated statement)

Fig. 12A.5. Year-to-date consolidated, front-shop, and dispensary comparative income statements (i.e., year-to-date compared to last year)

Fig. 12A.6. Schedule of inventory by key product groupings

Fig. 12A.7. Schedule of sales by key product groupings

Fig. 12A.8. Schedule of cost of goods sold by key product groupings

Fig. 12A.9. Schedule of salaries and benefits

Fig. 12A.10. Schedule of occupancy costs

Fig. 12A.11. Schedule of other expenses

Allocation of Expenses

The various expenses of the pharmacy must be attributed to either the front shop or the dispensary. This division of expenses requires detailed analysis for each individual pharmacy. Some guidelines, however, will apply generally.

WAGES

The attribution of some of the salaries (together with benefits and any bonuses that might apply) will be obvious: pharmacy assistants' and staff pharmacists' salaries will be charged against the dispensary; front-shop clerks' wages will obviously be charged against the front shop. However, the salaries of the owner, cashiers, bookkeeper, delivery personnel, and various others are not as obvious. The pharmacy owner must review the activities of such staff members (as well as his own) and make an equitable split. Once the division of wages is determined between the two operational areas, a standard journal entry can be prepared each month to charge the dispensary with its fair share of the wages and attribute the remaining costs to the front shop.

OCCUPANCY COSTS

Occupancy expenses include rent (or the interest on a mortgage and depreciation of the building), utilities, property taxes, and repairs and maintenance. Allocating occupancy costs to the dispensary can be a difficult task. The average pharmacy of approximately 4000 square feet normally has a dispensary that occupies approximately 400 square feet. This would suggest that the occupancy cost charged against the dispensary should be 10 percent of the total. This, however, does not take into account storage areas, the waiting area, aisles, the entrance, the cashier's area, or other space utilized by individuals purchasing prescription drugs. Further analysis indicates that a more appropriate method of allocating occupancy cost to the dispensary is on a percentage-of-sales basis. If, for example, dispensary sales represent 40 percent of total sales, then 40 percent of the occupancy costs should be allocated to the dispensary operation.

OTHER EXPENSES

Each of the expenses that fall under the category "other" must be analyzed in detail. Again, some are obvious. For example, the cost of the dispensary computer is 100 percent dispensary, as are the costs of dispensary supplies, pharamacists' licences, and professional liability insurance. Allocation of general insurance and financing costs (interest payments) should correspond to the relative net investments in the front-shop and dispensary operations. Net investment in the dispensary is composed of the applicable accounts receivable, dispensary inventory, and certain fixed assets (including the dispensary computer), less the applicable accounts payable. The same applies to the front shop. Depreciation for fixtures should be allocated according to the department to which the fixtures belong. Accounting, legal, and other professional services should be allocated on a percentage-of-total-sales basis. Any other expenses that are not logically attributable to either the front shop or the dispensary should also be allocated on the basis of relative sales. Since each pharmacy is different, the particular percentage allocations for each will also be different.

This may seem like an onerous task. Once it is resolved, however, a standard journal entry can be prepared for each month for the allocation of each category of expense. All expenses should be charged to the front-shop operation in the general ledger, with one journal entry reserved for the allocation of the appropriate dispensary charge as determined at the first of each accounting year. If there are any major changes in the financial operation of the pharmacy, the accounting entry should be reviewed to make the allocation as close to actual as possible.

CONCLUSION

Unfortunately, most pharmacy owners do not prepare (or have their accountants prepare) monthly financial reports. Of the minority that do, most do not break the overall activity down by front shop and dispensary. However, knowing the combined gross margin of the pharmacy is of little use, since an increase in the percentage of front-shop sales will register a reduction in the consolidated gross margin percentage (because the margin on front-shop sales is significantly lower than on dispensary sales). Conversely, an increase in the trend of sales in the dispensary will register an increase in the consolidated gross margin percentage. Both results will only mislead the pharmacist-owner.

At the Practice Management Seminar conducted jointly by the Ontario Pharmacists' Association and the Canadian Foundation for Pharmacy each year, the participants work through the allocation of their pharmacies' expenses to the front shop or dispensary in the manner that we have described here. Usually more than half of the pharmacies represented show losses in the front shop, of which, in many cases, the owner was unaware. If the relevant information had been prepared and reviewed monthly, these pharmacists would no doubt have taken action to correct the loss situations. Many argue that obtaining monthly financial statements is too costly and reviewing them too time-consuming. In some cases, the pharmacy owner is happy with the pharmacy's ongoing profits and is not interested in the fine-tuning required to optimize those profits. Pharmacists starting out on their own, however, cannot afford such complacency. The model for monthly financial reports can be set up for any pharmacy by an accountant, who can then teach an in-house staff member or a part-time bookkeeper to prepare the actual monthly reports. Alternately, the statements can be generated on a computer system by the pharmacist, an outside accountant, or a computer service, which would streamline the reports and make them available at a nominal cost on a monthly basis. The latter is the best approach, especially since computer facilities or services are by now readily available and relatively affordable.

RECOMMENDED READING

Davidson, W.R.; Sweeney, D.J.; Stampfl, R.W. *Retailing Management.* 6th ed. New York: John Wiley & Sons, 1988.
Federal Business Development Bank. *Minding Your Own Business.* Vol.1. Montreal: FBDB, 1980.
Olenick, Arnold J. *Managing to Have Profits.* New York: McGraw-Hill Book Co., 1989

APPENDIX: SAMPLE FINANCIAL REPORTS

Figure 12A.1
WELL-MANAGED PHARMACY IINC.
Balance Sheet
As at January 31, 1988

Assets

Current Assets			
Bank		0.00	
Third party		0.00	
Master Charge/Visa		0.00	
Accounts receivable	0.00		
Allow. for doubt accounts	0.00		
Inventory		0.00	
Prepaid expenses		0.00	
Security deposits		0.00	

Fixed Assets				0.00
	Cost	Accumulated Depreciation	Book Value	
Furniture and fixtures	0.00	0.00	0.00	
Computer	0.00	0.00	0.00	
Leasehold improvements	0.00	0.00	0.00	
	0.00	0.00		0.00

Other Assets		
Goodwill		0.00
Incorporation expenses		0.00
		0.00
		0.00

Liabilities

Current Liabilities

Bank loan	0.00	
Accounts payable	0.00	
Payroll deductions payable	0.00	
Other accrued liabilities	0.00	
Retail sales tax	0.00	
Corporate income taxes	0.00	
		0.00

Long-Term Liabilities

Bank term loan	0.00	
Shareholder loans	0.00	
		0.00
		0.00

Shareholders' Equity

Capital

Authorized:

x preferred shares at	0.00	0.00	
x common shares at	0.00	0.00	
		0.00	

Issued and fully paid		
common stock	0.00	
	0.00	

Retained Earnings

Retained earnings	0.00	
Profit for the period	0.00	
	0.00	
		0.00
		0.000.00

Figure 12A.2
WELL-MANAGED PHARMACY INC.
Statement of Income
Consolidation
For the 4 months ended January 31, 1988

	Current Period	%	Year to Date	%
Sales	0.00		0.00	
Cost of Goods Sold	0.00	00	0.00	00
Gross Margin	0.00	00	0.00	00
Expenses				
Salaries	0.00	00	0.00	00
Occupancy costs	0.00	00	0.00	00
Other expenses	0.00	00	0.00	00
Net Operating Income (or Profit)	0.00	00	0.00	00
Income Taxes	0.00	00	0.00	00
Net profit (Loss) for the Period	0.00		0.00	

Figure 12A.3
WELL-MANAGED PHARMACY INC.
Statement of Income
Front Shop
For the 4 months ended January 31, 1988

	Current Period	%	Year to Date	%
Sales	0.00		0.00	
Cost of Goods Sold	0.00	00	0.00	00
Gross Margin	0.00	00	0.00	00
Expenses				
Salaries	0.00	00	0.00	00
Occupancy costs	0.00	00	0.00	00
Other expenses	0.00	00	0.00	00
Net Operating Income (or Profit)	0.00	00	0.00	00
Income Taxes	0.00	00	0.00	00
Net Profit (Loss) for the Period	0.00		0.00	

Figure 12A.4
WELL-MANAGED PHARMACY INC.
Statement of Income
Dispensary
For the 4 months ended January 31, 1988

	Current Period	%	Year to Date	%
Sales	0.00		0.00	
Cost of Goods Sold	0.00	00	0.00	00
Gross Margin	0.00	00	0.00	00
Expenses				
Salaries	0.00	00	0.00	00
Occupancy costs	0.00	00	0.00	00
Other expenses	0.00	00	0.00	00
Net Operating Income (or Profit)	0.00	00	0.00	00
Income Taxes	0.00	00	0.00	00
Net Profit (Loss) for the Period	0.00		0.00	

Figure 12A.5†
WELL-MANAGED PHARMACY INC.
Comparative Statement of Income
Consolidation
For the 4 months ended January 31, 1987 and January 31, 1988

| | January 31, 1987 | | January 31, 1988 | |
	Amount	%	Amount	%
Sales		100.00		100.00
Cost of Goods Sold	0		0	
Gross Margin				
Expenses				
Salaries	0		0	
Occupancy costs	0		0	
Other expenses	0		0	
	0		0	
Net Operating Income (or Profit)				
Income Taxes	0		0	
Net Profit				

†**Note:** Separate comparative statements of income must be prepared for the front shop and the dispensary, using the same format and listing the same details as presented in this consolidated Comparative Statement of Income.

Figure 12A.6
WELL-MANAGED PHARMACY INC.
Schedule of Inventory
For the Period December 31, 1987 to January 31, 1988

	Opening Balance	Net Change	Closing Balance
Health and beauty aids	0.00	0.00	0.00
Tobacco	0.00	0.00	0.00
Greeting cards	0.00	0.00	0.00
Cosmetics	0.00	0.00	0.00
Paper products	0.00	0.00	0.00
General	0.00	0.00	0.00
OTC products	0.00	0.00	0.00
Prescription drugs	0.00	0.00	0.00
Miscellaneous	0.00	0.00	0.00
	0.00	0.00	0.00

Figure 12A.7
WELL-MANAGED PHARMACY INC.
Schedule of Sales
For the 4 months ended January 31, 1988

	Current Period	%	Year to Date	%
Health and beauty aids	0.00	0.00	0.00	0.00
Tobacco	0.00	0.00	0.00	0.00
Greeting cards	0.00	0.00	0.00	0.00
Cosmetics	0.00	0.00	0.00	0.00
Paper products	0.00	0.00	0.00	0.00
General	0.00	0.00	0.00	0.00
OTC products	0.00	0.00	0.00	0.00
Prescription drugs	0.00	0.00	0.00	0.00
Miscellaneous	0.00	0.00	0.00	0.00
	0.00	0.00	0.00	0.00

Figure 12A.8
WELL-MANAGED PHARMACY INC.
Schedule of Cost of Goods Sold
For the 4 months ended January 31, 1988

	Current Period	%	Year to Date	%
Health and beauty aids	0.00	0.00	0.00	0.00
Tobacco	0.00	0.00	0.00	0.00
Greeting cards	0.00	0.00	0.00	0.00
Cosmetics	0.00	0.00	0.00	0.00
Paper products	0.00	0.00	0.00	0.00
General non-taxable	0.00	0.00	0.00	0.00
OTC products	0.00	0.00	0.00	0.00
Prescription drugs	0.00	0.00	0.00	0.00
Miscellaneous	0.00	0.00	0.00	0.00
	0.00	0.00	0.00	0.00

Figure 12A.9
WELL-MANAGED PHARMACY INC.
Schedule of Salaries and Benefits
For the 4 months ended January 31, 1988

	Current Period	%	Year to Date	%
Staff wages	0.00	0.00	0.00	0.00
Management	0.00	0.00	0.00	0.00
Pharmacist	0.00	0.00	0.00	0.00
Other	0.00	0.00	0.00	0.00
Employer share CPP/UIC	0.00	0.00	0.00	0.00
Benefits	0.00	0.00	0.00	0.00
Workmen's Compensation	0.00	0.00	0.00	0.00
MINUS Allocation to dispensary	(0.00)	(0.00)	(0.00)	(0.00)
	0.00	0.00	0.00	0.00

Figure 12A.10
WELL-MANAGED PHARMACY INC.
Schedule of Occupancy Costs
For the 4 months ended January 31, 1988

	Current Period	%	Year to Date	%
Rent	0.00	0.00	0.00	0.00
Insurance	0.00	0.00	0.00	0.00
Utilities	0.00	0.00	0.00	0.00
Realty taxes	0.00	0.00	0.00	0.00
Maintenance & repairs	0.00	0.00	0.00	0.00
MINUS Allocation to dispensary	(0.00)	(0.00)	(0.00)	(0.00)
	0.00	0.00	0.00	0.00

Figure 12A.11
WELL-MANAGED PHARMACY INC.
Schedule of Indirect Expenses
For the 4 months ended January 31, 1988

	Current Period	%	Year to Date	%
Advertising & promotion	0.00	0.00	0.00	0.00
Bad debt expense	0.00	0.00	0.00	0.00
Legal & accounting	0.00	0.00	0.00	0.00
Cash (over) short	0.00	0.00	0.00	0.00
Delivery and car expense	0.00	0.00	0.00	0.00
Amortized goodwill	0.00	0.00	0.00	0.00
Depreciation/amortization	0.00	0.00	0.00	0.00
Computer expenses	0.00	0.00	0.00	0.00
Store expenses	0.00	0.00	0.00	0.00
Membership dues	0.00	0.00	0.00	0.00
Wrapping supplies	0.00	0.00	0.00	0.00
Credit-card expenses	0.00	0.00	0.00	0.00
Charitable donations	0.00	0.00	0.00	0.00
Interest & bank charges	0.00	0.00	0.00	0.00
Licences and fees	0.00	0.00	0.00	0.00
Postage	0.00	0.00	0.00	0.00
Gain/loss asset disposal	0.00	0.00	0.00	0.00
Sales-tax credits	0.00	0.00	0.00	0.00
Investment – dividends	0.00	0.00	0.00	0.00
Capital tax	0.00	0.00	0.00	0.00
General	0.00	0.00	0.00	0.00
Telephone	0.00	0.00	0.00	0.00
MINUS Allocation to dispensary	(0.00)	(0.00)	(0.00)	(0.00)
Total	0.00	0.00	0.00	0.00

13

PROFESSIONAL RESOURCES

INTRODUCTION

The successful operation of a community pharmacy requires the expertise of a range of professionals – both working within the store and supplying services from without; both from the pharmaceutical profession and from the business-related professions. No pharmacist who owns or manages a pharmacy can be – nor would wish to be – entirely self-reliant. Perhaps two of the owner/manager's most important skills are to be able to recognize and understand the need for expert assistance and be prepared to search out the most appropriate and best-equipped professional resources available to meet the need.

Employing the services of such professionals can entail a significant expense, but prospective owners should recognize that they are thereby making an invaluable long-term investment. The benefits of trusted relationships with skilled and knowledgeable professionals and specialists are realized not only at the commencement of the business venture but throughout its lifetime.

This chapter is designed to provide you with a sort of practical catalogue and guide to the professional expertise you will find it necessary, or desirable, to employ in the operation of a pharmacy.

PROFESSIONALS WITHIN THE PHARMACY

Accompanying the changes that have been observed in community-pharmacy practice, we have seen an increase in specialization. The responsibility of the pharmacy manager or owner involves both achieving professional goals and producing an optimum return on investment. In general, pharmacies have grown in size, sales are much higher per pharmacy, product assortment is more diversified, and services such as patient counselling and home health care have expanded rapidly. All of these factors have contributed to the need for specialists in pharmacy practice. Many owners and managers of pharmacies have become acutely aware that they require several individuals with various skills to help them realize both their professional and entrepreneurial objectives. Some have analyzed their own strengths and directed their efforts accordingly, delegating those tasks that are not their specialty to others better qualified to perform them. We shall examine some of the tasks involved in the operation of a contemporary community pharmacy – both in the dispensary and the front store – and the types of individuals required to perform them. The number and variety of personnel will depend, of course, on the size of the pharmacy. Regardless of size, however, one guideline is critical for all pharmacy owners and managers: areas of professional responsibility must be well defined and the reporting relationships of dispensary managers (head pharmacists) and front-store managers must be clearly specified. It is also essential to the success of the operation that a compatible relationship be developed between dispensary and front-store management to ensure that each understands the benefits their efforts bring to the success and profitability of the business. They must work as a team and understand that they share a common goal.

Responsibilities of the Head Pharmacist

In the dispensary, we require one, two, or more pharmacists, who, in addition to their professional responsibilities, often have some management responsibilities. A typical pharmacy may have a head pharmacist (sometimes in the person of the pharmacy owner or manager), whose responsibilities include the following:

1. Supervising professional staff, including pharmacists and technicians, employed in the dispensary area.
2. Ensuring that products requiring pharmacist participation in their sale are sold in compliance with relevant legislation.
3. Arranging the schedules of dispensary staff to guarantee efficient service at all times.
4. Ensuring that a proper inventory-control system is in place and that pharmaceuticals are ordered correctly.

5. Ensuring that tasks associated with the pharmacy computer, such as backups, purging, and reports, are conducted regularly.
6. Ensuring that accounts are remitted to cash customers and third-party-plan administrations, and that they are reconciled. (In larger pharmacies, this task is delegated to office personnel.)
7. Being responsible for security in the pharmacy's professional area, particularly with regard to narcotic and controlled drugs.
8. Ensuring that any reports required by law are properly completed and submitted to the appropriate authorities.
9. Being responsible for establishing and monitoring the pricing systems used in the dispensary.
10. Being able to perform all the duties of staff pharmacists in case the need arises to assume them.
11. Depending on the organization of the pharmacy, the head pharmacist normally reports to the pharmacy owner.

Responsibilities of the Staff Pharmacist

The responsibilities of staff pharmacists include the following:

1. The compounding and dispensing of prescriptions, including
   a. receiving the prescription and obtaining authorization for refills as necessary;
   b. ensuring that all orders are legal;
   c. ensuring that prescribed dosages of the medication are correct;
   d. checking for allergies and interactions;
   e. ensuring that the prescription is labelled properly;
   f. where appropriate, providing specific instructions regarding storage;
   g. being certain that the correct drug, in the correct, prescribed amount, is dispensed.
2. Taking all patients' drug histories and ensuring that proper patient profiles are maintained.
3. Monitoring patient profiles prior to dispensing prescriptions to ensure that the patient is not allergic to the prescribed drug(s) and that there are no interactions with other medication being taken by the patient.
4. Providing consultations with patients when a prescription is dispensed to ensure that
   a. the patient understands the use of the medication
   b. the patient understands any precautions associated with the use of the medication
   c. the patient understands any special storage requirements.
5. Consulting with physicians as needed with regard to the appropriateness of the prescribed therapy.
6. Monitoring patient compliance with the medication regimen.

7. Providing patients with information about non-prescription drugs, particularly those for which a pharmacist is required to participate in the sale.
8. Disposing of outdated or overstocked drugs, as well as of any that may have been recalled by the drug manufacturers.
9. Participating in adverse-drug reporting programs.
10. Participating in practical training programs for pharmacy students.
11. Pricing prescriptions and billing them appropriately.
12. Supervising all tasks delegated to pharmacy assistants or technicians; training pharmacy assistants as necessary.
13. Participating in selecting the drug(s) to be dispensed.
14. Participating in continuing-education programs to maintain competence.

In community pharmacy practice today, the provision of clinical services has a high priority with consumers. It is therefore important to hire staff pharmacists who are well suited to providing such services. In general, the pharmacist-owner/manager must recognize that the marketing of professional clinical services has become a very important competitive factor in community-pharmacy practice.

Certain provincial licensing bodies have established standards of practice for pharmacists that can be a useful guide for owners and managers. (One such example is the Nova Scotia Pharmaceutical Society's *Standards of Practice*, which served as one of our sources for the responsibilities of staff pharmacists listed above.)

PHARMACY ASSISTANTS

As noted earlier, pharmacy assistants generally report to staff pharmacists. Their responsibilities may include:

1. Stocking pharmacy supplies, such as containers.
2. Cleaning, after the preparation of extemporaneous compounds.
3. Counting tablets, pouring liquids after medication is selected by the pharmacist, and prepackaging commonly dispensed pharmaceuticals under the instruction of the pharmacist.
4. Accepting written prescriptions from the patient.
5. Preparing labels and receipts for prescription drugs.
6. Transcribing prescription data from prescription to patient profile or entering prescription data into the computer, activities which are always to be checked and initialed by the supervising pharmacist.
7. Preparing third-party insurer claims forms.
8. Checking orders received for the dispensary and, where appropriate, pricing products and placing them on the shelves.
9. Looking after inventory control for the dispensary under a staff pharmacist's (or the head pharmacist's) supervision.

10. General clerical duties related to the dispensary.
11. General maintenance duties related to the dispensary.

Front-Store Management Professionals

With increased size, sales, and specialization, pharmacy owners and managers have found it difficult to make the time and acquire the expertise necessary to manage the front-store area of their operations as well as the dispensary, and now normally hire professional personnel with expertise in merchandising to serve as front-store managers. In the average Canadian pharmacy in 1986–87, prescription sales accounted for about 43–50 percent of total sales. The balance of 50 percent or more must be managed competently to ensure the pharmacy's profitability. Depending on the size of the pharmacy, the front-store manager might report to the pharmacy owner or the manager; in a multi-store operation, to the regional supervisor.

The front-store manager is responsible for operating the front store in accordance with company policy and for ensuring (1) that it is properly staffed and orderly, with proper signage; (2) that the pharmacy's marketing and merchandising plans are effectively realized; (3) that the front store has an inventory appropriate to its needs; and (4) that products are priced in accordance with existing market conditions. Among the tasks for which the front-store manager is responsible are the following:

1. Receiving all merchandise, recording it properly, and distributing it to the appropriate departments; ensuring that proper security procedures surrounding the receipt of merchandise are being followed. (Most of the shrinkage evident in small retail businesses can be attributed to sloppy receipt procedures. See the discussion in Chapter 11.) The front-store manager is responsible for ascertaining that all staff assigned to this task are well-trained and responsible individuals.
2. Pricing merchandise in accordance with store policy. This includes the pricing of merchandise for sales (and re-pricing after sales). For pharmacies using point-of-sale systems, this task is made much simpler (see Chapter 11).
3. Purchasing merchandise. This task involves working in conjunction with staff responsible for various sections within the pharmacy. It also involves meeting with suppliers' representatives and dealing with wholesalers to obtain the best terms available.
4. Establishing an efficient inventory-management system. This task includes maintaining appropriate records and ensuring that they are kept current (see Chapter 11).
5. Arranging the display of merchandise in a manner that encourages sales (see Chapter 15). This includes setting up promotional displays throughout the store, keeping them current and seasonal, and emphasizing special merchandising events. The front-store manager must

also see to the signage related to promotions, such as the hanging of banners and the placement of sale signs.

6. General housekeeping. This involves keeping the store clean and orderly and making sure that burned-out lighting is replaced, windows and showcases are kept clean, and aisles are free of clutter.
7. Training staff. Training is a particularly important task, as properly trained staff is the key to a successful operation. This task includes keeping front-store staff informed and up-to-date on store policy through regular staff meetings.
8. Recruiting personnel. The front-store manager has the responsibility for selecting and recruiting staff for the front-store (see Chapter 10).
9. Depending on store policy, front-store managers are often responsible for cashiers and for the preparation of daily cash reports. In many stores, however, this responsibility is assigned to office personnel.

There are a number of other specialists who can be involved in the operation of a contemporary community pharmacy, depending on its size. They include the office manager, who assists with cash management, accounts receivable (including third-party plans), and accounts payable, as well as with other bookkeeping functions. In larger stores, there may also be a merchandising manager and a bookkeeper. Cosmeticians are frequently employed to offer specialised consultation and service in the cosmetics department. In stores offering home health care, orthotic consultants may be on staff to provide advice on products such as ostomy supplies and equipment, surgical garments, and patient aids, such as canes, crutches, walkers, and wheel chairs. Some community pharmacies employ registered nurses in such positions, who may also conduct blood-pressure clinics and provide advice on immunization.

In addition to the specialists required to operate today's community pharmacy, a full staff of well-trained and competent employees is necessary to make the store operate smoothly and efficiently. It has often been said that the most valuable asset of any business is its personnel. In a service-oriented business/profession such as a pharmacy, this could not be truer.

Professional Resources: Business, Finance, Law

The pharmacist-owner or manager must employ the services of a variety of outside professionals, who might be viewed collectively as a sort of management team, consisting of an accountant, a lawyer, a banker, an insurance professional, and a real-estate professional or a developer. There are a myriad of other resources available to assist the pharmacist-owner as well: professional pharmacy organizations, manufacturers and wholesalers, government services such as Statistics Canada and the Federal

Business Development Bank, schools of pharmacy, extension departments of universities and junior colleges, chambers of commerce or boards of trade and, last but not least, colleagues in pharmacy practice.

Let us examine how these professional resources can assist the community pharmacy owner or manager.

Accountants

As we saw in Chapter 6, the skills of an accountant are probably indispensable to most small businesses. Accountants can provide the following services:

1. An accounting-system design, including electronic accounting services supplied by the accounting firm or the firm's assistance in selecting an appropriate in-house system.
2. Financial analysis. Accountants normally have a good knowledge of the particular industry or profession they serve, and have access to pertinent information that will assist the pharmacist-owner in charting the progress of the business and comparing it against trends in the industry.
3. Securing loans. Success in dealings with lending institutions can hinge on the manner in which they are approached: business people have often failed to secure loans because their applications were not properly prepared. Accountants know what bankers require, and their services are well worth the expense if they result in prompt acceptance of a loan application.
4. Preparing returns. The taxation of small businesses, and especially of limited corporations, is complex and frequently misunderstood by the lay person. The professional services of an accountant include not only accurate preparation of income-tax returns but assistance with tax planning to maximize the benefits of the pharmacy's earnings.
5. Auditing. An accountant will implement a reliable audit system to verify the pharmacy's accounts periodically.
6. Preparing budgets and general business plans. Accountants can offer expert assistance in the overall financial and operational planning of the business.
7. For pharmacy owners, accountants can assist in integrating personal financial planning and business planning to maximize the benefits from each in the long run.

Lawyers

There are various legal requirements that must be observed in the course of establishing and operating any business. With regard to the practice of pharmacy in particular, legal requirements may vary from province to province. The provincial licensing bodies can advise the pharmacist-owner of applicable provincial laws and regulations (see the detailed discussion in Chapter 7).

Included among the services provided by lawyers are the following:

1. Advice on the form a business should take.
2. Information about zoning by-laws and local ordinances.
3. Advice on federal laws that relate to the operation of a business, including legal requirements surrounding employees of a business.
4. Advice about the various contracts and agreements, such as leases or partnership agreements, connected with the operation of a business.
5. Information about legal requirements for record keeping in a pharmacy.
6. Advice on the legal aspects of acquiring or disposing of property.
7. Advice about legal options in the face of credit problems that may arise in the operation of the business.
8. Advice on the liability of the business owner with respect to consumers.

Bankers

The first thing that comes to mind when we think of bankers or representatives of other financial institutions is the provision of loans and credit (for a detailed discussion refer back to Chapter 6). But bankers can also generally supply useful information about sound investment practices, as well as mortgages and refinancing schemes. Recent changes in financial laws have resulted in an expansion of the services that banks can provide, including computerized payroll and accounting services. Some pharmacies are now using banks for electronic payroll services, often at very reasonable rates.

Where large loans are outstanding, managers must meet regularly with their bankers. This provides an opportunity to use the banker's business knowledge to help improve operations or take advantage of new opportunities. Bankers, for example, will know about business developments in the trading area that may influence the pharmacy practice.

Insurance Agents

One of the most important aspects of the management of a pharmacy is protecting the business against risk. The services of a good insurance agent or broker are required to provide coverage protecting the business against such risks as fire, public liability, malpractice, business interruption, and crime or vandalism (refer back to Chapter 8 for a detailed discussion of insurance protection). In addition, insurance companies can provide life and health insurance plans as well as pension plans for employees. A buy–sell agreement backed by insurance can protect an owner in the event of the death of a partner. Again, the cost of these services must be accepted as part of the normal operating cost of a business. Failure to consult with an insurance professional and to obtain sufficient coverage to protect your business could be disastrous.

Other Professional Resources

Professional organizations established to serve the interests of pharmacists, such as the Canadian Pharmaceutical Association and its provincial member associations, the provincial licensing bodies, and the Canadian Foundation for Pharmacy, have become an important resource for pharmacists in the area of continuing education in pharmacy management. More details on the nature of available programs are given in Chapter 26. The professional organizations also provide information on marketing services, government relations, public relations, research, legal services, and insurance services. The provincial pharmacy associations have engaged in various endeavours to assist their members, publishing brochures on specific aspects of pharmacy management or policy and procedures, organizing seminars with professional speakers on specific business-related topics, and conducting and publishing province-wide surveys on various financial aspects of pharmacy operation.

Drug wholesalers who offer full service are also a valuable resource. Among the services they are able to provide are the following: promotional and advertising programs; inventory-control and electronic order-entry services; marketing information and services; information to assist with location analysis; and assistance with store layout and design. Some also market pharmacy computer systems and provide related services.

Schools of pharmacy should not be forgotten by practising pharmacists and pharmacy owners. Their library collections and continuing-education programs, as well as their expanding undergraduate and graduate programs in pharmacy administration, can benefit all pharmacists.

A major resource available to prospective pharmacy owners is the Federal Business Development Bank. The FBDB is a Crown Corporation established in the 1940s to assist Canadian businesses. It focusses on small- to medium-sized businesses, and offers financial, investment-banking, and management services. Branches of the FBDB exist in most Canadian cities. Although it is best know as a source of funding for small business, one of the FBDB's major contributions in recent years has been in the area of education in management through published materials and seminars. The FBDB offers joint programs with various businesses and professions, such as the Personnel Management in Pharmacies program, as well as others on inventory management and time management. Another excellent service offered by the FBDB is the Counselling Assistance for Small Enterprises (CASE) program, which provides consulting services in all areas of business, at nominal cost, to small-business operators. It has been used by some of our most successful independent pharmacies.

The value to the pharmacy owner of institutions such as Statistics Canada and municipal chambers of commerce and boards of trade was discussed in detail in Chapter 3. It should be reiterated here that, as sources of demographic data, information on purchasing patterns, and statistics on local retail growth, they can be extremely important to the new or established pharmacy owner. Chambers of commerce and boards of trade can provide a forum for retailers to meet together to discuss business concerns in the community. As their membership is very diversified, opportunities are often available to discuss business concerns with experts in the field, who will have a particular concern for the well-being of the businesses in the community.

Real-estate professionals are particularly valuable in providing information on new and/or expanding local residential and commercial developments. Developers will often have valuable information concerning market share conditions in the community.

CONCLUSION

It should now be evident that the pharmacist entering the world of small business has recourse to various – and valuable – professional resources. (For quick reference, see the Professional Resources Checklist.) However, the responsibility to draw on the available resources rests with the individual. What is essential is a willingness to take the first step and to invest intelligently in the potential benefits of professional services.

Professional Resources Checklist

In-house Professionals
Senior or head pharmacist
Staff pharmacist
Pharmacy technician or assistant
Front-store manager
Merchandising manager
Office manager
Bookkeeper
Cosmetician
Orthotic consultant
Registered nurse

Outside Professionals and Professional Resources
Accountant
Lawyer
Banker
Insurance agent or broker

Real-estate agent or broker
Pharmacists' professional organizations
Pharmaceutical manufacturers
Wholesalers
Statistics Canada
Federal Business Development Bank
Schools of pharmacy
Extension departments of universities and colleges
Chambers of commerce or boards of trade
Market researchers
Colleagues in pharmacy

RECOMMENDED READING

Effective Pharmacy Management. 4th ed. Kansas City, Mo.: Marion Laboratories, Inc., 1987.

Federal Business Development Bank. *Minding Your Own Business.* Vol.2. Montreal: FBDB, 1980.

Guide to Good Pharmacy Management. Vaudreuil, Que.: Hoffman-La Roche, Inc., 1978. See especially *Personnel* and *Customer Care.*

Patterns for Success in Managing a Business. New York: Dun and Bradstreet Business Education Division, 1970.

Smith, Harry A. *Principles and Methods of Pharmacy Management.* 3rd ed. Philadelphia: Lea & Febiger, 1986.

Tharp, C.P., and Lecca, P.J. *Pharmacy Management for Students and Practitioners.* 2nd ed. St. Louis, Mo.: C.V. Mosby Co., 1979.

14

POLICY AND PROCEDURES

INTRODUCTION

Formalized policies and procedures dictate how internal activities in the community pharmacy are conducted. A policy defines a method or course of action to guide decision making, whereas a procedure specifies a particular way of acting or accomplishing something.

By defining "how we do things around here," policies and procedures promote efficiency and implement the pharmacy owner/manager's strategy for the direction and image of the pharmacy. They promote consistent communication and assist the owner and management personnel in directing business activities.

Policies and procedures should accomplish the following:

1. promote uniformity among different departments, units, or functional areas;
2. ensure continuity despite management or personnel changes;
3. restrict the kind of independent action by individual staff members that could detract from the overall direction and image planned for the pharmacy;
4. provide answers and decisions to routine questions;
5. provide guidelines for handling issues that are predicted to arise in the future;
6. facilitate training and integration of new employees;
7. provide a set of standards for all employees that can be used as a basis for control, evaluation, or discipline.

Policies can be developed either on an ad-hoc basis as the need for them becomes evident or in a planned, pro-active way. The number of policies and procedures and the degree to which they are formalized will vary widely depending on the size and age of the business, the diversity of its operations, and the management style and philosophy preferred by the pharmacy owner.

Certain aspects of policy and procedure will naturally pertain to areas of management and finances that are the exclusive domain of the pharmacy owner and, perhaps, of management personnel; many others should be made explicit to general pharmacy staff. Pharmacy owners will take different approaches to communicating store policy and procedures to staff members; however, in general, providing guidelines in writing is preferable to relying on verbal communication. Taking the time to collect and formalize ideas into concrete policies and procedures will benefit both management and staff. A policy and procedures manual may be produced as individual sets of typewritten or word-processed sheets dealing with the various aspects of the operation, to be photocopied and distributed to the appropriate staff members. This approach is simple and allows for easy updating as the need arises. (A manual must be updated and current, even if written changes are incorporated. In the latter case, changes should be initialled to document that they are authorized.) A larger enterprise or chain operation may choose to publish a comprehensive, printed employee handbook, as well as a separate managers' guide. A comprehensive manual setting out both policies and procedures can be invaluable both to new staff members, who are attempting to learn their jobs properly and to adjust to the preferred style of the operation, as well as to long-time staff members, who can rely on it as a reference. The various policies and procedures should be reviewed regularly with the staff members to whom they apply – particularly when changes or updates have been made.

MARKETING POLICIES

Marketing policies cover four critical areas: product and service mix, supply and distribution, merchandising, and pricing.

To support the pharmacist-owner's chosen direction and desired image for the pharmacy, policy will specify the products and services to be included in the mix or, conversely, those that are to be excluded. If the pharmacy is more professionally oriented, its product mix may be restricted to medications and personal-care items; if it is oriented toward high-volume, discount sales and mass merchandising, the product range may be loosely identified and may include any items that can be physically accommodated, purchased on deal, and turned over rapidly at a desired profit level.

The service mix of the pharmacy includes specific professional services, general retail services, and, possibly, complementary services. Patient counselling about prescription and non-prescription drugs, fittings, delivery and installation of home health-care products, and auxiliary services, such as newsletters and group counselling, comprise the potential professional-service mix. Examples of general retail services include: accepting major credit cards or personal cheques, allowing personal charge accounts, or offering delivery or parcel pickup. Complementary services, which are not directly related to community-pharmacy practice, but which can add to the store's appeal for its target market, can include anything from post office substations, the sale of lottery tickets, and photo processing to optical dispensaries, photo studios, or travel agencies. Service policies define which services will be offered and procedures detail how those services are to be conducted.

The second area that marketing policy addresses is supply and distribution. Policy on sources of supply may be open-ended, leaving purchasing decisions to individual buyers, such as the cosmetician, pharmacist, and front-store manager, or it can be strictly specified, particularly when continuity of supply, price stability, and uniformity of product mix are issues critical to the pharmacy. Policy can specify preferences for certain suppliers or exclusivity to one supplier; it should also address the questions of whether to buy direct or through wholesalers and, possibly, whether to join a buying group.

Closely linked to source of supply is the question of distribution. In the case of chain pharmacies, it must be determined how the company will get products into the different stores and whether it will operate its own warehouse. Decisions made regarding distribution will ultimately affect inventory levels and procurement costs and will have a major impact on the profitability of the business.

Once the products are in the pharmacy, merchandising policies and procedures govern how they will be presented and sold to the buying public. Policies may specify store decor, fixtures, signage, store layout and design, and location of product categories. The placement of individual items within categories and the handling of out-of-section displays should be outlined in the store's merchandising procedures. As you will see in Chapter 15, merchandising techniques have a pronounced impact on consumers' purchase decisions and therefore on sales and profitability. Procedures and policy should be developed accordingly.

Pricing policies should reflect and support the pharmacy's desired growth, market share, return on investment, competitive position, and overall image. Pricing rules and regulations specify how to set a retail price for each item or service offered. The approach can be based on cost, competition, or demand. For example, a particular pharmacy's policy might be to determine its regular prices on health and beauty aids by calculating a desired profit margin from cost, but to base its sale prices on matching (or going below) competitors' prices, regardless of cost or profit. Pricing policy is discussed in detail in Chapter 16.

A pharmacy's promotional strategy includes media advertising, publicity, personal selling, and in-store promotional tactics. Because this area of marketing is highly creative and constantly changing, the uniformity and continuity that derive from policies and procedures are usually unnecessary. Policies in this area may stipulate the use of a store trademark or logo in advertising copy, specify particular individuals as media contacts, limit advertising on certain products, or establish rules and guidelines to cover in-store promotional events.

OPERATING POLICIES AND PROCEDURES

Establishing standardized operational policies and procedures might be viewed as writing down a store's "recipe for success": a policy and procedures manual would itemize and communicate the ingredients and steps required to achieve a desired outcome. In a community-pharmacy setting, operating procedures cover a wide range of tasks and duties, from the most critical, such as purchasing, inventory management, and pricing, to the more routine, such as janitorial and maintenance functions. The basic operating-policy areas are as follows:

1. general operating policies;
2. janitorial and maintenance;
3. purchasing and inventory control;
4. receiving, marking, and stockroom management;
5. security;
6. public relations.

GENERAL OPERATING POLICIES

General operating policies affect the entire pharmacy and address the following types of questions: What days should the business be open? What should the daily hours be? Is there a need for emergency hours and how should they be handled? What kind of physical image should the pharmacy project?

JANITORIAL AND MAINTENANCE

Janitorial procedures govern daily housekeeping tasks, such as check-out counter care, floor care, garbage removal, cleaning of staff-only areas, refilling check-out supplies (wrapping, bags, tape, staples, pens), and checking the orderly presentation of merchandise. Some janitorial services may be contracted to outside services, including floor and window washers and dry cleaning services (for floor mats, towels, and mops). Various items require regular maintenance or intermittent repair. These items include store fixtures, exterior and interior signs, floor coverings, cash registers, auxiliary power packs, fire extinguishers, pricing machines, alarm systems, lighting, plumbing, heating and air conditioning, and items requiring carpentry or painting. Policy may specify the outside services to be engaged and when and how maintenance or repair should be conducted. Payment procedures might also be outlined.

PURCHASING AND INVENTORY CONTROL

Fundamental to the success or failure of a pharmacy are its purchasing and inventory-management practices. Policy questions will involve product range and inventory levels. Targets for both dollar value and number of units may be established to help maintain a particular image or service level.

Policy must address the entire purchasing system. Will the pharmacy centralize the buying function in one person or decentralize to each department (or, in a chain situation, to each store)? Will the pharmacy join a co-operative or buying group? Who will decide what merchandise to stock in each department or store? When ordering, what systems and procedures should be followed? Should buyers complete written purchase orders at all times? Is an "open-to-buy" purchase system to be used? Is it feasible to establish economic order quantities or minimum and maximum inventory-level criteria? Should specific purchasing intervals be established for particular product groups? Should separate policies be considered for purchasing seasonal products not carried throughout the year? What guidelines should govern purchasing items on deal? How will the pharmacy handle premiums (monetary or product incentives from suppliers)? Will they be viewed as store property or be available to individual buyers?

Policy governing purchasing and inventory control also addresses supplier relations. Setting appointments, supervising sales representatives, maintaining a suppliers' or visitors' log, and regularly paying accounts are examples of rules of conduct in supplier relations.

RECEIVING AND STOCKROOM–MANAGEMENT PROCEDURES

Product receiving procedures, stockroom management, and product marking and ticketing practices, if properly conducted, maximize efficiency and reduce loss. Receiving procedures generally specify that certain documents (packing slips, waybills, and invoices) must be retained, a receiving log used, narcotic and controlled drugs treated with greater caution, and back orders, refused shipments, and damages and shortages handled in a specified manner. Receiving hours are specified and a time period stipulated within which merchandise must be removed from the receiving area.

If the pharmacy uses a scanning system, prices are entered into the system and price labels on shelving may be sufficient; if no scanning system is in place, each product item will require a price ticket. Questions to be addressed regarding ticketing procedure include: What type and colour of ticket will be used? Where should it be placed on the item? Should all items be ticketed? If items are to be stored for a period of time, should they be ticketed? Who should do the price inputting or ticketing, and where and when should they do it? How should price inputting or ticketing be handled if the product is on sale for a specified time period? When and how should the price information be changed once the sale is over? Should other information, such as cost, department code, or date received, be recorded for each item?

Procedures concerning merchandise stored in a stockroom should address the following questions: How should the stock be organized? How should bulk items, such as disposable diapers and toilet paper, be handled? What about seasonal carry-over? Is a special area required for damaged items? What security measures should be taken for tobacco, confection, and high-value items? Should items be stored in complete cases or in specified multiples to improve security?

SECURITY

Policies addressing the physical security of the store begin by listing areas that require locks and keys (see Chapter 19). They should also identify the personnel who will have access to the keys and perhaps stipulate that a key registry be kept. Specific store opening and closing procedures should be outlined, as they can both reduce the possibility of robbery and internal theft and increase the safety of the individuals required to follow them. Policy might also identify the type of alarm system to be used in the pharmacy, the individuals entrusted to set the alarms, and the procedure for regularly checking their working condition.

Security policy, in addition to focussing on the physical security of the store, should deal with loss prevention. Procedures should be established for handling cash at the check-out counters, administering the major change fund or cash float, cash counting, and banking procedures.

Policies to reduce product losses cover buying, pricing, ticketing, receiving and storage, product display, selling procedure at the cash registers, staff purchases, and refund and exchange procedures. In compiling the pharmacy's policy and procedures manual, the owner or manager may determine either to include all aspects of security that relate to these various functions in one section of the manual or to treat them separately in subsections to the policies on each function (for example, "Receiving and Stockroom-Management – Security").

Security policies governing the purchasing function include the necessity to supervise sales representatives; confidential treatment of inventory statistics, pricing policies, and sales and marketing data; specific procedures for handling damaged goods; guidelines for submitting claims to suppliers for monies owed; and examination and control of products sold on consignment.

Rules that could be established with regard to pricing and ticketing include the following: checking invoice prices against purchase-order prices; ensuring price accuracy by conducting pricing spot checks; commencing sale pricing as close to the start date of a sale and reverting to regular pricing as soon after the end date as possible; and ensuring that pricing machines and pricing tickets are kept secure and inaccessible to customers.

Receiving and storage procedures that reduce loss might include ensuring that case counts are verified against waybills; verifying shipments against purchase orders; securing tobacco, confection, and high-value items in a locked area; locking the stockroom when unsupervised; breaking all packing cases to ensure they are empty; inspecting trash prior to removal; removing trash at specified times; and storing products in designated areas only.

Merchandising and display policies should aim not only to increase sales but also to minimize loss from shoplifting, damage, or obsolescence. For example, policy might demand regular product rotation to ensure that older stock is sold first, thus minimizing loss through obsolescence.

Specified procedures regarding staff purchases are also advisable and all staff purchases should be held in a designated area. There should be a policy regarding free goods from manufacturers as well.

It is important to implement a definite policy regarding refunds and exchange of merchandise, and to provide staff with rules or guidelines for handling such situations with customers.

Accounting and administration policies can also help to minimize the potential for loss. It is advisable to designate individuals and specify procedures for handling incoming mail, recording daily sales, preparing and banking deposits, handling staff sales, following up on returned cheques, preparing and double-checking payroll information, scrutinizing merchandise written off for store's use, following up on claims to suppliers, reviewing bank statements and bank reconciliations, conducting regular financial reviews, reviewing inventory, comparing purchase orders to invoices, and reviewing backup material such as invoices, purchase orders, or expense vouchers prior to issuing cheques.

Pharmacies can be protected in various ways against the possibility of theft, fraud, and fire. Precautions that should be taken are described in detail in Chapter 19, and the pharmacy owner would be well advised to develop formal policies and procedures around them. To give just a few examples, the possibility of fraud can be reduced by having specific policies on cheque, personal-credit, and credit-card acceptance. Similarly, fire-prevention procedures should be outlined clearly. They would include following all Fire Marshall regulations, ensuring that fire extinguishers work, clearing all fire exits, unplugging small electrical appliances when the store is empty, and having all products off the floor.

Closely related to security policies are company insurance policies. Owners should consider property insurance, business interruption insurance, fidelity insurance, and comprehensive or general liability insurance that covers personal injury, malpractice, or advertising liability, and should list the chosen options in a policy and procedures manual.

PUBLIC RELATIONS

Most operating policies indirectly affect the pharmacy's public relations. However, the store can institute policies and practices that will directly enhance their image with the public. A pharmacy may wish to influence not only customers but other groups as well, including the store's employees, the community at large, suppliers, and professional groups.

To improve customer relations, store policies can be established regarding customer service at check-out areas; post-purchase services, such as parcel pickup; and pre-purchase services, such as phone-in ordering. Systems can also be developed to handle or follow up on customer requests, customer complaints, and out-of-stock situations. The pharmacy owner or manager may also wish to develop means to communicate with customers, either to provide information (via a newsletter or information pamphlet) or to gather information (through customer surveys) or simply to reach potential new customers.

Community involvement with schools, non-profit groups, seniors' groups, youth groups, and local service clubs can be enhanced and controlled if there are policies or guidelines governing the amount of money available for, and the time to be allotted to, such endeavours. Some means by which notices would be posted or information distributed on behalf of such groups could be considered. Since there are never sufficient funds or time available to respond to the requests of all groups, policy can identify which of them will be assisted and how.

The pharmacist's relationship with other professional groups, including physicians, dentists, and nurses, also entails certain policy questions. For example, should regular meetings be held with prescribing physicians? If so, should patient-profile reviews be conducted? Does the store wish to circulate a pharmacy newsletter? Should discounts or other shopping privileges be extended?

Policies can also be developed to ensure involvement with pharmacy associations or societies and with merchant, mall, or other business associations. Such policy could require managers and pharmacists to attend meetings or conventions or to remain informed and potentially influential by some other means.

Operating policies provide a solid foundation for a successful business and, to some extent, can be used as the criteria by which to evaluate the performance of managerial and other staff. However, while operating policies can provide the framework for good business practice, they must be fleshed out with ongoing, innovative management. They should be revised and updated on a continual basis to reflect new strategic directions adopted by the pharmacy owner.

PERSONNEL AND HUMAN-RESOURCE DEVELOPMENT POLICY

Policies covering personnel and human-resource development ensure compliance with government employment regulations and facilitate fair employment practices by reducing favouritism and discrimination. They promote job satisfaction and dedication among employees. When developing or reviewing personnel policies, consider all provincial labour laws, competitors' employment and personnel practices, and any union contracts that could affect the store or the competition. Also consider the pharmacy's business strategy, particularly with respect to growth and diversification, which will affect the type and number of employees required.

There are seven policy areas within the personnel and human-resource development field:

1. personnel records, including payroll records and employee files;
2. wages, vacations, and benefits;
3. recruitment and hiring;
4. orientation, training, and development;
5. performance review and planning;
6. control and discipline;
7. motivation, coaching, and employee relations.

PERSONNEL AND PAYROLL RECORDS

Policy should define who will maintain the personnel records. In a large and diversified company, there may be a personnel department, but in an independent community pharmacy, the owner or manager will likely keep all records or delegate the responsibility to a bookkeeper or secretary. As well as designating who will keep the records, specify where the files should be kept, who will have access to them, and what type of information at what intervals will be included.

Employee files generally include hiring information, such as a copy of the résumé or job application form, reference checks, and all other relevant documents and correspondence, as discussed in Chapter 10. Policy might also stipulate that wage and salary information be included in an employee's file, including starting rate and rate adjustments, holidays and vacations used, attendance and punctuality records, sick leave taken, and any accidents or injuries that may have occurred.

Employees should have access to their employee files (in some provinces this may be a legal requirement – employers would be well advised to check with their provincial ministries of labour); a formal policy and procedures manual should address this point.

Businesses are legally required to keep separate payroll records for each employee, not only during, but for a period of time after, his or her employment with the firm. Payroll records include such information as gross pay, legal deductions, other deductions (and the reasons for them), net pay, holiday and vacation pay, and amount paid during illness. Once again, policy in this area should specify who keeps the records, where they are kept, what information is to be included, and how it is to be presented.

WAGES, VACATIONS, BENEFITS

As discussed in Chapter 10, pharmacies must develop policies with respect to wages, vacations, and benefits. This is necessary to remain competitive and to avoid discrimination. When establishing wage policy, check minimum-wage laws in the area of operation, union wage agreements, professional association guidelines, and competitive factors. Wage policy generally stipulates the starting wage per job category, a specified probationary period, and a time frame for wage increments, with a particular grid or system for establishing what they will be. It also specifies the length of the pay period and answers questions regarding paid hours, such as the following: Should the particular employee or job position be paid on a salaried or hourly basis? How will overtime be handled? What is the shortest paid shift? If there is a changing schedule, how much advance notice of work hours will the employees receive? Will time for meals or breaks be paid? What are the maximum hours per day or per week an employee will be required to work?

If the pharmacy offers bonuses or incentive plans, policy should stipulate the positions that are eligible for such plans, the eligibility criteria, and the manner in which the total amount will be calculated and paid.

Regarding vacations and holidays, policy must comply with provincial legislation and should once again be competitive. Questions include: If the store is open on statutory holidays, who will be required to work and how will they be reimbursed? How will vacation time be arranged or allocated? What length of vacation will be offered after what length of service for both full-time and part-time employees and for different job categories?

Some of the questions to be addressed regarding employee benefit programs are as follows: Who will be eligible for employee benefits? What benefits will be offered? Will some be mandatory and some optional? Which benefits will be entirely employer-sponsored and which shared by the employer and employee? Which will be paid entirely by the employee, but administered by the pharmacy?

Benefits can include sick leave, group life insurance, long-term disability, maternity and paternity leave, compassionate leave, dental plans, provincial health-care plans, extended health-care plans, pension plans or group RRSPs, retirement programs, jury duty, provision of uniforms, shopping privileges or discounts, and payment or leave for further education.

RECRUITMENT AND HIRING

Policy regarding recruitment and hiring should address the various issues discussed in detail in Chapter 10, and specifically answer such questions as the following: Will family members, spouses, or co habitants of existing employees be eligible for hire? Who will be responsible for the hiring, the immediate supervisor for the job position, a designated manager, or the pharmacy owner? For more senior positions, does the store wish to adopt a policy of hiring from within? How are drop-in applicants to be handled? Does the pharmacy wish to use standardized application forms? Should there be a specific recruitment program directed toward high schools, trade schools, or universities?

ORIENTATION, TRAINING, AND DEVELOPMENT

Policies regarding orientation, training, and employee development should reflect the pharmacy's philosophy toward its employees. During the orientation procedure, a new employee should be advised of policy regarding individual responsibility to the store, from observing regulations concerning parking, storing personal belongings, dress codes, and logging work hours to following the rules that govern personal behaviour.

Issues surrounding training, development, and continuing education include assigning responsibility for the training; making available the time, place, and materials needed; addressing the training expectations; and establishing measurements of results. Consideration should be given to cross-training of personnel to facilitate coverage during illness and vacations. Policy should outline the pharmacy's position on outside training or education, including any payment an employee would receive during the time he or she was absent from work for a course or training program, as well as subsidization of incidental costs, such as travel, meals, and materials.

PERFORMANCE REVIEW AND DISCIPLINARY ACTION

A formalized performance review and planning policy might specify the intervals between performance reviews, the persons responsible for conducting the performance interviews, and the forms or documents to be completed in the course of the procedure (see Chapter 10). Detailed policy regarding disciplinary action and termination procedures is also extremely important. Policy should outline a specific disciplinary procedure that requires the supervisor to discuss performance problems with employees and to draft plans of action to correct such problems. Documentation of all such meetings should be mandatory.

Termination policy should specify exit-interview procedures, final work-day determination, calculation of termination pay, severance arrangements, resignation options, and follow-up support, such as references the store would be willing to provide. Termination procedure should also ensure that all store property, such as uniforms and keys, is returned, that outstanding staff charges are fully paid, and that locks be changed if necessary.

MOTIVATION AND EMPLOYEE RELATIONS

The final policy area governing personnel and human-resource development revolves around motivation and employee relations. Policy and procedure questions to consider in this area include the following: How much authority and responsibility will be delegated to whom? What degree of sharing of information about the business and its goals will there be? Will the pharmacy sponsor get-togethers during leisure time? Will there be an employee suggestion system? Should regular meetings and conferences be held? Is it feasible to have a staff sports team or a one-day tournament to foster cohesiveness? Will the pharmacy have an "employee-of-the-month" program, and how and by whom will it be conducted?

POLICIES OF FINANCE AND ACCOUNTING

The finance and accounting policies and procedures established depend on the form of the business organization, the size and diversity of the company, and the company's growth rate. Policies are often developed in the following areas: (1) capital structure; (2) working capital; (3) debt; (4) profit disbursement; and (5) accounting.

Capital-structure policies set restrictions or guidelines on the amount of debt and the amount of equity held by the company, and identify sources for both debt and equity.

Working-capital policy establishes target levels for each working-capital category and defines financing methods for these assets. Policies streamline the handling of major accounts receivable, such as third-party prescription payments, bank credit cards, and store credit.

Further working-capital policies regulate inventory and cash-flow management. Methods for valuing inventory, either at retail or cost, and procedures to determine actual inventory levels through stock counts need to specified. Banking procedures for cash received and payment procedures for timing cash disbursements will synchronize cash inflows and outflows.

Policies on debt concern financing current assets with short-term credit (mainly credit with suppliers and short-term bank loans) and financing fixed assets. Examples of policy questions are as follows: Should the company lease or buy desired land or equipment? How much credit can be carried with suppliers and how should payments be handled? Which bank or other financial institution should be used? What criteria should govern the choice of debt instrument, such as an operating line of credit versus a short-term loan?

Finally, a pharmacy may establish policies regarding profit disbursement. The questions to answer include: How much profit is to be retained in the business? How much is to be disbursed to owners and shareholders? How much is available to be disbursed to employees in the form of incentives or bonuses?

Accounting policies and procedures cover a variety of areas. What kind of bookkeeping, data processing, and information systems and methods should be implemented? What kind of accounts should be established? What types of financial reports are desired and how frequent and comprehensive should they be? Should the company conduct only internal auditing or is external auditing required? And, with regard to forecasting and budgeting, who should be involved and how often should it be done?

SUMMARY

This chapter has focussed on the specific policies and procedures that pharmacy owners and managers can establish and implement to improve the efficiency of their enterprises and to ensure that the overall direction chosen for the pharmacy is realized. The extent to which such policies and procedures are formalized and the manner in which they are communicated to staff will depend on the size and nature of the organization and on the management approach preferred by the pharmacy owner or manager. It is suggested, however, that a policy and procedures manual, brochure, or handbook of some description can be invaluable in both fostering a clear understanding between management and staff and ensuring order and continuity in the way the pharmacy's business is conducted over the years.

Recommended Reading

Brigham, Eugene; Kahl, Alfred I.; and Rentz, William F. *Canadian Financial Management, Theory and Practice.* Toronto: Holt, Rinehart and Winston of Canada, Ltd., 1983.

Kotler, Philip, and McDougal, Gordon H.G. *Principles of Marketing.* Toronto: Prentice-Hall Canada Inc., 1983.

Thompson, Arthur A., Jr., and Strickland, A.J. *Strategy Formulation and Implementation: Tasks of the General Manager.* Plano, Texas: Business Publications, Inc., 1983.

15

MARKETING AND MERCHANDISING

THE MARKETING APPROACH TO PHARMACEUTICAL SERVICES

Marketing is the process by which the demands of the public for goods or services are not only satisfied, but also – by means of collecting and analyzing market information – predicted and enhanced; marketing enables such goods and services to be made available for sale to the public at appropriate prices. In this chapter, we will deal primarily with the marketing and retailing of pharmacy-related products and services. Retailing is part of the marketing process; it involves the provision of the physical environment in which the exchange of goods and services for a price is accomplished – in our case, the community pharmacy.

There is an increasing tendency among business experts to define the marketing approach as consumer-oriented, anticipating and meeting the needs of the public, rather than as a selling or merchandising approach. The consumer-oriented marketing approach has proved successful in providing consumers with what they want and generating profits for the businesses that perform best.

CHANGES IN RETAILING

Over the past 25 years, there have been enormous changes in retailing, which have evolved partly in response to societal changes in culture,

223

education, technology, and patterns of trade and partly as a result of the competitive nature of the retail marketplace. Many of these changes are reflected in the ways in which pharmaceutical products and services are currently sold.

Shopping has become a recreational pursuit in its own right. Stores have become larger as a greater array of products flows onto the market. In most of the categories of goods sold in retail, there has been a marked increase in the variety and kinds of products available. This is certainly true for pharmacies, where there are many new types of non-prescription drugs, home-care products, giftware, paper goods and cards, sunglasses, watches and clocks, confectionery, health and beauty aids, and cosmetics. As Canadian consumers became more affluent and sought a wider variety of products, pharmacies grew in size from approximately 2000 square feet in the 1960s to an average of approximately 4000 square feet in the 1980s, with prospects of even larger pharmacies in the future.

As we saw in Chapter 9, one of the major changes that has taken place is in the design of metal shelving, which now allows for mass displays of leading non-prescription drugs and other products. These new fixtures were part of an overall change in decor, involving new methods of layout, the use of softer colours, a more clearly defined departmental layout, more emphasis on signs, and an attempt to make the customer feel comfortable at all times while in the pharmacy. The initial emphasis on well-lit, clean, and orderly pharmacies has evolved into a demand for convenience, a wide variety of products and a high level of professional service.

A market demand for services is prevalent today, and pharmacies, particularly chain stores, advertise and promote a service-oriented image. The concept of "image" in advertising refers to the promotion of a type of store or service rather than the specific goods and services it provides. In response to the perceived needs of their customers, pharmacies now promote a professional service image, which is reflected in the appearance of the pharmacy and the provision of fast and efficient service and convenience.

THE CONSUMER ENVIRONMENT

Awareness of the Environment

In marketing, consumer desires and needs must be anticipated. In pharmacy, successful marketing depends on an accurate interpretation of societal trends that relate, directly and indirectly, to health and health care. This subsumes aspects of a wide range of societal trends, from political, economic, and technological changes to sociocultural and demographic shifts. Several chapters in this book will introduce you to the major health-care and health-related trends currently prevalent in our society or anticipated for the future: Chapters 20 and 22 discuss technological advances; Chapter 23 offers insight into demographic shifts and changes in society's perception and approach to health care and the new service opportunities they represent for the pharmacist; and Chapter 24 provides an overall picture of the political, economic, demographic, and health-care environments in which the pharmacist operates and to which he or she must become attuned.

"Environmental scanning," a technique used in marketing, is the process of continually noting current events and analyzing them for their impact on the business environment. Reading newspapers and journals and discussing issues with colleagues or salespeople will help to develop a sense of emerging trends and developments. It is clear that only a few relevant issues can be isolated and given close attention; hence, the key is to scan large amounts of information from which the relevant items are gleaned. This process is very subjective and requires skill, judgment, and experience. It is also an exciting and challenging exercise for the entrepreneur.

An example of environmental scanning is detecting an upward trend in interest rates, which might call for an adjustment to the financial plan of the business. It is equally important, however, to try to anticipate the impact of the interest-rate shift on customers. How will it change their purchasing patterns? Will they have more or less disposable income? If your consumer market is relatively young and in the process of establishing families and purchasing homes, the impact of higher interest rates will be to markedly reduce their incomes. If they are tenants, the higher interest rates will make it even more difficult for them to purchase homes and they will consequently have more disposable income for other purposes. Either direction will have an effect on the marketing and management of the pharmacy, for which the pharmacist-owner or manager should be prepared.

Understanding the Contemporary Consumer

Health has always had a high value in human society, but perhaps never more than today. This is reflected in current trends toward health and fitness, preventive health care, self-care and self-treatment, and holistic medicine and "natural" products. With this interest comes a general increase in consumer demand for a full range of pharmaceuticals and health-care products, from basic hygiene products, health and beauty aids, and non-prescription drugs to natural-source vitamins and self-diagnostic equipment. Each year, firms market new, more effective products for self-care and self-diagnosis (see Chapter 23). Economic circumstances, such as the high cost of medical and hospital care, have prompted governments to support the trends toward self-care and home care. The growing proportion of the elderly in our society contributes to the increased demand for home health-care products. With these changes, today's consumer is predisposed to rely more heavily on the products offered by pharmacies and the information, assistance, and counselling services that pharmacists can provide. Recent surveys have in fact documented that the pharmacist enjoys the high opinion of the community as a health-care provider(see Chapter 24), and all indications are that this trend will continue.

Generally speaking, the contemporary consumer aspires to a high quality of life, attempts to avoid or minimize stress, and seeks pleasure and relaxation. This is reflected in the kinds of products that people desire: the products that enable them to relax, make them feel and look healthy, and in some way make life easier are in greatest demand. Younger families tend to try to achieve a high standard of living in a relatively short period of time, satisfying desires as soon as possible, and such objectives are achieved through accessibility to funds using credit or long-term borrowing. Credit has thus become a major force in retailing and, as we saw in Chapter 12, must be managed to the pharmacy's best advantage.

Although the object of perhaps the greatest thrust in North American marketing and advertising today is the aging generation of baby boomers (people born between 1946 and 1965 – and tagged with various labels to describe their characteristics, such as "yuppies"), there is a growing focus on people over the age of 50 who are affluent and now have the time and inclination to spend money in various ways. Because these people place great value on their health, they tend to be a group to whom a wide variety of pharmacy-related products can be sold. Of course, the pharmacy owner cannot ignore young people, among whom fads change rapidly and can cause sizable shifts in the market for a wide range of goods. The marketer must try to anticipate and utilize such apparent shifts in the pharmacy's marketing strategy.

The pharmacist-owner may or may not agree with or understand the preferences of consumers, whether they be related to popular trends or cultural differences, but is obliged to observe them in order to properly meet the demands of the public. For example, the pharmacist may doubt the scientific validity of the current trend that favours natural-source vitamins and herbal medicines, but will nonetheless purchase and promote these products. (The ethics involved in their sale must of course be kept in mind so that the patient is not taken advantage of through lack of knowledge.) Another example involves cultural or religious groups whose beliefs might prevent them from using certain product groups, such as birth-control products. An awareness of this will enable the pharmacist to provide alternate products to help the patient control conception.

Consumer Behaviour

In marketing, demographic analysis is commonly used to understand the purchasing preferences and habits of consumers. Demographic analysis focusses on factors such as age, sex, income, family structure, education, ethnic background, socio-economic class, residence, religion, and politics. More and more, however, marketing has come to draw heavily on psychological analyses of human behaviour to determine how decisions are made by consumers. A variety of models of consumer behaviour have been proposed, which can be found in the literature on the subject (several useful titles are included in the Recommended Readings for this chapter).

Individuals have a particular psychological make-up based on their perception of themselves and of their role in society. In other words, the personality of the individual and his or her general pattern of behaviour is what distinguishes one individual from another. One new approach to market research that is now in wide use is called psychographics. It combines personality theory with lifestyle analysis, paying attention to individuals' activities, interests, opinions, and ambitions. A similar tool, called psychometrics, has also been advocated. Psychometrics differs from psychographics in that it focusses more exclusively on personality and the individual's need to structure experience, and less on lifestyle.

These tools measure various dimensions of personality, then group individuals on the basis of shared psychological-need configurations. For example, one configuration might be self-indulgence or autonomy. The size of the various identified groups and their purchasing patterns can then be evaluated and assessed against one another. This approach has been used to differentiate the purchasing patterns of French-speaking Canadians in Quebec from English-speaking Canadians in other parts of Canada.

In the fall of 1986, the Non-prescription Drug Manufacturers' Association of Canada (NDMAC) sponsored a psychographic study of 4000 adult consumers, which resulted in the classification of Canadians into five groups: activists or enthusiasts (20 percent of the population), traditionalists (24 percent), self reliants (24 percent), passivists or free spirits (14 percent), and naturalists (18 percent). Each of the groups had distinct behavioural characteristics as consumers. The study assessed the proportion of each group in each of the provinces – a potentially useful tool for pharmacy managers in designing an approach to the marketing of non-prescription drugs. For example, the study found a high proportion of activists in British Columbia. These are described as people who have a positive attitude to non-prescription drugs and take the most active role in looking after themselves. They are motivated by convenience, good prices, and a good selection. In contrast, the province of Quebec is claimed to have a very high proportion of traditionalists, whose consumption of non-prescription drugs is described as below average. Traditionalists tend to be loyal to one or two pharmacies and are primarily concerned with service and staff, consulting frequently with their pharmacists and valuing home delivery more than does any other segment.

The usefulness of this type of information is partly dependent on the size of the organization. A small market area would not justify such a complex research procedure and, in fact, this method is used largely by national manufacturers or distributors. Also, the results of such studies must be weighed critically against possible compensating factors, such as differences in the nature and quality of services offered by the different pharmacies that members of the survey group patronize. Such differences could clearly affect the participants' attitudes to pharmacies in general. Finally, the results of such a study might be called into question because of the relatively small size of the survey group. Nonetheless, pharmacy owners will benefit by an awareness of current research into consumer behaviour, which may contribute valuable new ideas to their marketing plans.

A MARKETING APPROACH

The pharmacy owner or manager must determine what the customer needs or wants and try to provide the kinds of activities or products that would satisfy these needs. There must, however, be a balance between the effort to meet the consumer's needs and the amount the consumer is willing to pay for the goods and services offered.

This means that a pharmacist must first assess the need for the particular goods and services that are to be provided in the given geographical area. The results of such an assessment will be reflected in the types of product lines carried and the depth in which they are stocked, the number of staff and nature of their training, and the availability of delivery services and credit accounts.

In a study of the attitudes of senior citizens to pharmacy services conducted by Johnson and Johnson in co-operation with the National Association of Retail Druggists in the United States, the services ranked as most important were: personalized service, home delivery, third-party billing, charge accounts, emergency-hour services, patient-information services, and computer-record services.[1] If a pharmacy is located in an area with a significant proportion of seniors, its owner would want to give such stated preferences the utmost attention in planning and marketing pharmacy services.

---

[1] *Aging Americans: Annual Audit of Attitudes 1988*, Johnson and Johnson, 1988, p. 5.

Consumer Market

As discussed in Chapter 3 on location analysis, the manager of a pharmacy must determine the size of the market that will be served – that is, define the trading area of the pharmacy. The "consumer market" is defined as the potential of a selected group of consumers to purchase the goods or services offered to them; for a pharmacy, this will be determined by the number of people in the trading area and the amount of money they are prepared to spend on health care and related products.

Assessment of the consumer market should be a dynamic process that defines the current number and the characteristics of the customer population and also considers apparent trends and their potential impact on future business. The pharmacist can examine the demographic characteristics of the trading area's constituent neighbourhoods to determine the kinds of families that live there and their potential needs.

The market may be changing from established families to younger families with less income, which would significantly influence the pharmacy's planning and marketing strategy. Similarly, it would be obvious that in an affluent neighbourhood, the people would be likely to spend more on personal products than in a neighbourhood with a lower income level. The relative affluence of a neighbourhood can be determined by looking at census data that will give average incomes by census tract.

The consumer market can be segmented into various groups. For example, the proportion of elderly in an area represents a potential demand for certain types of goods and products, whereas another neighbourhood with a large number of infants and young children would represent a very different kind of demand. One of the determinants of the kind of market one is dealing with would be the nature of family composition in the area. Again, from census data, one can determine market segments by the proportion of single individuals, married couples with no children, families with children and two parents, single-parent families, older couples with no children, or single elderly individuals: each group will clearly require a different range of products and services. Similarly, the age of the children and the number in each age group would indicate the potential kinds of merchandise to be sold.

The pharmacy owner may choose not to try to build client loyalty by marketing to all the identified consumer groups, but to focus on one predominant group. In other words, services might be customized to the surrounding market or a selected service might be targeted to specific market segments. If there is an even demographic mix, marketing experts suggest that you identify who your competition is targeting, and pursue the remaining market segments. Such choices are commonly referred to as "positioning the business in the marketplace."

Assessment of market need should be balanced against the estimated cost of operating the pharmacy over a period of years. A pharmacy offering a high level of service, with high rental costs and a low sales volume, could not effectively compete with low-priced, high-volume competitors if the customers in the trading area were very sensitive to price.

Marketing Information Systems

While the initial planning for a pharmacy is complex, subjective, and filled with risk, once a pharmacy is in operation there is a wealth of marketing information that can be used to refine marketing activities.

INTERNAL DATA

From sales data, accounts receivable, and prescription records, pharmacies can collect information such as customer names and addresses, the amount purchased per visit or per year, and the fluctuations and trends in sales.

Sales information from the cash register can be recorded by product or product line. The rate of purchase and sale of an individual item is referred to as its sales velocity; reports on sales velocity are often available from wholesalers. Sales velocity can be assessed by different groups of products or by department. The effectiveness of special promotions and sales can also be assessed by regularly monitoring quantities sold over the period of the sale. Profitability should also be assessed periodically by product and product line, by groups of customers, and by the sales and special efforts undertaken in each department.

Such monitoring will provide the pharmacy owner or manager with information essential to formulating a marketing plan, in that it reflects the degree to which customer needs are being met. Failure to meet consumer needs can also be monitored more directly, by putting a system in place to record and deal with customer complaints.

MARKET RESEARCH

Market research is the study of the attitudes and beliefs that shape the consumer's response to a product or service. Market research can be initiated in a pharmacy as an informal system, based on verbal comments and suggestions from customers and written comments obtained by request, for example, in a suggestion box. This is a common approach among community pharmacies. Through their close relationships with customers and other staff members, pharmacy staff can develop a good idea of the issues and problems facing the pharmacy, but they must be sensitive and alert to these issues and must have a means of using the information they gain to improve service.

To evaluate the image of your pharmacy, try to see it through the eyes of a customer and mentally compare it to other pharmacies. What is the visual impact and image conveyed? Has a professional atmosphere been achieved through cleanliness, orderliness, and comfort? Is the pharmacy well stocked and are products well displayed and uniformly marked with prices? Observe competitive pharmacies in the same way to derive a sense of the different approaches used and how they might influence your customers' choice of pharmacy.

Regular analysis, or environmental scanning, of the advertising of competitors should be conducted in order to stay abreast of activities in the competitive market and to be able to respond to them quickly and effectively. Regularly checking competitive prices is now standard practice in community-pharmacy market research. Such information will show competitors' reactions to market changes and will provide insight into the overall strategy of the competing pharmacy. Newspapers, newsletters, and advertising flyers should be read with an eye to both institutional and product advertising.

A more formal method of market research involves the systematic collection of information that is of specific interest to the pharmacy owner. Companies such as A.C. Nielsen specialize in market research, generating data on product movement and trends in market shares for various industries, including the pharmaceutical industry. While larger pharmacy organizations can hire market research firms to address specific problem areas, smaller firms will probably have to conduct their own research.

Questionnaires are a usual form of market research and are easy to use, although it can be difficult to design a good questionnaire that gives accurate, unbiased results. An open-ended format can be used, requesting customers' views on the services or products they would like to see in the pharmacy. Another, simpler, questionnaire format is the checklist on which people can indicate their preferences for services. Figures 15.1 and 15.2 show samples of the open-ended questionnaire and the checklist.

Information on competitors can be obtained through competitive pricing studies that are conducted by chain pharmacies and wholesale-based or co-operative groups. Regular information on the relative position of prices enables the manager to set competitive prices on selected items.

One method of collecting information that may be appropriate for pharmacies is the ongoing questionnaire – one that the same group of customers would be asked to complete periodically over time. This approach gives continuous feedback as to customers' perceptions of service levels, product offerings, and general image and enables the pharmacy to keep in touch with a client base and to adapt to better meet their needs. Questionnaires should be mailed out regularly, say, three times per year, and should include general questions that are repeated each time as well as questions that address specific issues of interest to the pharmacy

Figure 15.1 OPEN-ENDED FORMAT QUESTIONNAIRE

☒ SHOPPERS DRUG MART.
HELP US TO HELP YOU!

What did you like about our store?

What didn't you like about our store?

Are there any products or services that you would like to see in our store?

Any additional comments?

OPTIONAL:

NAME

ADDRESS

PHONE

PLEASE DEPOSIT IN OUR CUSTOMER
COMMENT BOX. THANK-YOU!
WE APPRECIATE YOUR INTEREST.

Source: Courtesy of Shoppers Drug Mart.

owner or manager at the particular time. As an incentive to participate, randomly chosen customers might be offered a prize or preferential treatment, such as prior announcement of sales. As customers drop out of the survey, new ones should be recruited.

THE MARKETING PLAN

From Strategic Plan to Marketing Plan

The strategic plan is the overall direction or goal that is set for the pharmacy. It outlines the philosophy by which the pharmacy will op-

Figure 15.2 Checklist Format Questionnaire

YOUR OPINION COUNTS

In order to better serve you, we would like you to complete this brief questionnaire. Please take a few minutes to answer the following questions. We will use the information you provide to serve you better.

Please use a lead pencil to fill out the form, do not use a pen. Completely fill in the circles of your choices. Do not mark outside of the circles.

Thank you for your assistance.

Fill in the one circle which best represents
your **agreement/disagreement** to each statement.

**SD = Strongly Disagree   D = Disagree   U = Undecided/Don't Know
A = Agree   SA = Strongly Agree**

1. The pharmacist(s) at this pharmacy provides excellent information about how to properly use each prescription.
   (SD)   (D)   (U)   (A)   (SA)

2. The employees at this pharmacy always make an extra effort to help me find what I need.
   (SD)   (D)   (U)   (A)   (SA)

3. The merchandise displays in this pharmacy are always attractive.
   (SD)   (D)   (U)   (A)   (SA)

4. The hours this pharmacy is open are convenient for me.
   (SD)   (D)   (U)   (A)   (SA)

5. The pharmacist(s) at this pharmacy provides me with useful information in selecting non-prescription medication.
   (SD)   (D)   (U)   (A)   (SA)

6. This pharmacy's prescription medication prices are competitive.
   (SD)   (D)   (U)   (A)   (SA)

7. The pharmacist(s) at this pharmacy is always available to answer my questions about non-prescription and prescription medication.
   (SD)   (D)   (U)   (A)   (SA)

8. The pharmacist(s) at this pharmacy always reviews my prescription medication with me to explain possible side effects or problems.
   (SD)   (D)   (U)   (A)   (SA)

9. The employees at this pharmacy are always friendly to customers.
   (SD)   (D)   (U)   (A)   (SA)

10. This pharmacy's non-prescription medication prices are competitive.
    (SD)   (D)   (U)   (A)   (SA)

11. This pharmacy always looks very neat and clean.
    (SD)   (D)   (U)   (A)   (SA)

12. This pharmacy carries the non-prescription medication I need.
    (SD)   (D)   (U)   (A)   (SA)

Overall, how satisfied are you with this pharmacy?

○ Not at all satisfied   ○ Somewhat satisfied   ○ Satisfied   ○ Very Satisfied

Please darken the circle that best represents the **importance** of these factors to you.

NI = Not Important   SI = Slightly Important
I = Important   VI = Very Important

Convenient Pharmacy Hours	(NI)	(SI)	(I)	(VI)
Clean and Attractive Pharmacy	(NI)	(SI)	(I)	(VI)
Wide Merchandise Selection	(NI)	(SI)	(I)	(VI)
Friendly and Helpful Service	(NI)	(SI)	(I)	(VI)
Competitive Prescription Prices	(NI)	(SI)	(I)	(VI)
Competitive Non-Prescription Prices	(NI)	(SI)	(I)	(VI)
Useful Prescription Information	(NI)	(SI)	(I)	(VI)
Useful Non-Prescription Information	(NI)	(SI)	(I)	(VI)
Concern for My Health	(NI)	(SI)	(I)	(VI)
Convenient Parking	(NI)	(SI)	(I)	(VI)
Convenient Location	(NI)	(SI)	(I)	(VI)

Please rate this pharmacy on each of the following factors
compared to other pharmacies available to you.

MW = Much Worse   SW = Somewhat Worse   S = Similar
SB = Somewhat Better   MB = Much Better

Convenient Pharmacy Hours	(MW)	(SW)	(S)	(SB)	(MB)
Clean and Attractive Pharmacy	(MW)	(SW)	(S)	(SB)	(MB)
Wide Merchandise Selection	(MW)	(SW)	(S)	(SB)	(MB)
Friendly and Helpful Service	(MW)	(SW)	(S)	(SB)	(MB)
Competitive Prescription Prices	(MW)	(SW)	(S)	(SB)	(MB)
Competitive Non-Prescription Prices	(MW)	(SW)	(S)	(SB)	(MB)
Useful Prescription Information	(MW)	(SW)	(S)	(SB)	(MB)
Useful Non-Prescription Information	(MW)	(SW)	(S)	(SB)	(MB)
Concern for My Health	(MW)	(SW)	(S)	(SB)	(MB)
Convenient Parking	(MW)	(SW)	(S)	(SB)	(MB)
Convenient Location	(MW)	(SW)	(S)	(SB)	(MB)

Where do you primarily buy your non-prescription medication?
○ This pharmacy.
○ Another pharmacy.
○ Grocery store.
○ Department store.

How frequently do you purchase your prescription medication from this pharmacy?
○ Always.
○ Some of the time.
○ Never.

Are you:
○ Male.
○ Female.

About how often do you shop here?
○ First visit here.
○ 1 or 2 times a month.
○ More than 2 times a month.

In which age group are you?
○ Less than 21 years.
○ 21-40 years.
○ 41-60 years.
○ Over 60 years.

In which income group is your family?
○ Under $15,000 annually.
○ $15,000 to $25,000 annually.
○ $25,001 to $35,000 annually.
○ Over $35,000 annually.

Source: Sandoz Consumer Health Care Group, 1987.

erate. For example, a strategic plan defines the image that is to be created, the pricing approach taken, and the levels of service offered. A small pharmacy in a clinic would have a very different philosophy from a large merchandising pharmacy in a shopping mall. The operational plan (on which the business plan is based) flows from the strategic plan, and sets out objectives in terms of sales, profits, gross margins, and market share, as we saw in Chapter 5. Based on the general directional guidelines of the strategic and operational plans, the pharmacy establishes a specific objective or set of objectives toward which to work, say, over the next five years. The operational plan is reviewed and revised annually in the context of the original projection of objectives. Each year, a marketing plan is also devised to implement those objectives (see Figure 15.3).

Figure 15.3.   STRATEGIC PLAN TO ANNUAL MARKETING PLAN

In establishing the annual marketing plan, it will be necessary (1) to review outside sources of data (consisting of international and national surveys and statistics) in order to gain a sense of general trends and new products, and (2) to conduct your own marketing research from internal sources. Some of the various factors involved and their influence on the marketing plan are described in the following sections.

To start, however, the manager should determine the average transaction sale of the pharmacy from cash-register data on total sales and total number of transactions. (This figure should be higher during sales due to the increased activity resulting from special promotions.) Examining such data by department will provide valuable insight into what is actually taking place in the store. Similarly, internal data on the pharmacy's customers should be reviewed. As mentioned earlier, prescription files and informal surveys will supply information on customer characteristics such as age, number of prescriptions purchased, non-prescription drug purchases, and patterns of repeat prescriptions.

The marketing plan may be guided by an objective either to increase the average sale per customer or to attract more customers to the pharmacy, or both. To increase the average sale per customer, the pharmacy must encourage the customer to buy more while in the store; that is, it must strive to increase impulse purchasing, for example, by expanding or varying the product mix or making the existing product mix more attractive to the customer. Revamping the merchandising approach will renew the customer's interest in the store. This approach can be supplemented by promoting existing or new professional services (such as blood-pressure measurement) through a mailing or in direct conversation with customers. Attracting more customers to the pharmacy would call for increased advertising and special promotions geared to the needs of potential customers (as determined through your market research) that would encourage them to come to the store.

Competition

A pharmacy faces competition not only from other pharmacies, but also from grocery stores, specialty shops, health and beauty shops, and natural-food stores. For pharmacies with a wider array of products, the list of competitors would be longer.

In drawing up the marketing plan, a manager would look at the different types of competition that exist within the trading area and analyze the competitors in terms of their prices, services, merchandise mix, and advertising. From this analysis, he or she might determine to strengthen some product lines, perhaps discontinue others, and possibly reduce (or raise) prices on certain items.

The question to be asked in analyzing the competitive situation in the trading area is whether the pharmacy is getting an appropriate share of the market. From estimates of total retail sales of pharmacy-related products in the area, the pharmacist could estimate the pharmacy's market share and judge whether it is reasonable. Another simple approach is to count the number of families served by your pharmacy and compare that to the actual number of families listed in the Canada Census for the census tract(s) that comprise your trading area. In addition, various city agencies, such as the Chamber of Commerce, can provide data giving an indication of retail growth in the area over the year; the percentage growth in sales for pharmaceuticals should be comparable to, or greater than, overall retail growth. If the pharmacy's sales increase is less than the average for the region, it is reasonable to assume that there has been a loss of market share. The pharmaceutical press publishes average rates of growth for pharmacies in Canada and the United States. Comparisons against these averages – taking into account, of course, any mitigating local circumstances – will also indicate whether the pharmacy's marketing plan has been effective or is in need of revision.

Performance in a particular trading area will depend on the overall strategy adopted. The community pharmacy that carries a large number of product lines and competes in such a way as to reach a large number of market segments would adopt a very different strategy than one specializing in health-care products and placing a greater emphasis on service. In the first instance, the manager would focus on communication with a large number of current and potential customers in the trading area, notifying them throughout the year of promotions of selected products. The emphasis would be on merchandise mix and merchandising. In contrast, a pharmacy featuring only professional products would search out ways of providing better service to existing customers and look for closely related products to add to the store.

Attracting Customers

The strategic plan adopted by a pharmacy should result in a particular image that is apparent to the public. Various segments within the population look for a particular kind of pharmacy to suit their needs. If the image matches what they are looking for, they are likely to patronize the pharmacy. A knowledge of the characteristics of the customers in your trading area will help determine the sort of image you will want to adopt for your store.

The range of goods and services provided will also have a major impact on the customers that are attracted. Generally speaking, a pharmacy that specializes in home-care supplies and has a good deal of interaction with older or handicapped people will have a very specific orientation and attract a particular type of clientele. Conversely, large pharmacies with low prices and a large volume of merchandise on display will usually attract price-conscious shoppers who like to take their time exploring the various bargains. Stores on busy streets are likely to attract people who do not have time to browse, but want to buy a particular item quickly (usually a commonly purchased one), and leave.

Attracting customers will depend in large part on the accessibility of the store. As we saw in Chapter 3, location has an enormous impact on the sales of a pharmacy, and good locations are in demand. Location will also influence merchandising to some extent. For example, rents are lower in suburban areas and pharmacies therefore tend to be larger, allowing for a wider range of products to be stocked. Also, since virtually everyone travels by car in the suburbs, people are able to transport more purchases (including bulky products) in a single trip than the downtown shopper can. Consequently, the suburban pharmacy is likely not only to stock a wider selection of merchandise than the inner-city store, but also a higher percentage of bulk paper goods. The opportunity is also there to handle products that fit into a lifestyle in which travel and automobiles play a major role (for example, certain automotive products, coolers and picnic items, maps, and so on). This would clearly not be appropriate for a store in a densely populated area where people tend to walk or use public transit.

ADVERTISING

The primary means by which people are attracted to pharmacies is advertising. One form is the institutional advertisement, which promotes the pharmacy and its services rather than specific products. An institutional ad might focus on the fact that the pharmacy specializes in prescriptions and provides a delivery service. If such an advertisement is run in a local newspaper on a repeated basis, people will come to remember the pharmacy for the advertised services, and will patronize it when they have need of those particular services. To be effective, however, institutional advertising must be repeated frequently so that its message remains fresh in the minds of the public.

The more common form of advertising is the product or promotional ad, which tells the public that products are available at the pharmacy at an attractive price. Although product ads are often run in local newspapers, they are most commonly distributed as printed flyers, mailed out by the pharmacy or by a bulk-mailing service. Flyers are normally used by pharmacies that are organized into groups, whether through ownership (chains such as Kent Drugs), franchises (Shoppers Drug Mart), wholesales (Guardian, IDA), or co-operative buying groups (Value Drug Mart, Price Watchers, Pharmasave, Big V).

The use of coupons in product ads in newspapers and flyers, calendars, or other promotional pieces is an effective tool in promotional campaigns. By redeeming the coupons at the store, customers receive special prices or discounts on advertised products. And, by counting the number of coupons redeemed, the pharmacy manager can evaluate how successful the promotion has been in attracting the attention of consumers.

MARKETING PLAN TO ADVERTISING PLAN

The annual marketing plan would set out the number of advertising promotions to occur during the year, the dates for which they were scheduled, and the overall annual advertising budget. For each promotion, an advertising plan and budget would be drawn up, specifying the media to be used (flyer, newspaper advertisement, radio or television advertisement, neighbourhood publication), the duration of the campaign, and the link to in-store merchandising (see Figure 15.4). Based on the expected sales, the promotion's contribution to profits would also be estimated.

It is important to note here the advantages with regard to promotional campaigns, advertising plans, and budgets that come with involvement in a centralized group, be it a franchise or wholesale-sponsored or co-operative buying group. Member pharmacies are provided with annual schedules of special promotions and sales – normally about 20 throughout the year, including the seasonal promotions, such as Easter, Christmas, and "back-to-school," and various other events, such as Valentine's Day and Mother's Day. Estimates of anticipated increases in sales for featured products or product lines may also be provided, assisting member pharmacies in their purchasing and merchandising for special promotions and in their own sales and profitability projections. In addition, advertising costs are naturally lower for participating pharmacies than they would be for pharmacies purchasing advertising independently. Finally, groups are often able to mount well-co-ordinated advertising campaigns that

Figure 15.4.   ADVERTISING PLAN WORKSHEET

1. Name or theme of promotion (eg., Easter Sale): _____

2. Dates of sale: _____

   Dates that advertising is to run: _____

3. Budget allocated for promotion: _____

4. Media to be used and cost:

   Flyer _____

   Newspaper _____

   Radio _____

   Other _____

5. Products to be promoted:

   _____

   _____

   _____

   _____

   _____

make use of all available media. For example, flyer promotions are usually supported by newspaper, radio, and TV advertising. When advertising budgets are prepared, an analysis may be made of the impact of each of the media on the advertising programs of the organization, relative costs are examined, and appropriate amounts allocated to each of the media forms.

Synthesis of Information for a Marketing Plan

Figure 15.5 shows examples of some of the objectives that might underlie an operational plan and drive the annual marketing plan. To prepare the marketing plan, a pharmacy manager would start by examining the store's business records for the past year or two. From ongoing environmental scanning, he or she would have an idea of general business conditions and sales prospects. This information, together with changes in prices, the introduction on the market of any new product lines, and changes in the competitive situation, would determine the kinds of products to be purchased, the emphasis to be given to the pharmacy's different departments, and the gross margin and sales to be expected for each department. These projections in turn would involve an assessment of the various target groups within the community and the prospects for penetrating them. This would also be the time to explore the possibility of offering new services in the pharmacy (see Chapter 23) or to seek an outside service contract: a tender to provide services to a nursing home could be drawn up, for example, and, if it had potential, pursued with vigour (see Chapter 24). Non-professional service opportunities, such as a post office sub-unit, could be investigated. The selling of lottery tickets has also recently become very popular in pharmacies and represents not only new revenues but also a mechanism to attract customers into the pharmacy who might also buy other products.

Allocation of Resources and Responsibility

An essential part of the marketing plan involves preparing a detailed list of responsibilities and duties in order to accomplish the objectives set. For the advertising program that is to be initiated, someone must design an institutional advertisement, negotiate space for it in a newspaper, and ensure that it is circulated on a regular basis as has been planned. For the promotional advertising, design of the flyer and arrangements for printing and distribution must be delegated or linked to a buying group. A budget should be established for the advertising program and monitored throughout the year.

Figure 15.5. EXAMPLES OF OBJECTIVES FOR AN ANNUAL
MARKETING PLAN

Sales	– Increase in sales of 8.5 percent (recognizing that a major part of this, about 5 percent, represents inflation).
Market Share	– Loss of market share in toiletries and confections expected due to grocery store competition, but will increase share in infant supplies in response to increased birth rate in the trading area by establishing infant-supplies department (see below).
Pharmacy Image	– Strengthen the image of the pharmacy as a family pharmacy with a wide range of products and everyday low (but not lowest) prices through a series of institutional ads.
Promotional Advertising	– Group promotions or independent in-store promotions to families in trading area, featuring new infant-supplies department and special sales of infant supplies.
Profit	– Increase in net profit from 4.2 percent to 4.5 percent; decrease in gross margin from 32.5 percent to 30.8 percent. (Increase inventory turnover rate; improve inventory-management system; reduce expenses; to maintain margins in face of increasing competition, consider eliminating products with less than 30 percent gross margin and turnover rate under 3.)
Staff	– Decrease complaints on service by 50 percent by introducing an orientation program for new employees, quarterly staff meetings to discuss customer complaints, and customer surveys via questionnaires.
Product Mix	– Establish a department featuring infant supplies and generating sales of $11,000 in the first year. (Assess space for best location; relocate other products and/or departments. Assess overall traffic flow; tie in with new family-pharmacy orientation.)

Control Procedures

For each of the objectives, progress must be analyzed and reviewed periodically, and, where necessary, corrective action taken. For example, if sales of infant supplies are much lower than anticipated, possible causes would have to be identified and addressed, either by increasing promotion, allocating more space within the pharmacy, training staff to sell related items more effectively, or lowering prices. In undertaking some of these activities, it might prove necessary to draw on other budgets and resources, which would in turn call for an assessment of the overall financial situation on a regular basis and of the progress and effectiveness of the revised marketing approach.

MERCHANDISING

Merchandising is part of the marketing process; it is often referred to as the art of having "the right product, at the right price, at the right time, and in the right place." It consists of activities that induce the customer to try your products and services. Such activities include purchasing products that will meet consumer demand, promoting them to the consumer at attractive prices, and displaying them in ways that will encourage their sale. Merchandising involves consideration of the target customers, competition, marketing objectives, and related financial objectives of the marketing plan.

Satisfied customers are the key to success in pharmacy, and customer satisfaction is obtained through the products offered, the service provided, and the customer's perception of comfort while in the store. Competition also plays an important role in merchandising. The degree of a pharmacy's success in relation to its competitors is largely determined by the products carried, their presentation, and their price.

Merchandising has five facets that must be considered.[2] They are as follows:

1. Administrative procedures
2. Occupation of suitable space and layout
3. Publicity about the products
4. Purchasing suitable products
5. Selling activities

---

[2] *Merchandising. Guide to Good Pharmacy Management*, (Vaudreuil, Que.: Hoffman–La Roche, 1978).

Merchandise Philosophy

Every pharmacy needs a merchandise philosophy that sets guidelines for the kind of merchandise to be stocked. Six areas are normally considered in this context: variety, price and quality, brands, turnover, gross margin, and inventory balance. In a pharmacy, the merchandise reflects the health-oriented professional nature of the organization.

VARIETY

The variety of products stocked in a pharmacy can vary enormously. Some pharmacies are very specialized in the range of products they handle (for example, prescription drugs only). Others carry health and beauty aids, OTC products, and home health-care supplies in addition to prescription drugs. More recently, the potential variety of products in a pharmacy has been increased by the inclusion of foods (particularly convenience foods), infant apparel, computers and electronic merchandise, and lottery tickets. In each product category, the number of different items stocked and the depth in which they are stocked (i.e., the quantity in stock) will reflect the merchandise philosophy adopted by the pharmacy manager. As pointed out earlier, the marketing plan, customer needs, and competition will determine the eventual variety that is to be stocked.

PRICE AND QUALITY

The kind of merchandise carried will depend partly on the area that the pharmacy serves. In lower-income neighbourhoods, pharmacies tend to carry more lower-priced convenience items, such as cigarettes, magazines, confectionery, and audio and visual tapes. In more affluent neighbourhoods, they would carry health equipment, electronic equipment, a wider variety of better-quality health and beauty supplies, and fairly expensive giftware. One exception to this is ethical pharmaceuticals (i.e., products purchased on the advice of a professional rather than those advertised to the public), which tend not to vary significantly in quality and price.

BRANDS

The term brand or brand name refers to the manufacturer's registered trademark on a product, such as Tylenol®, which is protected by law. The success of a brand and the customer loyalty it can generate makes brand-name products valuable in the retail marketplace. Traditionally, pharmacies have been more receptive than supermarkets to introducing new brands – especially in the health and beauty lines – and they have thereby generated customer loyalty to the store as well as to the particular brands.

Where brand-name products have been successful, private brands or house brands of those products are now commonly introduced. These private-label products are manufactured on contract to the retailer and labelled with a brand name unique to the pharmacy or chain of pharmacies. For example, vitamins and other products are manufactured for Shoppers Drug Mart and sold under the Life Brand label.

"No name" or generic products are also currently popular. They do not bear a manufacturer's brand name, but only the generic name of the drug. These products are sold on the basis of low cost and minimal advertising.

TURNOVER

The merchandising philosophy of a pharmacy will influence its rate of inventory turnover. A pharmacy that operates with high sales volume and low prices will have a high inventory turnover rate. On the other hand, smaller pharmacies and pharmacies with specialized inventories would have lower turnover rates in some of their departments. A high turnover rate is not usually characteristic of the high-price/high-quality merchandising philosophy typical, for example, of cosmetics, which tend to have a lower turnover rate.

GROSS MARGIN

The gross margin on pharmaceuticals has traditionally been approximately 40 percent. As a result of competition in the marketplace, the gross margin on non-prescription drugs is considerably lower and on other product lines lower still. One of the challenges of pharmacy management is to maintain margins and still attract customers. Product lines with less competition and higher margins are constantly sought, and the most promising among them are currently in the field of durable medical equipment (DME).

INVENTORY BALANCE

In stocking merchandise, one must balance the variety, breadth, and depth of the stock. The combination of these three factors determines the inventory balance of the pharmacy.

Pharmacies today typically have very limited storage space, so products must be purchased on the basis of predetermined criteria in order for the store to maintain a suitable inventory balance at all times.

Pharmaceuticals differ from other items in that out-of-stock situations are less acceptable. Also, pharmacies routinely stock all new prescription drugs.

Merchandise Display

In the display of merchandise, visual impact is extremely important – in fact, it is an essential sales tool. Products must be clearly visible to the customer, attractively arranged in good lighting, and placed in proximity to other related products. Although the techniques of merchandise display are essentially straightforward, it requires a good deal of effort to maintain a tidy, well-displayed stock of merchandise at all times. The importance of visual impact in selling may be illustrated by the fact that the visual appeal of product packaging alone is responsible for most impulse sales, which account for appproximately 60 percent of all pharmacy sales.[3]

The principles of merchandise display combine aesthetic appeal with other known determinants of consumer behaviour to direct shoppers' attention to particular products and to expose them to different product areas in the store. Effective stock placement, manipulation of traffic flow (as discussed in Chapter 9), and the use of promotional displays are all important elements of merchandise display.

The resulting effect of such efforts is to create a positive image in the mind of the consumer – one that is in keeping with the overall image intended for the pharmacy.

VISUAL BALANCE

Visual balance refers to the appealing arrangement of products on shelves by size or colour. For example, larger packages should be placed on the lower shelves and smaller items on the upper shelves. Similarly, colour gradations should run from dark to light, with bright colours at the ends of the aisles. Mass displays of shampoos and other hair products, for example, can be structured vertically or horizontally, achieving symmetry and striking blocks of colour. (Vertical grouping refers to the placement of different sizes of the same product above and below one another on different shelves; horizontal grouping involves placing them side by side on the same shelf, with smaller sizes to the left and larger sizes to the right.) By varying the approach, more aesthetically pleasing visual effects can be obtained from the combinations of colours, sizes, and arrangements of product packages.

Although visual balance is important, it should not take precedence over other essential selling criteria: top-selling products must be at eye level, with related products appearing nearby, even if this detracts somewhat from visual balance.

---

[3] "Impulse Behind Many Purchases: POPAI/Dupont Study," *Drug Merchandising* 66, no. 4 (April 1985): 40–41.

PRODUCT FACINGS

An important aspect of the relationship between merchandise display and sales activity is the role of product facings. A facing is simply a product package on the shelf, facing out to the consumer, with stock of the product lined up behind the front package. A rule of thumb in merchandising is that "a product will generate 36 percent more sales when its facings are increased from two to four."[4] Hence, to a point, the number of facings of a stock item should be proportional to its sales. A slower-selling item might have a single facing, but if an item sells very well, it should be given four or more facings. Similarly, increasing the number of facings will push up the sales of new products. Suppliers, especially wholesalers, can provide data on the relative sales of the products they distribute, but in-store data should also be used to track fluctuations in sales and adjust product facings accordingly.

It is important to note here that consistent price ticketing improves the visual quality of displays and encourages customers to buy. The placement of price stickers should therefore be done within a set of guidelines by trained staff. Price tickets must be placed on product packages where they will be in clear view, without obstructing printed information that the consumer may need to know about the product (for example, the strength of a vitamin or instructions for use). Tickets are normally placed in the upper right-hand corner on the front of the package, although in the case of very small containers, they may have to be placed on the top. Containers with removable tops, such as aerosol containers, are normally priced on the body of the container. Uniformity in the placement of price stickers will not only improve the appearance of the display, but will also help sales clerks when they ring up purchases.

PLANOGRAMS

Another factor influencing stock placement is the relative effect on sales of various locations in a gondola. The highest sales are associated with products placed in the centre of the gondola, sometimes referred to as the "hot-spot cross" because the consumer's eye travels from left to right at eye level, then up and down at the centre of the gondola, as shown in Figure 15.6. Note the numbering from 1 through 6 that indicates most to least desirable locations for products on the gondola.

Products with the highest sales velocity should be placed in the hot-spot cross area and should have the greatest number of facings (normally three to five). Translating this scheme into stocked shelves with the thousands of items found in a pharmacy is a formidable task. The tool to help solve the problem is called a planogram.

[4]A. Archambault and H. Segal, *Merchandising. Pharmacy Management Program, Module 3* (Kirkland, Que.: Nordic Laboratories Inc., n.d.), pp. 4–5.

Figure 15.6.   THE HOT-SPOT CROSS MERCHANDISE DISPLAY
PRINCIPLE

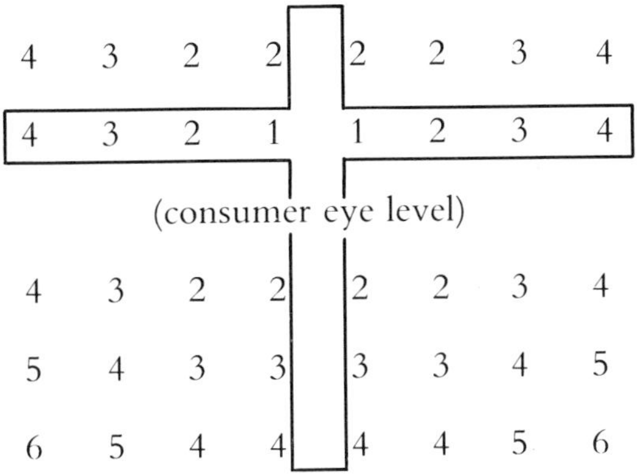

```
4   3   2   2 | 2   2   3   4

4   3   2   1 | 1   2   3   4

        (consumer eye level)

4   3   2   2 | 2   2   3   4

5   4   3   3 | 3   3   4   5

6   5   4   4 | 4   4   5   6
```

Source: Courtesy of H.J. Segal.

A planogram is a precise, detailed scheme for merchandise display within given product categories. It specifies stock levels and the optimal number of facings for each product, as well as the optimal positioning of products in relation to one other on the shelves. Planograms are often designed and supplied to pharmacies by the headquarters of chains or by the wholesalers of co-operative groups, in the form of photographs of ideally stocked gondolas (see Figure 15.7). Pharmacy staff then follow the photographs closely in stocking shelves. In a planogram, the positioning of each product and the space allocated to it are determined on the basis of the product's sales velocity and profitability (per square foot), combined with factors such as historical sales patterns, current trends, and expectations for the future. Planograms can also be drawn up by the pharmacy on the basis of its inventory, purchasing, and sales records, together with data on item performance that is obtainable from wholesalers and manufacturers. Today, point-of-sale (POS) systems that record sales by item will give pharmacy owners instant access to sales velocity data and other relevant information (see Chapters 11 and 20). In addition, computer programs have now been developed to design planograms for pharmacies.

ALLOCATION OF SPACE

The allocation of space to various product groups throughout the pharmacy is determined by calculating their relative sales and profitability

Figure 15.7.　SAMPLE PLANOGRAM (PAIN-RELIEF PRODUCTS–
8-FOOT ISLAND

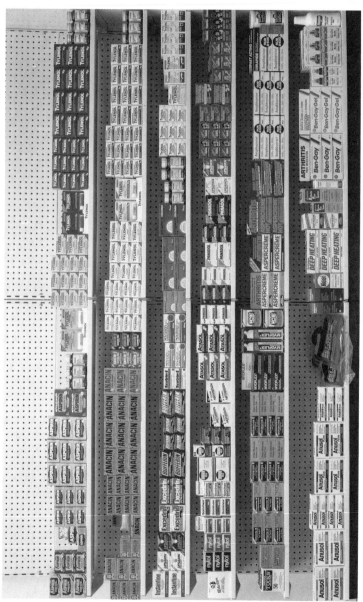

Source: Courtesy of Drug Trading Company Limited.

per square foot. The principle behind the allocation of space is to maximize sales per square foot of the selling area, hence to allocate more space to the most profitable product groups and less to the least profitable ones. Figure 15.6 shows a sample calculation of profit per square foot in several different product areas. Sales in the various product groups should be monitored periodically to determine if adjustments are needed in existing allocations of space in the pharmacy.

In some cases, space will be made available for merchandise or services that bear a low profit but are known to attract people into the store. This is usually the reason for introducing post-office substations or lottery ticket sales in pharmacies.

Promotional Displays

One important way of drawing customers into the pharmacy is through special promotions, where featured items are sold at a special price over a specified period of time. In order for displays of the featured products ("promotional displays") to be effective in generating sales, they must have sufficient impact to attract the consumer's attention and interest. As customers look for the advertised items, they will be drawn into various parts of the store, where effective promotional displays will engage their interest in the full range of products offered there.

Promotional displays generally involve separating featured products out from their regular product areas in the store through the use of floor displays, end displays, dump bins, impulse units, and special areas promoting seasonal items. Research has shown that sales per customer can be significantly increased in this way. In addition, promotional displays induce customers to travel through parts of the pharmacy that they might otherwise have no reason to explore.

The overall impact of a pharmacy's merchandise display will depend on the effective use and placement of the various types of promotional displays.

FLOOR DISPLAYS

Where space allows, one or two floor displays may be used – too many can detract from the pharmacy's orderly image. A floor display should contain quite a large amount of stock if it is to be visible and have impact, which means that the product used should have a high sales potential (otherwise, the amount of inventory needed to create a substantial display would be more than the store could sell.) However, the display should not be so tall that it blocks the consumer's view of the rest of the store. Care should also be taken to allow adequate space for traffic to move around the display. Floor displays must be continually replenished with

Figure 15.8 CALCULATING SALES AND PROFITABILITY PER SQUARE FOOT

(1) Product Category	(2) Sales ($)	×	(3) Gross Margin (%)	=	(4) Gross Margin ($)	(5) Square Footage	(2) ÷ (5) Sales per Sq. Ft. ($)	(4) ÷ (5) Gross Margin per Sq. Ft. ($)
Rx	150,000		40		60,000	400	375	150
Health and beauty aids	120,000		28		33,600	1200	100	28
Tobacco	50,000		15		7,500	150	333	50
Cards	30,000		50		15,000	700	42.9	21.4
Cosmetics	30,000		40		12,000	200	150	60
Miscellaneous	120,000		31		36,900	1350	88.9	27.6
Total	500,000		33		165,000	4000	125	41.25

Source: Adapted from *Merchandising. Guide to Good Pharmacy Management* (Vaudreuil, Que.: Hoffman–La Roche, 1978), p. 13.

stock, and taken down once their visual impact decreases because of depleted stock.

END DISPLAYS

Displays at the ends of shelving should have a theme, such as protection from the sun, and should feature no more than two different products, which must complement each other. A thematic approach tends to increase sales. It is generally held that competing products should not be placed together in an end display as this will encourage comparisons and a process of looking for the best bargain. The purpose of the display is to convey clearly the single message that the product featured is an exceptional value and, in this way, to prompt customers to consider replenishing their home stock of the item. End displays should be restocked regularly (ensuring that the number of facings remains sufficient to stimulate sales) and changed periodically to ensure that they do not lose their impact on consumers.

DUMP BINS

Dump bins are an inexpensive, versatile, and easy way of generating sales for promotional merchandise. Repositioning dump bins can give the store a new look and draw customers into its various departments.

If the bin is transparent, some of the product packages should be used to line the sides and the remaining stock can be dumped into the centre. Another tip is to avoid putting a variety of products into a dump bin – no more than two different products (or, where applicable, two different colours or flavours) should be used, and preferably only one. Similarly, if two products are used, try to establish one price for both: confusion arises if there are several prices. When stock has been reduced and there is not enough to fill the bin, a false bottom can give the appearance of fullness. Dump bins should carry the same product for only a week or so. Bins are particularly useful for impulse, seasonal, or trendy items, but they should not be used to sell off damaged merchandise or products that could break or leak.

IMPULSE PURCHASE AREAS

Impulse items are normally located at or near the check-out counter where traffic flow is high and people have time to browse while waiting, cash in hand, to pay for their purchases. We have all seen the racks with candy bars and gum, batteries, or sunglasses. Other products, such as photo supplies, magazines, trial sizes of health and beauty aids, novelties, pens, and seasonal items, are also sometimes featured. Both counter units and free-standing units near the check-out counter are generally used for the display of impulse items.

SEASONAL ITEMS

Most pharmacies reserve a high-traffic aisle in the store for seasonal promotions, and rotate the product groups displayed there throughout the year. Seasonal promotional displays should be fully stocked and kept up to date. All seasonal merchandise should be introduced at the same time in one massive display that appears overnight and stays in place until the occasion for the display has passed. Treating a seasonal display as a new event in the store is much more effective than gradually building up partial displays as stock comes in. Additional displays of related merchandise (for example, gift items and boxed chocolates during the Christmas promotion) should appear close to the main seasonal aisle where they will be noticed by the customer. It is wise to introduce seasonal items well in advance of the onset of the season, as many people shop early while selection is good or want time to make price comparisons before purchasing. A pharmacy whose full seasonal display is not up early will undoubtedly suffer losses in sales.

The progress of each seasonal promotion should be recorded in terms of changes in stock levels over time and total sales of each item, so that a plan for the next year can be prepared immediately upon the display's removal.

SIGNS

Signs are one of the most important sources of information about products in the store. People immediately look for information on prices, specials, and the location of particular products. The easier it is for the customer to find products, learn their prices, and determine how much of a bargain they are getting, the more likely they will be to make a purchase. Signs can be used in an effective way that will generate sales. They should be brief, simply worded, and clearly printed, using a consistent style throughout the store. Prices should always appear in the largest characters to draw people to good values. The key element to remember is to use signs and to use them freely.

End units need signs, as they are separated from the regular product area and the consumer's attention must be drawn to them. The kinds of products in the display, the reason they are being displayed, and their price should be clearly identified. Floor displays also require signs. In this case, the signs must be legible from all directions and, if possible, visible through the front windows to attract people into the store. Because the floor displays are quite large, correspondingly large signs should be used. Bin displays require signs to ensure clarity as to the products inside and their prices. When the bin contains more than one product, it is important for the sign to be clear and specific about the contents.

SUMMARY

The marketing of the consumer products found in a pharmacy calls for anticipating and meeting the needs of the public. This entails keeping abreast of new products and the changing demands of consumers. Hence, pharmacy owners and managers must learn the principles of environmental scanning and market research. Analyzing and meeting the special needs of selected consumer groups is also a critical tool, known as market segmentation.

Marketing information is essential to pharmacists in managing their stores. It is becoming increasingly important for pharmacists to establish market research programs that will keep them in touch with the attitudes, needs, or complaints of their customers. These can be informal systems or more formal methods of data collection. Questionnaires are now being used more frequently by pharmacies to collect market information.

A pharmacy's marketing plan should take into account the competition, ways of attracting customers, product lines to be carried, and the image of the store that is to be projected. It should set out the responsibilities and duties of staff members in accomplishing the stated objectives. Control procedures that trigger corrective action when objectives are not being met should also be established.

A key component of marketing is merchandising, which refers to the assembly, promotion, and presentation of products in a visually appealing way. Merchandising guidelines should include variety, price and quality, brands, turnover, gross margin, and inventory balance. Decisions relating to these factors will combine to create a particular image for the pharmacy.

Merchandising is sometimes defined as visual selling, in recognition of the power of visual impact in promoting sales. Product display is consequently a central concern in merchandising. Pharmacists can increase sales and profitability in their stores by observing certain proven principles for effective stock presentation. Some of the factors influencing product display are visual balance, facings, and space allocation according to a product's sales potential and profitability. These factors inform the design of planograms, which are an invaluable aid to pharmacy owners in achieving effective stock presentation. Equally important in stimulating sales is the creative use of promotional displays and signage throughout the pharmacy.

RECOMMENDED READING:

Aaker, David A., and Myers, John G. *Advertising Management*. 3rd ed. New York: Prentice-Hall, 1987.

Archambault, A., and Segal, H. *Merchandising. Pharmacy Management Program, Module 3*. Kirkland, Que.: Nordic Laboratories Inc., n.d.

Arnold, Danny R.; Capella, Louis M.; and Smith, Garry D. *Strategic Retail Management*. Toronto: Addison-Wesley Publishing Co., 1983.

Breen, G.E. *Do-It-Yourself Marketing Research*. Toronto: McGraw-Hill Ryerson, 1977.

Coleman, Thomas E. *Modern Drug Store Merchandising*. Chain Store Age Books, 1975.

————. *Retail Drug Store Management and Control*. New York: Friedman Books, 1978.

Coté, Bob. "How to Buy Advertising Space." *Drug Merchandising* 67, no. 11 (November 1986): 12.

————. "How to Get the Most for Your Broadcast Dollar." *Drug Merchandising* 67, no. 12 (December 1986): 54–55.

————. "Opportunity Knocks: Prepare Your Marketing Plan." *Drug Merchandising* 67, no. 7 (July 1986): 14.

————. "What to Shoot for in Your Advertising Plan." *Drug Merchandising* 67, no. 8 (August 1986): 20.

————. "Which Medium for Ads? Pros and Cons of Each." *Drug Merchandising* 67, no. 10 (October 1986): 36.

Davidson, W.R., Bates, A.D., and Bass, S.J. "The Retail Life Cycle." *Harvard Business Review* (Nov.–Dec. 1976), p. 89.

Effective Pharmacy Management. 4th ed. Kansas City, Mo.: Marion Laboratories, Inc., 1987.

Guide to Good Pharmacy Management. Series of booklets published by Hoffman-La Roche, Vaudreuil, Quebec, 1978. See *Merchandising* and *Advertising*.

Haltje, Bert, and Book, James Peter. *How to Be Your Own Advertising Agency*. New York: McGraw-Hill, 1981.

Hawkins, Del I.; Coney, Kenneth A.; and Best, Roger J. *Consumer Behavior*. Dalles, Texas: Business Publications, Inc., 1980.

McCarthy, Jerome E., and Shapiro, Stanley J. *Basic Marketing*. 1st Cdn. ed. Georgetown, Ont.: Irwin-Dorsey, 1975.

Weilbacher, William M. *Advertising*. New York: Macmillan Publishing Co., 1979.

16

PRICING

The product mix in a pharmacy includes three distinct types of products: prescription drugs, non-prescription drugs, and non-drug products. The range and type of service provided with the sale of each of these product categories differs. Because of this, and because pharmacists are educated to make professional judgments in the sale of pharmaceutical products, methods of pricing for these product categories should be different.

Non-drug products, for example, are offered for sale in a wide variety of outlets, consumers are familiar with them, and little or no service is required in their sale. As a result, their selling price is determined by calculating a percentage of their cost and adding this amount (the markup) to the cost to arrive at a retail price. The percentage used may vary depending on competition, volume sold, and the retailer's pricing strategy.

Non-prescription drug products have traditionally been priced in a similar fashion. In this instance, however, the involvement of a pharmacist may occur, either at the customer's or the pharmacist's instigation. An example to consider is that of the diabetic looking for a cough syrup. The pharmacist must first determine that the person is diabetic and then recommend an appropriate (sugarless) product. Even though the product is priced on the basis of its cost, the percentage added to represent the difference between the product's cost and its selling price should be higher to reflect the cost of services provided.

Prescription products highlight the uniqueness of pharmacy as a business. These products cannot be sold in the same way as ordinary merchandise, because the consumer must be advised on the proper way to consume or use them. Hence, pharmaceutical services, based on professional judgment, are involved. As a result, the final price of a prescription product must reflect the cost of the product plus a separate charge for this specialized and individualized service. A professional fee is the method of choice.

Although pharmacies carry the three distinct product categories that we have just described, our discussion in this chapter shall narrow them down to two – non-prescription merchandise (including drug and non-drug products) and prescription drugs. This will enable us to analyze the two main approaches to pricing – the first using a percentage markup and the second, the application of a professional fee.

PRICING NON-PRESCRIPTION PRODUCTS

The value of any product or service is its "exchange value" in the marketplace. In other words, it is only worth what someone is willing to pay for it at a given point in time. Hence, its price is its exchange value.

Individual preferences determine how much utility or gratification is represented by a specific product or service. Thus, consumers are faced with decisions as to what and how much to purchase. The price system helps them decide in that it influences the way in which they will disperse a fixed amount of money among an almost limitless number of products and services.

Consumers attempt to maximize the value of their purchases and merchants attempt to set prices that will attract buyers. Price, then, becomes an important component of overall marketing strategy and results in a firm's ability to generate sales and earn a profit.

Pricing Objectives

Pricing objectives can serve many purposes. For example, some firms will place a very high price on a new or innovative product for one or more of the following reasons: (1) because they believe this invests the product with value in the mind of the consumer; (2) to recoup research and development costs as soon as possible; (3) to take advantage of market exclusivity before competitors bring out a similar product; and (4) simply to maximize profits.

Other firms are committed to very low pricing. This, too, creates a certain image, attracts customers, increases the volume of products sold, and deters competitors from entering the marketplace.

Both of these approaches, with their different effects but similar objectives, are employed in the pharmaceutical industry and, perhaps to a lesser degree, in community practice. Different consumers have different expectations with regard to value, which translate into a willingness to purchase products only at what they think are appropriate prices. Pricing policies, therefore, must strive to find an equilibrium between a pharmacy's price levels and its consumers' expectations and perceptions of value at those prices.

Pricing Policies

There are a number of pricing policies available to the pharmacy owner or manager, which tend to be classified in the following general categories: market-oriented pricing; discount pricing, which includes leader and loss-leader pricing; and traditional pricing, including markup on cost and gross-margin pricing.

Market-oriented pricing is most often applied to general pharmacy merchandise, that is, to products that can be purchased at most pharmacies. This type of pricing occurs in a competitive environment and is accepted, and even expected, by consumers. A market-oriented policy can involve setting the price on a product at, below, or above the prevailing market price.

The approach that prices products at the market-price level serves to retain, but not necessarily to increase, market share and may be applied to items such as cough syrups or certain analgesics, which are used by consumers regularly and are purchased as needed. Price reductions on such products would serve little purpose, as most pharmacies sell identical items at similar prices and consumers are unlikely to go out of their way to find bargains on them.

Pricing below market levels constitutes a discount policy and is used to attract traffic and increase sales. Competing outlets are likely to monitor prices in the market and may be forced to follow suit when they discover that discount prices are being offered elsewhere. Therefore, this type of pricing policy is most effective when implemented at random times on different categories of merchandise, for example, by holding theme sales. Health and beauty aids are typical examples of goods that are priced below market at random times. This approach has the advantage of drawing customers into the store because they know that they can occasionally obtain items at less-than-regular prices; it also stimulates impulse buying and may increase sales of selected items. The risk involved is that below-market pricing can create an unwanted discount-pharmacy image; consideration should therefore be given to the frequency and manner in which this approach is used.

Above-market pricing is used when it is unlikely that customers will shop elsewhere for the products sold or where service is required in the sale of the goods. Above-market pricing policies are most likely to be found in pharmacies that carry home health-care supplies, provide delivery service, or have extended store hours.

The main objective of discount pricing is to achieve a greater volume of sales – either in units sold or dollars generated or both. There are several variants of discount pricing. Leader pricing is meant to create an image of an innovative, aggressive retail store that is a "leader" in setting competitive prices. It attempts to attract new customers as well as to retain regulars. Customer interest is maintained by using the strategy on weekends or holidays, promoting them as special sale days. Items for the sales must be selected carefully to suit the particular theme of the sale and the pharmacy must be able to purchase the merchandise in appropriate quantities at appropriate prices. An extension of leader pricing is loss-leader pricing, where certain products are priced *below cost* for an aggressive merchandising policy. This approach is intended to attract customers in large numbers, diminish stock levels of selected items, and discourage competition.

A continuous application of leader and loss-leader pricing will lead to the perception that the store is a discounter. Such pricing policies result in low-margin retailing and a dependence on high turnover and large sales volumes. Caution must be exercised to avoid creating the wrong impression in customers' minds: they may come to expect the so-called discount prices to extend to the dispensary for prescription drugs as well, if they perceive the operation to be a "discount drug store." If the two major departments of the pharmacy (the front shop and the dispensary) do not have compatible pricing policies, customers may simply decide to shop in the front store for the bargains and take their prescriptions elsewhere. Therefore, the pharmacy must attempt to communicate to the public the important relationship between price and value with regard to prescription products in order to retain their loyalty and continued patronage.

Pharmacies generally adopt a one-price policy for all consumers. This is reflected by the fact that a price sticker displaying a retail price appears on each item in the store. In some instances, however, special prices may be offered to identified individuals or groups. For example, employees and certain groups of customers, such as senior citizens, may be given the privilege of purchasing items at special discounts.

Traditional or routine methods of pricing refer to the traditional practice among pharmacies of applying markups on the cost of goods. Two variants of the traditional method – gross-margin pricing and markup on cost – are practised. Traditional pricing methods generally result in prices that are consistent with market levels, and, if they fail to generate sales at expected rates, may be combined with a selective use of discount policies in order to stimulate business.

Gross-margin pricing has routinely been adopted by pharmacies. The cost of an item is taken as the base to which a markup value, calculated as *a percentage of the selling price*, is added, in order to obtain a desired *gross margin*. Hence, if the cost of an item is one dollar and the desired gross margin is 30 percent, the following formula would provide the appropriate selling price:

$$\text{Cost price } + 30\% \text{ of Selling price } = \text{Selling price}$$
$$\$1 + .30x = x$$
$$x = \$1.43.$$

By definition, the gross margin is the difference between the selling or retail price and the cost of the item; in our example, then, the gross margin is 43 cents, or 30 percent of the retail price. (It should be noted here that, in practice, gross margins are generally set for product lines rather than individual products; for example, an average 30 percent margin might be required on the various sizes and formats of a particular brand of toothpaste.)

A markup may also be expressed as *a percentage of the cost price* and is hence referred to as a "markup on cost." In our example, the markup on cost is 43 percent. As you can see, there is an important difference between a markup based on retail price and a markup based on cost price. The two should not be confused. There is of course a relationship between them as well. Let us illustrate this with a second example.

If a particular bar of soap cost the pharmacy $1.00 and the supplier's catalogue suggested it sell for $1.50, the gross margin is $0.50 – the difference between the selling price and the cost. In terms of a percentage markup, this $0.50 is (0.50 ÷ 1.00) × 100 = 50% of cost or (0.50 ÷ 1.50) × 100 = 33.3% of the retail price. Table 16.1 develops this principle for selected values.

Table 16.1.   MARKUP CONVERSION VALUES AND RETAIL PRICE

Percentage Markup on Cost	Percentage Markup on Retail (Gross margin %)	Retail Price Using $1.00 as Cost
5.3%	5.0%	$1.05
11.1	10.0	1.10
14.9	13.0	1.15
17.7	15.0	1.18
19.9	16.6	1.20
25.0	20.0	1.25
33.3	25.0	1.33
50.0	33.3	1.50
66.6	40.0	1.67
100.0	50.0	2.00

The conversion from a cost base to a retail base and vice versa is facilitated by the following formulae:

$$\text{Markup on cost} = \frac{\text{Markup \% on retail}}{100\% - \text{Markup \% on retail}}$$

$$\text{Markup on retail} = \frac{\text{Markup \% on cost}}{100\% - \text{Markup \% on cost}}$$

An adaptation of gross-margin pricing is a sliding gross-margin policy. In this approach, a higher markup is applied to low-cost items and a lower markup to higher-cost items. This is usually done to achieve a reasonable approach to pricing: it serves to minimize the inequity that results from an "across-the-board" markup on all items.

Considerations in Cost-Based Pricing

As can be seen, price-setting is not a simple matter. Most retailers have now adopted cost-based pricing, as opposed to market-oriented or discount pricing, in order to ensure at least that product costs are recouped. Historically, manufacturers set the retail prices on their products and specified discounts to wholesalers and to retailers (known as trade discounts). The discounts represented payment for services provided in the distribution channels and in selling the products to the public. They were expressed as percentages of the retail price. Increased competition led to the decline of this system, as prices charged from store to store varied widely and the suggested retail price became meaningless. Also, when retail chains began to buy in bulk, the relationship between cost price and suggested selling price became less important. However, the principle of using percentages in pricing survived.

In many cases today, the only known values are the product cost and the retailer's required gross-margin percentage, which explains the importance of the data in Table 16.1. The process of establishing a price based on cost involves totalling all costs associated with an item offered for sale. Among these costs are the product cost itself, the freight cost, allowances for advertising, and the cost of labour involved in getting the product to the shelf and maintaining it. In many cases, although they no longer set the retail price on products, manufacturers (and wholesalers) still provide a *suggested* retail price, which can serve as a guide to the retailer and provide a level from which to discount. In addition, because suggested retail prices take into account the cost of the item to the retailer, they are also useful in suggesting both a gross margin amount and a markup figure.

If a product does not come with a suggested retail price and the pharmacist-manager wishes to establish a markup (or verify the markup where a suggested retail price *is* given), the traditional formula for calculating initial markup (on retail) can be applied. It is as follows:

$$\text{initial markup percentage} = \frac{[(\text{expenses} + \text{profit}) - \text{cash discounts from suppliers}] + (\text{markdowns} + \text{stock shortages} + \text{employee discounts} + \text{customer discounts})}{\text{net sales} + (\text{markdowns} + \text{stock shortages} + \text{employee discounts} + \text{customer discounts})}$$

Note, however, that:

1. expenses + profit = gross margin;
2. markdowns (i.e., any price reductions for the purpose of stimulating sales) + stock shortages (due to theft, breakage, or unsaleable items) + employee and customer discounts = reductions;
3. gross margin – cash discounts from suppliers = maintained markup.

Therefore:

$$\text{initial markup percentage} = \frac{\text{maintained markup} + \text{reductions}}{\text{net sales} + \text{reductions}}$$

The value of calculating an initial markup percentage is evident, for example, when a pharmacy owner or manager is planning to carry a new line of products. The planning procedure should involve the following steps:

1. Establish a sales goal for the new line over a specified period of time, for example, $20,000 in one year.
2. Calculate the expenses to reach this goal. They will include fixtures and a portion of staff salary and overhead for a cost of, say, $5000.
3. Estimate the retail reductions such as markdowns, employee discounts, and customer discounts. Let us say these total $1000.
4. Set a profit goal, for example, six percent of sales, or $1200.
5. Account for cash discounts on purchases, at, say, $500.

Remember that:

gross margin = expenses + profit: $5000 + $1200 = $6200
reductions = markdowns + stock shortages + employee and customer discounts: $1000
maintained markup = gross margin − cash discounts: $6200 − $500 = $5700.

Therefore, in order to meet the obligations of the business and earn a six percent profit, the initial markup on this new line of products must be:

$$\frac{\text{initial markup}}{\text{percentage}} = \frac{\text{maintained markup} + \text{reductions}}{\text{net sales} + \text{reductions}}$$
$$= \frac{\$5700 + \$1000}{\$20,000 + \$1000}$$
$$= 31.9\%.$$

Cash discounts from suppliers must be subtracted from gross margin because "cash-discount" dollars, earned as a result of the business's ability to pay its invoices on time, reduce the cost of the goods. If included, it would mean that they were in effect being counted twice, because the cost of the merchandise would be artificially inflated by the value of the discount taken and any markup calculated on cost would be increased as well.

Reductions must be added back because they represent discounts from the proposed retail price. If they are not added back, the resulting gross margin or markup based on retail price will be smaller, resulting in a lower markup on cost also. Reductions are included in both the numerator and denominator to increase both elements of the equation relatively, in order that reductions will not affect the initial markup percent abnormally.

This formula may not be widely used in community pharmacies because individual departments are often not sufficiently well defined in terms of allocation of overhead costs. The value of the formula is in its ability to define costs better and allow judgmental pricing decisions to be made when there is cause to deviate from full-margin pricing.

Importance of Cost Recovery in Pricing

All prices calculated at a full gross margin must cover the cost of the item plus expenses and profit, as follows:

1. direct expenses incurred in operating the business (labour costs)
2. indirect expenses incurred in operating the business (overhead costs)
3. reductions in inventory (shrinkage) or reduction of markups (discounts)
4. anticipated profit or return on investment
5. the actual cost of the item

By calculating a correct retail price, the pharmacy owner will be able to recover these costs and expenses and earn the desired profit upon selling the merchandise. The only cost that is known with some certainty is the actual cost of the merchandise. The other costs must be determined as accurately as possible and reflected in the final price charged. Anything less will not ensure the recovery of all operating or overhead costs, let alone the anticipated profit.

PRESCRIPTION PRICE DETERMINATION: A COST-RECOVERY MODEL[1]

Historic Approaches to Prescription Pricing

The community pharmacist is both a health-care professional and a businessperson. Because of the dichotomy of the role, there is a persistent dilemma in determining an adequate and reasonable remuneration for a pharmacist.

Traditionally, pharmacists have been identified with a product – prescription medication. Deriving revenue was therefore a simple matter, since it was tied directly to the product. Indeed, the revenue collected represented a portion for the cost of the product and a portion for overhead expense that included professional income and profit.

Over the years, the mechanisms used to determine prescription prices have been erratic. In the United States, for example, drug catalogues were in circulation as early as the 1760s, but the prices of products were not listed until 1828.[2]

The 1828 catalogue that published prices was the result of three years of deliberations by several committees and bore the name "Catalogue of the Materia Medica and of the Pharmaceutical Preparations with the Uniform Prices of the Massachusetts College of Pharmacy." This catalogue represents the first known attempt in North America to establish a uniform dispensing fee for prescription drugs on the basis of agreement by an association of pharmacists. This fee was to be charged in addition to the cost of ingredients.

Pharmacists were fairly quiet about their fees until 1908, at which time the National Association of Retail Druggists, aided by F.W. Nitardy, published a "Prescription Pricing Schedule," which "called for a charge for the ingredients plus a charge equal to the cost of the ingredients."[3] It was believed at the time that, by doubling the cost of ingredients for an average prescription, enough revenue would be derived to cover the cost of maintaining the prescription department, the pharmacist's salary, and a profit consistent with "respectability."

---

[1] This discussion is adapted from "Prescription Pricing: Financial Considerations," an invited paper by H.J. Segal, presented before the Annual Meeting of the Association of Faculties of Pharmacy Research Symposium, Halifax, Nova Scotia, 27 May 1985.

[2] G. Griffenhagen, "Fair Trade in 1828," *Journal of the American Pharmaceutical Association* (Practical Pharmacy Edition) 20, no.3 (March 1959): 156.

[3] F.W. Nitardy, "Prescription Pricing Schedule," *NARD Notes* 6 (30 July 1908): 17.

Two basic concepts emerged from this first organized approach to pricing: (1) that a prescription was an article of merchandise and (2) that it was to be priced relative to its cost. It appears that this philosophy sparked further investigation and other methods of determining prescription prices. Both McEvilla[4] and Myers[5] have examined the historical beginnings of prescription pricing, tracing its evolution from a markup system to one of calculating a dispensing fee.

The major change in philosophy occurred in the early 1950s. As pharmacists became more sophisticated in their practice, moving from the compounding of prescriptions to the use of an ever-increasing range of manufactured dosage forms, the methods used to price prescriptions started to reflect this change. Professor Swinyard of the University of Utah developed the "computation system," which involved calculating the price of each prescription "on the basis of the cost of material and the time required for filling."[6] The system was considered to be exact and fair, but it proved to have a disadvantage in that individual pharmacists did not dispense prescriptions at a uniform pace. With standardized dispensing times, the method became one of computing cost plus a flat rate for dispensing. The flat rates were simply taken from a predetermined list based on the quantity and type of preparation dispensed.

The computation system was significant for recognizing the different cost factors involved in prescription-price determination. Swinyard identified these as the cost of material, container, and service fee. Thus, each pharmacy could set its own fee on the basis of its overhead, salary expense, and "professional skill rendered [to] the patient."

A further refinement was described by Fuller in 1957 in a report on prescription pricing methods.[7] Most of the methods examined added a fixed gross margin to the cost of ingredients, then added in the cost of a container. To arrive at a final price, a dispensing fee was also added. Fuller observed at the time that this method was unsound from a cost-accounting perspective.

At about the same time, Professor S.B. Jeffries of the Brooklyn College of Pharmacy identified the cost factors involved in pricing a prescription as the costs of the ingredients, the container, labour, and overhead. Jeffries defined the first three of these as variable costs and the last as a fixed cost (fixed, at least, for a certain period of time). A dispensing fee was added to these four costs.

[4] J.D. McEvilla, "Pharmacy and the Professional Fee in Theory and Practice," *Journal of the American Pharmaceutical Association* NS2, no. 9 (September 1962): 520.

[5] M.J. Myers, "Professional Fee: Renaissance or Innovation?" *Journal of the American Pharmaceutical Association* NS8, no. 12 (December 1968): 628.

[6] "Rx Pricing by Computation Plus Flat Rate Favoured by Educator," *Drug Topics*, 2 January 1950.

[7] H.J. Fuller, "Prescription Pricing Methods," *Canadian Pharmaceutical Journal* 90, no. 2. (February 1957): 42.

The problem with such pricing methods was the determination of the cost of overhead. Fuller handled this by defining overhead as all expenses related to the pharmacy department (excluding materials and labour for a specified period of time. He suggested dividing this total overhead amount by the total number of prescription transactions to arrive at a standard overhead cost per transaction. This approach is reasonable, since, in the long run, *all* costs must be recovered before any profit can be made. To accurately determine the dispensary's total overhead, however, the pharmacy's financial record keeping must be organized in such a way that a proper and valid allocation of the store's overhead costs is made to the prescription department. Today, with computerization of both the front store and dispensary, this undertaking is perhaps more likely to produce accurate results than could be obtained in the late 1950s.

What set Fuller's method apart from the others was his philosophy for using a professional, or dispensing, fee. He articulated it as follows:

1. A prescription is not an article of trade, capable of being bought and sold by anyone.
2. The services rendered by the pharmacist in dispensing and/or compounding a prescription are of a professional nature, requiring specialized knowledge and judgment and, therefore, the reward he gets for these services is a fee.
3. The professional services rendered by the pharmacist are not, and never have been, a function of the cost of ingredients used.[8]

In 1962, Abrams distilled this approach to dispensing-fee determination when he indicated that

the utilization of a percentage markup is an admission that the final price of a prescription is a function of the cost of the product. It is not and should not be. The ultimate consumer fee should be, in all fairness, related to the professional services rendered and the costs involved in making these services available.[9]

He further pointed out that, calculated properly, the fee is designed to meet all operating expenses and provide a reasonable return to the pharmacist. Therefore, each prescription, regardless of its ingredient cost, would (1) bear the same charge for the professional services rendered; (2) be based on each individual pharmacist's actual costs; and (3) probably be competitive within most communities.

[8] H.J. Fuller, "The New Philosophy of Professional Fees," *American Professional Pharmacist* 26, no. 8 (August 1960): 503.
[9] R.E. Abrams, *Focus on Pharmacy, 1962* (Detroit: Wayne State University, College of Pharmacy, March 1962).

In an attempt to standardize a procedure to identify a standard fee per prescription, Abrams put forward the following formula:

$$\frac{\left(\begin{array}{c} \text{Prescription sales} \\ \text{as a \% of total sales} \end{array} \times \begin{array}{c} \text{Total pharmacy expenses} \\ \text{[excluding proprietor's salary]} \end{array}\right) + \begin{array}{c} \text{Proprietor's} \\ \text{salary} \end{array}}{\text{Number of prescriptions dispensed in the year}}$$

This was the first attempt at standardizing the method of allocating expenses to the prescription department. This method, by first taking out the proprietor's (i.e., the pharmacist-owner's) salary and then adding it back in, is sound only if the ratio of escription sales to total sales is very high. If this ratio is low, the cost of dispensing calculated in this manner will be disproportionately high, as the costs are spread over a relatively low number of prescriptions. Therefore, Fuller modified Abram's formula by not adding back the proprietor's salary, but, in its place, adding a direct labour charge, which he originally set at $0.50 per transaction plus an arbitrary amount for net profit. (Abrams later added an amount for net profit to his formula as well). Thus, the Fuller Formula is:

$$\frac{\left(\begin{array}{c} \text{Prescription} \\ \text{sales as a \%} \\ \text{of total sales} \end{array} \times \begin{array}{c} \text{Total expenses} \\ \text{[excluding} \\ \text{proprietor's salary]} \end{array}\right) + \begin{array}{c} \text{Direct} \\ \text{Labour} \\ \text{Cost} \end{array} + \begin{array}{c} \text{Net} \\ \text{Profit} \end{array}}{\text{Number of prescriptions dispensed in the year}}$$

If similar data are applied to each formula, the resulting fee is somewhat different. Nevertheless, the value of these formulae is in the breakthrough in thinking that they represent and in the fact that they establish useful criteria for the calculation of a professional fee that does not take into account the cost of ingredients. They also made the important contribution of recognizing that overhead costs should be distributed equally over all prescriptions dispensed. The use of a standard overhead cost per transaction is supported by the fact that, on average,

1. the time it takes to dispense each prescription is almost equal;
2. the service provided with each prescription is almost equal;
3. the responsibility assumed for dispensing each prescription is equal;
4. the liability assumed for dispensing each prescription is equal.

The flaw in Fuller's approach is in the arbitrariness with which the labour cost and the amount for net profit are assigned in his formula. These values can in fact be calculated to reflect the actual costs of labour and a legitimate return on investment. In calculating dispensing fees, there must be a recognition of the costs involved in stocking a basic inventory of prescription medication and of the expense of a pharmacist's salary, which is incurred throughout the time the pharmacy is open – whether prescriptions are being dispensed or not. The model that is described in the following section addresses these issues.

Dispensing-Cost Identification

As private and government insurance carriers became involved in paying claims on behalf of their subscribers, pressures to restrain prescription prices grew. The PARCOST (Prescriptions at Reasonable Cost) Program in Ontario was based in part on setting maximum professional (or dispensing) fees while allowing individual pharmacies to charge less than the negotiated maximum if they so wished.[10] It thus became critical for pharmacists to be able to accurately determine and document their dispensing costs, if only to verify that the maximum allowable fees under the program would compensate them adequately. In April 1971, the Ontario Pharmacists' Association (OPA) circulated an information letter explaining how to calculate the direct and indirect costs of dispensing, and enclosed a special form for the purpose. To a large extent, the OPA's recommended method of calculation in itself legitimized the fact that the dispensing function could be broken down into fixed (direct) and variable (indirect) costs and that these costs would be different for each pharmacy operation.

The calculations in the model proposed by the OPA are made by isolating the cost factors in the dispensing function, then assigning costs to them as shown in Figure 16.2 (based on the amounts in the income statement in Figure 16.1). This cost-recovery model also includes a cost factor to allow for a return on investment in prescription-drug inventory, under the category "opportunity cost."

Professional labour cost is a cost directly attributable to the dispensing function. It includes a pharmacist's salary for each hour the pharmacy is open. In our example in Figure 16.2, the pharmacy is open 74 hours per week and employs one full-time pharmacist (40 hours per week), in addition to the pharmacist-owner. The pharmacist's hourly rate is as follows:

$$\frac{\$46,197}{40 \text{ hours} \times 52 \text{ weeks}} = \$22.21 \text{ per hour,}$$

for a total pharmacist's salary cost of 74 hours × 52 weeks × $22.21 = $85,464 (as represented in Figure 16.2 by the pharmacist's full salary and a portion of the pharmacist-owner's – $46,197 + $39,267). Also to be included are the labour costs connected with any additional personnel

[10] H.J. Segal, "PARCOST: Its Origins, Mechanics, and Impact," *Medical Marketing and Media* 8, no. 8 (August 1973): 11.

Figure 16.1
Income Statement
Hypothetical Pharmacy Limited

Sales		$1,302,190
Prescription	$562,805	
Other	739,385	
Cost of Goods Sold		915,139
Gross Margin		387,051
Expenses		
Pharmacist-owner's salary	$ 66,985★	
Pharmacist's salary	46,197	
Other salaries (including pharmacy assistant)	74,342	
Rent	30,150	
Heat, light, power	5,725	
Accounting, legal, professional fees	5,516	
Taxes and licences	5,505	
Insurance	3,544	
Interest paid	7,805	
Repairs	5,041	
Delivery	4,951	
Advertising	15,303	
Depreciation	9,947	
Bad debts	602	
Telephone	3,109	
Miscellaneous	39,749	
Total expenses		324,471
Profit (before tax)		$ 62,580

Other Pertinent Information
    Total number of prescriptions dispensed annually: (approximately
                                                             36,638   100/day)

Hours open per week: Mon.-Fri. $- 5 \times 12 = 60$
                         Sat. $- 1 \times 9 = 9$
                        Sun. $- 1 \times 5 = 5$
                                     74

    Total hours worked per week by
    pharmacist-owner: 50
    Prescription inventory value: $50,500

★ The pharmacist-owner's salary breaks down as follows: $39,267 (as pharmacist) + $27,718 (as manager, 43.2% or $11,974 of which is attributable to the dispensary).

working in the pharmacy department on a full-time or part-time basis. In our example, one pharmacy assistant is employed. The other direct costs that apply are for the labels, containers, and forms that are required in the dispensing process.

The operational costs of the pharmacy department – the indirect costs – are represented by that portion of the pharmacy's total expenses (excluding salaries) that is attributable to the dispensary. As we saw in Chapter 12, the most appropriate way to allocate occupancy costs is on the basis of the relationship of prescription sales to total sales. Although certain other expenses should be allocated either according to different criteria (eg., relative net investment) or entirely to the dispensary (eg., professional licences, professional liability insurance), we have based the allocation of operational costs in our example exclusively on relative sales, for the sake of convenience.[11] Therefore, since prescription sales in our example represent 43.2 percent of total sales, we have calculated the operational costs of the pharmacy department at 43.2 percent of total pharmacy costs.

The calculation of indirect costs for the purpose of professional-fee calculation should be a simple matter for pharmacy owners who insist that monthly financial reports reflect the activities of the front shop and dispensary separately, as recommended in Chapter 12.

Opportunity costs are the dollar costs involved in maintaining an inventory of prescription drugs, viewed as a return for risk on invested capital. In other words, if these dollars were not invested in prescription inventory, they could be invested elsewhere to earn a return commensurate with the risk; the opportunity cost factor in the model compensates for that forgone return. (Another way to interpret opportunity cost is as profit. Contrary to popular belief, businesspeople are not *entitled* to a profit; profit is rather the financial reward for effective management of resources or assets. This return on investment, then, is justified on the basis of capital invested at risk and of efficient management of that investment.) The rate is arbitrary, but it must be in line with alternative opportunities for return on investment in the marketplace, modified to reflect the greater risk associated with investment in a business enterprise. We have chosen a rate of 30 percent in our example, which is considered an acceptable rate of return for the risk of investment in prescription inventory among community pharmacies at present.

The general and administrative costs of the pharmacy department consist of the management time invested in administering this area. For example, a typical pharmacy usually employs two pharmacists, an employer or manager (often the pharmacist-owner) and an employee or staff pharmacist. During the week, the manager or owner divides his or

---

[11] Review the discussion in Chapter 12 on allocation of expenses (wages, occupancy costs, and other expenses).

Figure 16.2.
COST-RECOVERY MODEL PROFESSIONAL-FEE CALCULATION

	Costs	Percentage of Total Costs
1. Professional Labour Cost (Direct Cost)		
Pharmacist:		
$22.21/hr × 40 hrs × 52 wks =	$ 46,197	
Pharmacist-owner:		
$22.21/hr × (74 − 40 = 34 hrs) × 52 wks =	39,267	
Pharmacy assistant:		
$12/hr × 40 hrs × 52 wks =	24,960	
Labels, containers, etc.: $0.20 × 36, 638 =	7,328	
Total Direct Cost	$117,752	57.7%

2. Operational Costs of Pharmacy Department (indirect Costs)

Rent	$ 30,150	
Heat, light, power	5,725	
Accounting, legal, professional fees	5,516	
Taxes and licences	5,505	
Insurance	3,544	
Interest paid	7,805	
Repairs	5,041	
Delivery	4,951	
Advertising	15,303	
Depreciation	9,947	
Bad debts	602	
Telephone	3,109	
Miscellaneous	39,749	
	$136,947	

	Costs	Percentage
Total Indirect Cost ($136,947 × 43.2%)	$ 59,161	29.0%

3. Opportunity Cost

	Costs	Percentage
Prescription inventory $50,500 × 30% =	15,150	7.4%

4. General and Administrative Cost of Pharmacy Department
(43.2% of the portion of proprietor's salary earned as a manager)

$$(1.5 \times \$22.21/\text{hr}) \times (50 - 34 = 16 \text{ hrs}) \times 52 \text{ wks} \times 43.2\%$$
$$\underline{11,974} \quad \underline{5.9\%}$$

5. Total Costs (1. + 2. + 3. + 4.) $\underline{\$204,037}$ $\underline{100.0\%}$

6. Cost to Dispense One Prescription

$$\frac{\text{Total Costs}}{\substack{\text{Number of} \\ \text{Prescriptions Dispensed}}} = \frac{\$204,037}{36,638} = \$5.57, \text{ rounded to } \$5.60$$

her time between dispensing and administrative or management tasks. It is this latter function that represents the base from which the pharmacy department's general and administrative cost is calculated. To be fair, only that portion of the manager's salary attributable to dispensary administration can be charged to this category. This portion can be calculated either on the basis of time or as a proportion of prescription sales to total sales (we have followed the second option in our example). Note that the remuneration for management activities is calculated at a higher rate (150 percent of the pharmacist's rate of pay, in our example) to compensate for effective management and increased responsibility.

This general and administrative cost category may also be viewed as representing a profit, earned on the basis of efficient purchasing, inventory control, and cost control (including bulk-purchase savings, taking cash discounts on accounts payable, and collecting receivables on time, thus preventing a drain on working capital and possibly saving interest on borrowed funds.) The difference that usually exists between the actual acquisition cost of prescription inventory and "published costs" in government benefit lists and formularies is explained by the purchasing advantage that pharmacies are able to obtain from suppliers. This is one aspect of effective management that is being recognized in the general and administrative cost category. The profit represented here should certainly not be construed as a markup based on the cost of ingredients or arbitrarily added to it as an entitlement.

All the costs we have described are finally totalled to reflect the dollar amount expended in operating the dispensary for a given period of time. The fee or "burden rate" per prescription is then calculated by dividing the total costs by the number of prescriptions dispensed during the period. The result is the average cost of dispensing a prescription. This model can be applied either on the basis of historical data for purposes of financial assessment or on the basis of forecasted costs in financial planning for a future period of time.

The professional fee determined for any particular pharmacy must be reviewed periodically to ensure that it continues to reflect current costs. This can only be accomplished by recalculating the fee at regular intervals, perhaps annually or semi-annually. Possibly the most reasonable approach to fee review would be to identify a cyclical period whose end point coincides with a change in costs, for example, when employees are due for performance reviews and labour costs are anticipated to rise or when overhead costs are expected to increase because of increasing rent or utility costs.

It is also useful to monitor the proportion of each of the cost categories relative to the total fee. For example, in our professional-fee calculation of Figure 16.2, direct costs account for 57.7 percent of total costs; indirect costs account for 29.0 percent; opportunity cost, 7.4 percent; and general and administrative costs, 5.9 percent. In this way it can be demonstrated that the majority of the professional fee goes to remunerate labour (direct costs and administrative costs are 63.6 percent of the total) and overhead (29.0 percent of the total). Inventory overhead costs represent only 7.4 percent of the total.

The cost-recovery model we have just described has been subject to criticism by some pharmacists who, under agreement with their provincial government, add a markup of approximately 10 to 15 percent of the cost of ingredients in addition to the dispensing fee. These pharmacists argue that when the cost of the ingredients in a prescription are already high, the professional fee calculated using the cost-recovery model appears too small in relation to the total cost of the prescription, and must therefore represent too small a gross margin. (It should be noted that during the 1980s, the cost of prescription drugs has indeed risen rapidly, outstripping the rate of increase of overhead-cost components in the professional fee, and resulting in lower gross margins than were typical for prescription products in the past.) Another objection arises in cases where pharmacies are required to pay a percentage of their sales for rent. This percentage of sales is sometimes equal to or even greater than the percentage of the total cost of the prescription represented by the dispensing fee – again, on prescriptions whose ingredients are costly. The pharmacy in such cases is dispensing prescriptions at a loss.

These perceived problems, although they appear to be related to the cost of the ingredients in the prescription, are really not a function of the product or its cost. In the first instance, the professional fee may appear to be small in dollars, but the method by which it was calculated took into account the service, responsibility, and liability of the pharmacist and remunerated him equitably. These are not, after all, functions of the ingredient cost. Neither is the rent-related dilemma associated with ingredient cost: it is rather a problem rooted in lease negotiation and, although an important cost consideration, it should not be confused with the process of professional-fee calculation. Notwithstanding the practical financial implications for the pharmacy, the situation in which landlords in effect share in one's business must be questioned seriously, particularly from the perspective that, in pharmacy, the situation amounts to a form of profiteering from illness.

Inventory costs are taken into account in calculating a professional fee by applying the concept of return on investment. If the inventory investment – and with it the element of risk – increases, the rate of return should be increased to reflect these changes. It thus becomes critical that inventory be monitored periodically – perhaps monthly – to track increases in investment and adjust the fee accordingly.

It should be stressed that if a markup-on-cost pricing system is selected for prescriptions, the cost of the product will only be recovered if and when it is dispensed and paid for. A markup on cost makes no provision for earning a return on the inventory that remains on the shelf. The cost-recovery model, however, provides for a return on investment on the average value of prescription inventory and amortizes it equally over all prescriptions dispensed and paid for. Thus, the entire inventory generates a return.

CONCLUSION

In summary, the dispensing fee – currently more accurately referred to as the professional fee – in prescription pricing has historically been determined either as a percentage of the cost of ingredients or as a distinct entity representing the cost of the service component in dispensing. Recently, the latter approach has found favour among pharmacists, as it attempts to identify and separate the professional functions involved from the commercial ones. It also allows the pharmacist to charge all clients fairly and equally for the services that are provided and, on average, the service provided to each client is the same. Furthermore, since the professional fee is based on the total number of prescriptions dispensed, the cost of the service is amortized and passed along equally to its users. In short, each user is charged an equal fee for the accessible, convenient, and responsible pharmacy services provided by the pharmacist, who, in turn, is able to recover the costs involved in providing those services.

RECOMMENDED READING

Pricing Non-Prescription Products

Applebaum, A.H.; Beckman, M.D.; Boone, L.E.; and Kurtz, D.L. *Contemporary Canadian Business*. Toronto: Holt, Rinehart and Winston of Canada Ltd., 1984. (See Chapter 13, "Prices and Pricing Strategy.")

Davidson, W.R.; Sweeney, D.J.; and Stampfl, R.W. *Retailing Management*. 6th ed. New York: John Wiley & Sons, 1988. (See Chapter 12, "Pricing and Gross Margin Planning.")
See Chapter 5, Evanson, R.V. "Pricing Decisions for Products and Services." *Effective Pharmacy Management*. 4th ed. Kansas City, Mo.: Marion Laboratories, Inc., 1987.
Smith, H.A. *Principles and Methods of Pharmacy Management*. 3rd ed. Philadelphia: Lea and Febiger, 1986. (See Chapter 15, "Pricing and Professional Fees.")

Prescription Price Determination

Fuller, H.J. "The New Philosophy of Professional Fees." *American Professional Pharmacist* 26, no. 8 (August 1960): 503.
———. "Prescription Pricing Methods." *Canadian Pharmaceutical Journal* 90, no. 2 (February 1957): 42.
———. "What Does It Cost to Dispense a Prescription?" *Canadian Pharmaceutical Journal* 102, no. 4 (May 1969): 7.
Griffenhagen, G. "Fair Trade in 1928." *Journal of the American Pharmaceutical Association* (Practical Pharmacy Edition) 20, no. 3. (March 1959): 156.
Jacoff, M.D., and Evanson, R.W. "An Expense–Cost Analysis for Professional Fee Planning." *Journal of the American Pharmaceutical Association* NS2, no. 9 (September 1962): 525.
McEvilla, J.D. "Pharmacy and the Professional Fee in Theory and Practice." *Journal of the American Pharmaceutical Association* NS2, no. 9 (September 1962): 520.
Myers, M.J. "Professional Fee: Renaissance or Innovation?" *Journal of the American Pharmaceutical Association* NS8, no. 12 (December 1968): 628.
Nitardy, F.W. "Prescription Pricing Schedule." *NARD Notes* 6 (30 July 1908): 17.
"℞ Pricing by Computation Plus Flat Rate Favoured by Educator." *Drug Topics*, 2 January 1950.
Segal, H.J. "PARCOST : Its Origins, Mechanics, and Impact." *Medical Marketing and Media* 8 (August 1973): 11.

17

PROFESSIONAL, COMMERCIAL, AND COMMUNITY SERVICES

INTRODUCTION

Prescription drugs are unique among consumer goods in that they are purchased on the order of a physician. Furthermore, all pharmaceutical products, both prescription and non-prescription, are unlike other consumer products in the following way: it is essentially the proper or improper use of such products that will determine whether they are beneficial or detrimental to their users. From a clinical point of view, it is only through appropriate use that a pharmaceutical product, correctly prescribed and properly dispensed, will function effectively as a therapeutic drug.

In effect, just like the photographic film that is transformed into a photograph only after it has been exposed correctly, developed, and printed, the pharmaceutical product does not become an effective medicine until it has been rationally prescribed by a physician or correctly recommended by a pharmacist, dispensed in the proper manner, and consumed properly by the patient. Drawing on another analogy, the rational use of pharmaceutical products in the context of the health-care system is comparable to a chain, in which the manufacturer, the physician, the pharmacist, and the patient are the links.

Should a single link in this chain give way, pharmaceutical products, though designed to act as medications, can subtly become hazardous or even poisonous substances. Pharmacists must therefore fully assume their exclusive and essential role in the health-care system to ensure that they do not become the weak link in the chain. In order to do this, they must first recognize and respect the underlying principles of professional responsibility, then develop and establish the services they intend to provide accordingly. Despite the commercial nature of the pharmaceutical profession, the pharmacist must consider the provision of an essential group of professional services as the foundation of the practice. Then, depending on the pharmacy's location and clientele, the pharmacist can evaluate the appropriateness of providing certain of the latest professional support services or even developing new and innovative ones. Finally, as a good manager, the pharmacist will assess the benefits of offering customers certain commercial services and of becoming involved in community services.

PROFESSIONAL SERVICES

ESSENTIAL SERVICES

No society would be able to survive if its members did not pool their individual talents and resources for the common good. It is with this idea in mind that the essential and complementary roles of physicians and pharmacists can be defined, as follows: while the physician has a duty to understand thoroughly the patient's medical pathology in order to prescribe the most appropriate treatment, the pharmacist's duty is to be thoroughly familiar with the patient's medication profile in order to adequately advise and inform the patient about his or her drug therapy on every occasion that medication is dispensed, whether by prescription or on the pharmacist's recommendation.

With the wide variety of pharmaceutical products that patients may be prescribed by specialists or general practitioners, in addition to drugs they may already be taking (all too often as a result of outside influences), patients need to be guided and advised by an expert. This expert is the pharmacist, whose vigilance in this role is critical. However, in addition to advising individual patients and monitoring their drug use, the pharmacist's responsibility includes acting as a consultant for physicians by handling therapeutic problems, assisting in the selection of patients for drug therapy, outlining treatment options, identifying adverse drug reactions and drug interactions, and supplying information in specialized areas such as comparative pharmacology. The pharmacist can also contribute to the education of other health professionals and the public by participating in seminars, conferences, and public forums. Thus the four essential professional services that the pharmacist must provide are: monitoring drug use; advising and informing patients about their drug treatments; acting as a consultant to physicians; and educating the public with regard to pharmaceutical products and their appropriate use.

MONITORING DRUG USE

In monitoring drug use, the pharmacist must observe the principle that a patient may consume only such drugs as his or her particular condition will permit and that those drugs must be compatible with any medication that the patient is already taking.

A prerequisite for effective drug monitoring is the patient file. The pharmacist must keep a file on each of the pharmacy's patients, if contraindications are to be detected and patients warned, at the outset, of possible interactions between drugs. By keeping patient files up-to-date and consulting them whenever medication is dispensed, the pharmacist will be better equipped to inform each patient of the most appropriate manner, for that particular patient, of using the prescribed drug in order to derive its optimal effect and to reduce the intensity of any side effects that could potentially develop.

To be effective, the patient file should be kept simple and clear for easy reference. It must, however, contain all the information necessary for providing proper care. As soon as a prescription is received – particularly for a new patient – information should be obtained about any medication the patient may already be taking and any adverse reactions or allergies to drugs that may have been experienced in the past. Female patients should be encouraged to inform the pharmacist if they intend to become pregnant or are pregnant or breast-feeding. Also, in the case of infants, chronic patients, and elderly people, some basic information, including age and weight, should be recorded in the patient's file in order to facilitate proper dosage evaluation by the pharmacist. (In fact, provincial licensing bodies encourage or require that the age and weight of all patients served by a pharmacy be entered into the patient's profile.) Patient files can be kept on record cards or stored electronically in a computer.

Ideally, technical tasks, such as tablet counting, labelling, and invoicing, should be delegated to technical personnel, with the pharmacist intervening only to supervise and check completed technical work. The pharmacist must verify that the correct product, dosage form, and dosage amount have been dispensed, referring back to the physician's prescription. Then, with the help of the patient file, the pharmacist must review the patient's drug profile and note all other remarks or observations already recorded there.

The pharmacist will thereby discover if there is any contraindication to the use of the new drug as prescribed. Should the risk of drug interactions be detected, their seriousness must be assessed and any necessary substitutions determined. Taking into account the patient's age and physical condition, as well as any other medication he or she is using, the pharmacist must assess the validity of the dosage and the directions for use prescribed by the physician. (It seems evident that, in the near future, pharmacists will be asked by physicians to provide pharmacokinetic consultation services.) If the need arises, the pharmacist must communicate with the physician to suggest either desirable or necessary changes in the prescription. Only after all these steps have been taken, and all problems resolved, should the pharmacist dispense the prescribed medication to the patient, along with any necessary information or advice.

If a patient is already taking medication and wishes to purchase a non-prescription drug product, he or she should be advised to consult with the pharmacist before making the purchase.

Once again, the pharmacist should check the patient's file to review the drugs that are already being taken and to ensure that the patient is not allergic to the non-prescription drug in question. It is also important in such cases to determine if female patients are pregnant or breast feeding. If a customer is new to the pharmacy, the pharmacist must solicit the pertinent information, since many non-prescription drug products can be harmful to individuals already under medication – particularly those who suffer from diabetes, hypertension, or heart problems. It is also essential that pharmacists direct patients to see their physicians if the symptoms they describe – or the failure of previous medication to alleviate symptoms – lead the pharmacist to suspect the need for medical consultation. Any non-prescription drug products that could prove harmful should be displayed in the immediate vicinity of the dispensing counter, or in such a way that the patient will be compelled to consult with the pharmacist. The pharmacist should always be able to survey and control the counter in order to intervene and advise customers on the use of such products as necessary. You will recall from Chapter 7 that a number of provincial licensing bodies regulate the sale of certain non-prescription drugs by stipulating where the involvement of a pharmacist in the sale is a requirement; imposing restricted-access laws or policies; or designating that the professional-products area must be adjacent to the dispensary.

Pharmacists would be well advised to refer to *Self-Medication: A Reference for Health Professionals*, published by the Canadian Pharmaceutical Association, when dealing with patients who are treating symptoms through the use of non-prescription drugs. Each chapter in this textbook ends with a list of questions that might usefully be posed to such customers, and may assist the pharmacist in the early detection of disease among the pharmacy's customers.

If a pharmacy dispenses approximately 600–700 prescriptions per week and keeps its files on computer, it would be wise for the pharmacist to consider purchasing a second terminal. The first could then be used to accomplish technical tasks, while the second would be devoted exclusively to the pharmacist's needs, affording immediate access at all times to the kind of information that is constantly required by the pharmacist.

ADVISING PATIENTS

In the role of adviser, the pharmacist must observe the principle that patients taking prescription drugs must previously have received sufficient information to motivate them to follow the physician's prescription closely. This is possible only if the pharmacist takes measures to achieve the following three objectives:

1. Ensure that the patient understands perfectly the purpose of the medication.
2. Supply complete instructions on the proper use of the product and ensure that the patient fully understands them.
3. Monitor patient compliance to the prescribed drug therapy; that is, take measures to ensure that the patient follows the instructions provided during the entire course of the treatment.

Although these objectives may seem too ambitious, they are not only well within the reach of every responsible pharmacist but are indeed a necessity, since failure to advise a patient adequately and correctly can constitute grounds for a negligence suit against the pharmacist. The pharmacist is obligated to take the time required to advise the patient, and explain

1. the purpose, mechanism of action, and anticipated effect of the medication (whether prescription or non-prescription);
2. how the medication should be taken (for example, on an empty stomach, with a little or a lot of water, etc.);
3. when the medication should be taken (a dosage schedule must be supplied for each drug dispensed);
4. the probable side effects of the drug and how best to eliminate or reduce them;
5. the non-prescription drug products that the patient must avoid while taking the medication;
6. the foods that the patient should avoid or, in some cases, increase consumption of, in order to obtain the full effect of the drug.

Finally, after determining that the patient has fully understood these verbal instructions, the pharmacist should supply a written copy that the patient can take home for reference throughout the course of the treatment. Patient-information aids, both printed and electronic, have been developed commercially to assist in this aim. They include PAL (Patient

Advisory Leaflet), produced by PharmaSystems Ltd.; SIM (Supplemental Information on Medication), produced by the CPhA; and PIS (Pharmaceutical Information System), developed by the University of Montreal's Faculty of Pharmacy.[1] Although each of these patient-information systems is well prepared, no single system is perfect and each requires constant revision and updating. A new computerized service is available from the USP-DI (United States Pharmacopoeia-Drug Information), which is compatible with DOS operating systems and capable of customizing and printing patient information for each individual customer. However, no auxiliary label or printed information sheet can adequately replace the verbal instructions given by the pharmacist. It is only through personal contact and conversation that the pharmacist can really assess the level of the patient's understanding and ensure that it is sufficient. Printed information, properly qualified by the pharmacist, serves as a necessary complement to encourage and assist the patient in following the pharmacist's verbal instructions throughout the course of treatment.

Monitoring patient compliance through the course of the treatment may involve, for example, follow-up calls notifying patients to come in for prescription renewals. Not only are such measures part of the pharmacist's responsibility in the provision of essential professional services, they have also proven to be cost-effective. Pharmacists should indeed plan and establish systems for encouraging patient compliance.

Pharmacists are often called upon to dispense medication to elderly people living in institutions. Generally, these patients are no longer able to cope for themselves and are cared for by a competent medical and nursing staff. This, however, in no way diminishes the responsibility of the pharmacist toward this patient group. Pharmacists should, through their use of computer software designed for institutionalized patients and their advice to medical and nursing personnel, remain the monitors of the drug therapies that these elderly patients receive.

CONSULTATION FOR OTHER HEALTH PROFESSIONALS

While pharmacy was once defined as the art of compounding drugs, today it embraces the full knowledge of drug properties that enables users to derive the beneficial effects of drugs without experiencing the potential adverse effects that could occur with improper use. Physicians, nurses, and other health professionals rely heavily on pharmacists today for advice and information about the potential adverse effects and interactions of the drugs they prescribe. The nature of these interprofessional relationships will be discussed in greater detail in Chapter 21.

---

[1] See the Appendix to this chapter for the addresses of these sources. Also, see Chapter 20 for further information on computerized patient-counselling aids.

In Canada, physicians and nurses may first refer to the *Compendium of Pharmaceuticals and Specialties*, but, not always finding the answers to their questions there, they will turn to the pharmacist. Except on rare occasions and unless entirely confident of the correctness of an answer, the pharmacist should first record the inquiry, then return the call personally after having consulted the available literature on the product in question. In some cases, the pharmacist will find it necessary to contact one of the many drug-information centres that exist in various locations across Canada. It is clear that the pharmacist's drug-information resources must be a great deal more exhaustive than those of other health professionals. To remain sufficiently knowledgeable and aware of new and existing drugs and their properties, pharmacists must expect to invest a minimum of $1000 per year to replace or update reference books, subscribe to several monthly pharmaceutical journals, and participate in continuing-education programs. See the Appendix at the end of this chapter for a list of the basic reference books, as well as some recommended journal titles, that should be represented in a pharmacy's reference library.

Communication among the various health professionals will continue to grow, and pharmacists will be integral players in this process. They should, indeed, encourage it. Pharmacists should not concentrate their attention on what is happening within their profession alone. They must also focus on matters that are of concern to the other health professionals with whom they interact. The pharmacist would therefore be well advised to subscribe to the leading Canadian medical, dental, and nursing journals. Again, a list of several Canadian health publications can be found in the Appendix at the end of the chapter.

EDUCATING THE PUBLIC

Every pharmacist should, in accordance with provincial regulations, employ his or her professional knowledge to protect and promote public health. In this sense, the pharmacist's role includes educating the public.

In promoting public health, the pharmacist must first respect and promote the principle that drugs are to be used only when absolutely necessary for therapeutic purposes, and ensure that the pharmacy operates according to this principle.

This is in part the reason why the pharmacist is obliged to advise customers thoroughly about all pharmaceutical products that are sold without prescription, informing the patient not only of the beneficial effects of the drugs they are purchasing but also of their dangers and limitations.

Furthermore, it is part of the pharmacist's role as an educator of the public not only to warn customers about potential health hazards, but also to provide advice and information about preventive health care. Pharmacists can easily educate their clientele about ways to control weight, blood pressure, and blood-sugar levels. Today, it is also important for the pharmacist to contribute to public awareness about the dangers of drugs and sexually transmitted diseases and, of course, the ways in which they can be prevented. The dangers of smoking are by now well known to the public, but the pharmacist who does not smoke nor sell tobacco products is likely to gain greater credibility with customers.

There are various publications designed to assist pharmacists in their role as educators, which are available free-of-charge or at nominal cost from professional pharmacy associations and other health-care organizations, such as the Canadian Cancer Society, the Council on Drug Abuse, and family planning organizations, to name but a few. Because these publications are expensive to produce, and in order to increase their effectiveness, the pharmacist may want to be somewhat discriminating in their distribution. In many cases, customers will treat these educational brochures and booklets more seriously if they are recommended to them personally by the pharmacist.

Finally, the pharmacist should never miss an opportunity – within or outside the pharmacy – to promote the essential role that the profession plays in the health-care system. Accordingly, when the opportunity presents itself, the pharmacist should not hesitate to remind customers that pharmaceutical products are not like other consumer goods and, since they are too important to be treated casually, should be used only with the advice and guidance of the pharmacist. Valuable opportunities exist to promote the profession in the media, in public lectures to groups of various ages and backgrounds, in primary and secondary schools, colleges, and universities, or to members of social clubs or senior citizens' groups. To this end, the majority of provincial pharmaceutical associations are able to supply their members with information sheets, lectures, or even slide shows and videos to help them better inform the public about therapeutic drug use.

SPECIALIZED SUPPORT SERVICES

Once essential services are assured, the pharmacist can also arrange to provide certain of the specialized support services that have been introduced in community pharmacies in recent times. We shall discuss several of these possibilities here, but a more detailed discussion can be found in Chapter 23, which focusses on new service opportunities.

It is evident by their behaviour that Canadians are eager to learn. As an example, consider the large number of Canadian adults who fill evening courses offered at colleges and universities in search of further education. This results in a much better informed and more critical public.

Along with their greater autonomy, the members of our society are intent on achieving a better quality of life. As part of this objective, they have demonstrated a greater interest in exercising their rights and responsibilities with regard to health-related decision making and the health-care process. It is therefore not surprising that pharmacists have been called upon increasingly to establish service centres for self-diagnostic and self-monitoring equipment. This new role, a result of the ongoing evolution of the profession, entails new responsibilities that pharmacists should embrace and from which they will benefit.

Such service centres need not take up a great deal of space in a pharmacy. Generally, 60 feet of shelf space should be sufficient for a full display of self-diagnostic products and equipment. The pharmacist should, however, anticipate the need for a private or semi-private area where techniques can be properly demonstrated. With such new products in the area of health care, demonstration and instruction are critical – manufacturers' directions cannot replace personal interaction. When an individual who suffers from hypertension takes matters in hand and decides to measure his or her own blood pressure on a regular basis, that person is looking for support. While tensiometers may be promoted through catalogues and sold in discount stores, people will undoubtedly prefer to buy such instruments at pharmacies if they can rely on the support, monitoring, and advice of the pharmacist, both in the course of the purchase and afterwards.

The provision of this type of service is time-consuming. For example, approximately half an hour is required to demonstrate the proper use of a tensiometer and up to an hour to teach a diabetic how to use a home blood-glucose monitoring device (a reflectance photometer). Pharmacists will naturally expect to be reimbursed for such services. The additional labour costs may be worked into dispensing-fee calculations, but consideration should also be given in future to negotiating with governments for a fee to be paid to pharmacists when they instruct welfare patients or senior citizens in the proper use of self-diagnostic instruments. Alternatively, pharmacists could negotiate for a higher markup on a product like a blood-glucose monitoring meter, to recoup the costs of the time required for patient training. In the process of such patient interaction, pharmacists are likely to become even more integral to the health-care system by assisting in the early detection of conditions such as diabetes and high blood pressure.

For today's pharmacist, keeping up with the times will involve offering a range of specialized services in self-diagnostic and monitoring equipment and products such as reflectance photometers, tensiometers, predictors of periods of fertility and sterility, pregnancy tests, and all other tests that are already available or soon to come on the market, such as detection tests for cancer of the colon, gonorrhea, urinary infections, and throat infections.

Pharmacists who decide to offer these services should do so in a thoroughly professional manner, or risk damaging the reputation of both the profession and the pharmacy itself. Pharmacists should therefore insist that competent sales representatives from the products' manufacturers give complete demonstrations and training in the relevant techniques for both the pharmacists and their assistants.

Pharmacy is constantly evolving as a profession. It is for this reason that today's pharmacist is first and foremost a monitor of drug use, adviser of patients, consultant to physicians, and public educator. But this does not mean that pharmacists have altogether abandoned the traditional role of compounding drugs: they are still called upon occasionally to make up unique, customized prescriptions, since the pharmaceutical industry could not possibly cater to the particular needs of every patient with drugs produced on a mass scale. It will therefore always be necessary for a certain number of pharmacists to devote their time to the specialized service of preparing unique formulas. Professional Compounding (Canada) Inc., of London, Ontario (see the Appendix for the complete address), offers pharmacists all the necessary materials and technical support for this purpose. Pharmacists could also offer their services for the preparation of sterile products. It is probably clear from these two examples that the quality and profitability of such services can be guaranteed only if they are offered by a very limited number of pharmacists in any given area.

As the population ages and the percentage of elderly people grows, a range of specialized long-term-care services will come into demand. Depending on location, a pharmacist might offer much-needed services to the population by selling or renting the home health-care equipment and accessories often prescribed by specialists, as follows:

1. Orthopaedic specialists recommend or prescribe the use of orthopaedic supports, corsets, walking aids, bathroom accessories, wheelchairs, walking sticks, and crutches.
2. Occupational therapists often recommend feeding aids, cleaning aids, and aids for writing, reading, and dressing.
3. Urologists prescribe aids for those suffering from urinary incontinence.
4. Surgeons often prescribe equipment for ostomy patients.
5. Respiratory technologists recommend accessories for oxygen therapy equipment.

Consult the Appendix at the end of the chapter for a selected list of suppliers of such aids, equipment, and accessories.

COMMERCIAL SERVICES

DELIVERY SERVICES

The number of single-parent households increases from year to year, as does the percentage of the elderly in the population. This situation virtually demands that pharmacies provide a delivery service for prescriptions. It is also obvious that, given the sheer size of our country, not all people have access to a pharmacy in their immediate neighbourhoods. In some cases, prescription and non-prescription drugs must be ordered and delivered by mail.

Although home delivery and postal services increase costs for the pharmacy, this should never be used as a pretext for diminishing the level of professional services offered in such cases. On the contrary, the pharmacist must always supply written information and instructions for use with each prescription delivered and, since the pharmacist is not in a position to assess the patient's comprehension of the instructions, the patient should be invited to call the pharmacist if any supplementary information is required.

CREDIT-CARD SERVICES

The use of credit cards is ubiquitous in our society, and pharmacists cannot survive today with a cash-only payment policy. In certain parts of the country, experiments are already underway using automatic debit cards that allow clients to settle a bill immediately by direct transfer of the amount due from their bank account to that of the supplier. As an efficient manager, the pharmacist should use all the instruments available that allow patients to deal easily with the monetary aspect of pharmaceutical services.

POSTAL SUBSTATIONS

Canada Post maintains a network of postal substations across the country to provide better service to the population, and often seeks to franchise these substations to pharmacies, whose stability – a result of the constant need for pharmaceutical services – makes them a reliable site. The extended hours frequently offered by pharmacies are another reason for locating substations there. The substations generally occupy little space in a pharmacy – roughly 40 square feet – and serve the population well, while simultaneously increasing the pharmacy's potential clientele.

It is up to each pharmacist to evaluate the cost–benefit ratio of introducing a post-office substation by estimating the costs involved (in terms of staff time, fixtures, and inventory of stamps) and the patronage the substation is expected to generate.

RETURNS POLICY

As in any business that sells both goods and services, pharmacies must establish a returns policy. However, in all matters pertaining to drugs, pharmacists must comply with Pharmacy Act regulations. As a result, they can under no circumstances accept the return of prescription or non-prescription drugs, unless they are to be destroyed immediately in the presence of the pharmacist and with the patient's knowledge. As an efficient manager, the pharmacist must establish a returns policy for other products and ensure that all personnel adhere to that policy closely.

COMMUNITY SERVICES

As a respected professional in the community, the pharmacist may be called upon to sponsor certain local programs, such as children's team sports. The pharmacist may also be asked to make financial contributions to local causes or to extend services in a professional capacity.

There are a number of ways in which pharmacists can participate in community services:

1. By serving on the boards and committees of voluntary health agencies, such as the Cancer Society, the Heart Fund, and the Ostomy Association.
2. By serving on local committees or joining organizations concerned with the control of drug abuse.
3. By becoming involved with hospital boards.
4. Some pharmacists even choose to participate, in some capacity, in municipal, provincial, or federal politics.

The pharmacist and the local community are mutually dependent. Always bearing this fact in mind, pharmacists, when approached to sponsor or participate in a community cause, should offer some measure of support. Each pharmacist must, of course, determine the reasonable limits of his or her personal or financial involvement in such endeavours.

SUMMARY

In order to establish a productive and beneficial practice, the pharmacist must recognize the absolute necessity of providing essential professional services of the highest standards, then evaluate the benefits of offering specialized professional services and certain commercial services, and finally, decide on the sort of community-service involvement to be undertaken.

The pharmacist's reputation will be based on the quality of the essential professional services he or she provides. The pharmacist must therefore excel as a monitor of drug use and adviser of patients in all aspects of their therapeutic drug treatments, and become a knowledgeable consultant for other health professionals, as well as an active educator for a public that demands ever-increasing levels of information. In this way, the pharmacist will have a greater involvement in the decision-making processes that relate to collective and individual health in our society.

RECOMMENDED READING

See the Appendix to this chapter for a list of basic reference books and recommended journal titles.

Effective Pharmacy Management. 4th ed. Kansas City, Mo.: Marion Laboratories, Inc., 1987.

Guide to Good Pharmacy Management. Vaudreuil, Que.: Hoffman-La Roche, 1980. (See especially *Customer Care*.)

The Milis Report. Pharmacists for the Future: The Report of the Study Commission on Pharmacy. School of Public Health, University of Michigan, Ann Arbor, MI. Health Administration Press, 1975.

Schoepp, G.H. "How to Win MDs: Physician-Oriented Pharmacy Practice – A Protocol for the Community Pharmacist." *Drug Merchandising* 65, no. 11 (November 1984): 22–30.

———. "Marketing Physician Consultations." *Drug Merchandising* 68, no. 11 (November 1987): 19–24.

Tharp, C.P., and Lecca, P.J. *Pharmacy Management for Students and Practitioners*. 2nd ed. St. Louis, Mo.: C.V. Mosby Co., 1979.

APPENDIX: PROFESSIONAL SERVICES – REFERENCES AND RESOURCES

Sources of Information on Pharmacy in Canada

Canadian Foundation for Pharmacy
603-123 Edward St.
Toronto, Ont.
M2B 8A8

Canadian Pharmaceutical Association
1785 Alta Vista Dr.
Ottawa, Ont.
K1G 3Y6

Sources for Patient-Information Systems

Canadian Pharmaceutical Association
1785 Alta Vista Dr.
Ottawa, Ont.
K1G 3Y6

Pharmaceutical Information Service (PIS)
Faculty of Pharmacy
University of Montreal
P.O. 6128
Montreal, Que.
H3C 3J7

PharmaSystems Ltd.
361 Steelcase Rd. W.
Markham, Ont.
L3R 3V8

Specialized Support Services: Selected Equipment

ConvaTec
Division of Squibb Canada Inc.
2365 Côte de Lisées
Montreal, Que.
H4N 2M7

FORMEDICA
1481 Bégin
St-Laurent, Que.
H4R 1V8

Hollister Ltd.
322 Consumers Rd.
Willowdale, Ont.
M2J 1P8

Kimberly-Clark of Canada Ltd.
365 Bloor St. E.
Toronto, Ont.
M4W 3L9

Pfizer Hospital Products Ltd.
United Division
546 Governors Rd.
Guelph, Ont.
N1H 6K9

Physio ERP Ltée
3232 autoroute Laval ouest
Laval, Que.
H7T 2H6

Proctor and Gamble Inc.
P.O. Box 589
Hamilton, Ont.
L8N 3L5

Professional Compounding (Canada) Inc.
10 Gore St.
London, Ont.
N5W 4A7

Basic Reference Books for the Pharmacist's Library (with publishers' addresses)

American Hospital Formulary Service
American Society of Hospital Pharmacists
4630 Montgomery Ave.
Bethesda, MD
20814 U.S.A.

AMA Drug Evaluation
American Medical Association
W.B. Saunders Co.
55 Horner Ave.
Toronto, Ont.
M8Z 4X6

Applied Therapeutics: The Clinical Use of Drugs, 4th ed.
ed. by Lloyd Yee Young and Mary Anne Koda-Kimble
Applied Therapeutics Inc.
P.O. Box 5077
Vancouver, WA
98668 U.S.A.

Self-Medication: A Reference for Health Professionals, 3rd ed.
ed. by Cheryl Clarke
Canadian Pharmaceutical Association
1785 Alta Vista Dr.
Ottawa, Ont.
K1G 3Y6

Compendium of Pharmaceuticals and Specialties
Canadian Pharmaceutical Association
1785 Alta Vista Dr.
Ottawa, Ont.
K1G 3Y6

Current Geriatric Therapy
by T.R. Covington and J.I. Walker
W.B. Saunders Co.
55 Horner Ave.
Toronto, Ont.
M8Z 4X6

Drug Facts and Comparisons
J.B. Lippincott
East Washington Square
Philadelphia, PA
19105 U.S.A

Drug Interaction Facts
(Mediphor Editorial Group)
J.B. Lippincott
East Washington Square
Philadelphia, PA
19105 U.S.A.

Drug Therapy for the Elderly
by K.A. Conrad and R. Bressler
C.V. Mosby Co. Ltd.
5240 Finch Ave. E.
Scarborough, Ont.
M1S 4P2

Drugs in Pregnancy and Lactation
by G. Briggs, R. Freeman, and S. Yaffe
Williams and Wilkins
428 East Preston St.
Baltimore, MD
21202 U.S.A.

Martindale
The Extra Pharmacopoeia
ed. by James E.F. Reynolds
The Pharmaceutical Society of Great Britain
1 Lambeth High Street
London SE1 7JN
England

Le Guide pédiatrique de l'hôpital Ste-Justine
Hôpital Ste-Justine
3175 Chemin de la Côte Ste-Catherine
Montreal, Que.
H3T 1C5

Handbook of Clinical Drug Data
by J.E. Knoben and P.O. Anderson
Drug Intelligence Publications, Inc.
1241 Broadway
Hamilton, IL
62341 U.S.A.

Medication Guide for Patient Counselling
by D. Smith
Consumer Health Information Corporation
8350 Greensboro Drive
Suite 521
McLean, VA
22102 U.S.A.

Pharmacy Practice for the Geriatric Patient
American Association of Colleges of Pharmacy/Eli Lilly
Health Sciences Consortium Inc.
103 Laurel Ave.
Carrboro, NC
27510 U.S.A.

Poison Management Manual
Canadian Pharmaceutical Association
1785 Alta Vista Dr.
Ottawa, Ont.
K1G 3Y6

Problems in Pediatric Drug Therapy
by L.A. Pagliaro and A.M. Pagliaro
Drug Intelligence Publications, Inc.
1241 Broadway
Hamilton, IL
62341 U.S.A

USP-DI
Vol. 1(A and B): *Drug Information for the Health Care Provider*
Vol. 2: *Advice for the Patient*
United States Pharmacopoeial Convention Inc. (USPC)
P.O. Box 2248
Rockville, MD
20852 U.S.A.

Suggested Journals for the Pharmacist's Reading (with publishers' addresses)

American Pharmacy
American Pharmaceutical Association
2215 Constitution Ave. N.W.
Washington, DC
20037 U.S.A.

B.C. Pharmacist
B.C. Pharmacists' Society
Westco Marketing Ltd.
2040 West 12th Ave.
Vancouver, B.C.
V6J 2G2

Canadian Pharmaceutical Journal / Revue Pharmaceutical Canadienne
Canadian Pharmaceutical Association
1785 Alta Vista Dr.
Ottawa, Ont.
K1G 3Y6

Drug Merchandising
Maclean Hunter Ltd.
777 Bay St.
Toronto, Ont.
M5W 1A7

Drug-Nutrient Interactions
Alan R. Liss, Inc.
41 East 11th St.
New York, NY
10003 U.S.A.

Drug Protocol
Trimel Corporation
5915 Airport Rd.
Suite 700
Mississauga, Ont.
L4V 1T1

Medical Letter
56 Harrison St.
New Rochelle, NY
10801 U.S.A.

Le Pharmacien
Maclean Hunter Ltd.
625 ave. Président Kennedy
Montreal, Que.
H3A 1K5

Pharmacist's Letter
5075 Cozad Way
Stockton, CA
95212 U.S.A.

Pharmacy Practice
Trimel Corporation
5915 Airport Rd.
Suite 700
Mississauga, Ont.
L4V 1T1

Pharmacy Times
Romaine Pierson Publishers Inc.
80 Share Rd.
Port Washington, NY
11050 U.S.A.

Québec Pharmacie
Les Publications Codex Inc.
1031 rue St-Denis
Montreal, Que.
H2X 3H9

U.S. Pharmacist
Jobson Publishing Corp.
352 Park Ave. S.
New York, NY
10010 U.S.A.

Selected Canadian Dental, Nursing, and Medical Journals (with publishers' addresses)

Journal of the Canadian Dental Association
1815 Alta Vista Dr.
Ottawa, Ont.
K1G 3Y6

Journal Dentaire du Québec
625 boul. Dorchester ouest
5ième étage
Montreal, Que.
H3B 1R2

Ontario Dentist
234 St. George St.
Toronto, Ont.
M5R 2P1

AARN Newsletter
Alberta Association of Registered Nurses
11620-168 St.
Edmonton, Alta.
T5M 4A6

The Canadian Nurse
Canadian Nurses Association
50 The Driveway
Ottawa, Ont.
K2P 1E2

Nursing Québec
l'Ordre des infirmières et infirmiers du Québec
4200 Dorchester ouest
Montreal, Que.
H3Z 1V4

RNABC News
Registered Nurses' Assn. of British Columbia
2855 Arbutus St.
Vancouver, B.C.
V6J 3Y8

RNAO News
Registered Nurses' Assn. of Ontario
33 Prince St.
Toronto, Ont.
M4W 1Z2

Alberta Doctors' Digest
9901-108th St. NW
Suite 300
Edmonton, Alta.
T5K 1G8

British Columbia Medical Journal
115-1665 West Broadway
Vancouver, B.C.
V6J 1X1

Canadian Family Physician
1200 Sheppard Ave. E.
Suite 507
Willowdale, Ont.
M2K 2S5

Canadian Medical Association Journal
1867 Alta Vista Dr.
Ottawa, Ont.
K1G 3Y6

Manitoba Medicine
60 Pearl St.
Rm LB 315
Health Sciences Centre
Winnipeg, Man.
R3E 1X2

Le Médecin du Québec
1440 Ste-Catherine ouest
Suite 1100
Montreal, Que.
H3G 1R8

Modern Medicine
1450 Don Mills Rd.
Don Mills, Ont.
M3B 2X7

The Nova Scotia Medical Bulletin
6080 Young St.
Suite 305
Halifax, N.S.
B3K 5L2

Nutrition
2498 Yonge St.
Suite 21
Toronto, Ont.
M4P 2H7

Ontario Medicine
777 Bay St.
Toronto, Ont.
M5W 1A7

18

FINANCIAL ASSESSMENT

Once a pharmacy practice is in operation, it becomes necessary to monitor its financial progress – in other words, to assess the performance of the business. Regular performance assessment allows problems to be identified and, once understood, those problems can be corrected through modifications that will ensure the continuing profitability of the practice.

As we saw in Chapter 12, it is possible to successfully increase sales, yet simultaneously run out of the cash necessary to replenish stock or pay wages, and thus to be operating the pharmacy at a loss. The reason may be as simple as accepting credit sales and failing to collect on the accounts receivable in full or within an acceptable period of time.

In response to such situations, techniques have been developed to monitor factors such as the average length of time required to collect accounts receivable (commonly referred to as the "average collection period") and the average length of time taken to pay invoices (known as the "average payable period"). The importance of comparing these two factors has also been recognized, and is based on the simple premise that collected receivables will provide the funds needed to pay suppliers. If the average collection period exceeds the average payable period, there are clearly no funds available to pay suppliers. If those funds are being borrowed, the pharmacy practice is incurring needless interest charges. The concept of "aging accounts," that is, the calculation of the number of days that accounts receivable have been outstanding, represents an important area for regular monitoring by pharmacy owners or managers. This technique is an example of financial ratio analysis, which is a systematic way of (1) determining how well the assets of a business are being managed; (2) identifying problem areas before they are out of control; (3) separating profitable from unprofitable products or services; and (4) providing the objective insight into one's business that someone examining it from outside might gain.

The results of financial ratio analysis do not explain *why* something occurred, only *that* it occurred. Therefore, when changes from the norm are detected through ratio analysis, the pharmacy owner is prompted to search out the causes. The implied comparison to norms involves two aspects: first, comparison of current data with the pharmacy's own historical data (internal comparisons), and, second, comparison with industry averages as reported in the professional literature (external comparisons).

The ratios that can be calculated are usually categorized into groups, reflecting liquidity, profitability, and solvency. Liquidity is the ability to turn assets into cash quickly, in order to repay debt from short-term capitalization. The ratios frequently used to determine liquidity are known as the current ratio and the quick ratio. Profitability refers to the firm's ability to generate sufficient revenue not only to pay its expenses but also to reward its owner(s). Profitability is usually expressed as a percentage of sales and is calculated on the basis of income *before* tax is paid. Solvency is a measure of the firm's ability to repay debt from long-term capitalization.

The tables that appear in this chapter categorize the more frequently used financial ratios, illustrate the methods by which they are calculated, and use industry averages from the Seventh Annual Survey of Community Pharmacy Operations for 1986 in the sample calculations. You will notice that the industry averages often fail to meet the standards described as ideal or desirable in the financial ratios. This is due in some cases to certain unique characteristics of pharmacy as a business. In others, however, it is simply attributable to the fact that industry averages do not represent the ideal, but include businesses that are either newly established or inefficiently managed together with those that are well established and distinctly profitable. Each individual pharmacy should, of course, strive to achieve the kind of ratios described in this chapter as attainable and desirable.

Read the tables along with the text, which elaborates on each of the ratios illustrated. Refer back to Chapter 4, Figures 4.1 and 4.2, for the complete financial statements on which we have based our examples in this chapter. You may also find it useful to review the material on financial statements in Chapter 4, on debt and equity capital in Chapter 6, and on minimizing assets and maximizing liabilities in Chapter 12.

Ratios Used to Assess Liquidity

Table 18.1 illustrates the liquidity ratios discussed in this section

CURRENT RATIO

The current ratio is "a measure of a firm's ability to meet its current obligations on time and to have funds readily available for current operations."[1] This ratio should have a value of 2:1, which allows current assets – the sum of cash, accounts receivable, inventory, marketable securities, and prepaid expenses – to shrink by 50 percent and still cover current obligations. Creditors like to see a high ratio indicating a wide

Table 18.1 LIQUIDITY RATIOS

Ratios	Calculation	Industry Average
Current Ratio	$\dfrac{\text{Current assets}}{\text{Current liabilities}}$	$\dfrac{323,060}{160,729} = 2.0$ times or 2:1
Quick Ratio or Acid Test	$\dfrac{\text{Current assets} - \text{Inventory}}{\text{Current liabilities}}$	$\dfrac{117,327}{160,729} = 0.7$ times or 07:1
Average Collection Period	$\dfrac{\text{Ending accounts receivable}}{\text{Annual credit sales}} \times 365$ days	data not available
Inventory to Net Working Capital	$\dfrac{\text{Inventory}}{\text{Current assets} - \text{Current liabilities}}$	$\dfrac{205,733}{162,331} = 1.27$ or 127%
Net Sales to Net Working Capital	$\dfrac{\text{Sales}}{\text{Current assets} - \text{Current liabilities}}$	$\dfrac{1,302,190}{162,331} = 8.0$ times or 8:1

margin of safety for claims against the business. However, a very high ratio – greater than 3:1 – may indicate that funds are not being used to greatest advantage and that inventory, receivables, and cash may be at levels that are higher than necessary. A ratio of less than 2:1 may occur during the early years of a new pharmacy's operations or may indicate continuing unprofitability or insufficient capital.

QUICK RATIO OR ACID TEST

This is the ratio "between the liquid, or 'quick,' current assets and the current liabilities. Quick current assets are cash, marketable securities,

[1] Paul H. Walgenbach et al., *Principles of Accounting*, 1st Canadian ed. (Toronto: Harcourt Brace Jovanovich Canada Inc., 1988), p. 759.

and receivables."[2] Because inventory is difficult to convert into cash readily, it is not included among quick current assets. The quick ratio is thus a more critical measure of liquidity than the current ratio, indicating the ability of *readily available resources* to meet current obligations. An appropriate value for this ratio is 1:1. If the current ratio is acceptable, but the quick ratio falls below 1:1, the size of the inventory relative to total current assets is probably too great, and requires the owner/manager's close attention. Pharmacies in fact tend to have a proven quick ratio than desirable because of their dependence on large dollar values of inventory, particularly in the dispensary. This is why efficient inventory-control systems are so critical in pharmacy practice.

AVERAGE COLLECTION PERIOD

Since most pharmacies grant credit, either personally to individual patrons, to drug-insurance programs on behalf of their patrons, or through credit-card acceptance, this is a useful ratio to calculate. Unfortunately, industry averages for annual credit sales are unavailable and we are therefore unable to calculate the ratio for the industry. This, of course, in no way diminishes its importance for individual pharmacies and should be calculated periodically in order to determine the number of days accounts receivable are outstanding.

The pharmacy owner or manager can establish parameters for the pharmacy's collection period and monitor deviations from those parameters. The average collection period should ideally be 30 days or less – and this goal is indeed frequently achieved by pharmacies that submit accounts to third-party payers promptly, train staff to complete billings properly, transmit billings electronically, and disallow personal credit accounts (or employ rigorous credit policies and collection procedures where they do exist). Refer back to Chapter 12's discussion on minimizing assets as part of good cash management in pharmacy practice.

The acceptance of credit cards as opposed to personal credit accounts in pharmacies is one way to control the collection of receivables. It must be remembered, however, that there is a cost charged to the business by the financial institution that issues the card and that staff will have to be trained in the proper use and validation of credit cards.

INVENTORY TO NET WORKING CAPITAL

This is another measure of liquidity and inventory balance, and is usually expressed as a percentage. As explained previously, when a large proportion of the pharmacy's assets is represented by inventory, it may be

[2] Walgenbach et al., *Principles of Accounting*, p. 760.

difficult to meet current obligations. An appropriate value for this ratio is 90–100 percent. A higher ratio, however, is not uncommon in newer pharmacies. A value over 100 percent may indicate that inventory is too high and that the cash position could be improved by liquidating some portion of it.

NET SALES TO WORKING CAPITAL

This ratio illustrates how many dollars of sales are supported by each dollar of working capital. Thus, it provides some indication of the amount of working capital that would be needed if sales volume were to be increased. An appropriate ratio is 5:1. If the ratio is too high, the business may be operating on scarce resources and the pharmacy may not have sufficient funds to meet any new liabilities that could be incurred in the near future. New pharmacies or those relying heavily on supplier credit tend to have higher ratios. A low ratio indicates that more working capital is being used to generate existing sales than should be necessary.

Ratios Used to Assess Profitability

Table 18.2 illustrates the profitability ratios discussed in this section. Note that the profitability ratios are normally expressed as percentages.

PROFIT ON SALES

This is a measure of managerial effectiveness in increasing owner's (or shareholders') equity. Although this value may vary greatly among phar-

Table 18.2 PROFITABILITY RATIOS

Ratios	Calculation	Industry Average
Profit† on Sales	$\dfrac{\text{Profit}}{\text{Annual sales}}$	$\dfrac{62{,}580}{1{,}302{,}190} \times 100 = 4.8\%$
Return on Investment	$\dfrac{\text{Profit}}{\text{Net worth (equity)}}$	$\dfrac{62{,}580}{195{,}331} \times 100 = 32.0\%$
Return on Total Investment	$\dfrac{\text{Profit}}{\text{Equity} + \text{Long-term liabilities}}$	$\dfrac{62{,}580}{250{,}460} \times 100 = 25.0\%$
Return on Asset Investment	$\dfrac{\text{Profit}}{\text{Sales}} \times \dfrac{\text{Sales}}{\text{Total assets}}$	$\dfrac{62{,}580}{1{,}302{,}190} \times \dfrac{1{,}302{,}190}{411{,}189} \times 100 = 15.2\%$
Profit on Net Working Capital	$\dfrac{\text{Profit}}{\text{Current assets} - \text{Current liabilities}}$	$\dfrac{62{,}580}{162{,}331} \times 100 = 38.6\%$

†*Note:* Profit *before tax* is assumed with each use of the term *profit* in this table.

macies, the average profit on sales in the industry over the years has been approximately five percent. This value will rise as the sales of departments that earn high gross margins assume a greater proportion of total sales. Yearly internal and external comparisons are useful in assessing the appropriateness of the profit-on-sales percentage.

RETURN ON INVESTMENT

This ratio evaluates how productively the owner's funds are being used. A valid return-on-investment figure can be derived only if a reasonable owner's salary and a fair rent value (if the premises are owned by the pharmacist) are included in the operating expenses. If this is not done, profit will be overstated, as will the return on investment value. At today's interest rates, an appropriate value is 20 percent or higher. This ratio can be increased by increasing the debt-to-equity ratio – if assets can earn more than the cost of borrowing, then financing through fixed or long-term debt is useful.

RETURN ON TOTAL INVESTMENT

This ratio evaluates income relative to total funds invested in the business, making no distinction between owner's equity and long-term liabilities. It measures how effectively the total funds invested in have been managed.

RETURN ON ASSET INVESTMENT

This ratio measures the productivity of total assets, making no distinction between owner's capital and borrowed capital. This ratio improves if sales increase while assets remain constant or if the rate of profit increases.

PROFIT ON NET WORKING CAPITAL

This ratio finds use in measuring profitability when a large portion of the operating funds is provided through long-term borrowing and when permanent capital is unusually low relative to sales.

Ratios Used to Assess Solvency

Table 18.3 illustrates the solvency ratios discussed in this section.

DEBT TO EQUITY

This ratio compares the total debt of the practice to its total equity and is expressed as a percentage. When total debt exceeds owner's equity, the practice will be in a precarious position should a dramatic change occur in the operation, such as a sudden or prolonged drop in sales or an increase in expenses. A pharmacy with a low debt-to-equity ratio compared to that of other similar pharmacies may not be using its borrowed funds effectively. Values of this ratio vary depending on the age of the pharmacy and its borrowing policy, but they should ideally be in the area of 50 percent and should not exceed 100 percent.

The industry-average ratio is calculated as 110.5 percent, indicating that many reporting pharmacies are either new establishments with a sizable debt load or are highly dependent on borrowed capital.

Table 18.3 SOLVENCY RATIOS

Ratios	Calculation		Industry Average
Debt to Equity	$\dfrac{\text{Total liabilities}}{\text{Net worth}}$		$\dfrac{215,858}{195,331} \times 100 = 110.5\%$
Current Debt to Net Worth	$\dfrac{\text{Current liabilities}}{\text{Net worth}}$		$\dfrac{160,729}{195,331} \times 100 = 82.3\%$
Sales to Net Worth	$\dfrac{\text{Sales}}{\text{Net worth}}$		$\dfrac{1,302,190}{195,331} \times 100 = 6.7 \text{ times or } 6.7:1$
Funded Debt to Working Capital	$\dfrac{\text{Long-term liabilities}}{\text{Working capital}}$		$\dfrac{55,129}{162,331} \times 100 = 34.0\%$
Fixed Assets to Net Worth	$\dfrac{\text{Fixed assets}}{\text{Net worth}}$		$\dfrac{88,129}{195,331} \times 100 = 45.1\%$
Average Payable Period	$\dfrac{\text{Outstanding accounts payable}}{\text{Annual purchases}} \times 365 \text{ days}$		data not available
Degree of Newness of Fixed Assets	$100\% - \dfrac{\text{Accumulated depreciation}}{\text{Fixed asset cost}}$		data not available

CURRENT DEBT TO NET WORTH

This ratio, also expressed as a percentage, illustrates the extent to which the new capital of the practice is dependent on short-term debt. It may also be interpreted as indicating the pharmacy's ability to meet its current obligations from its net worth or equity capital. The ratio is usually higher in new pharmacies. If this ratio is high (over 80 percent), severe undercapitalization will occur in the event that a debt is recalled. Again, newly established pharmacies may constitute a high proportion of the pharmacies reporting to the annual survey, as the ratio here is 82.3 percent, which indicates a relatively poor credit position. Pharmacy owners should be aware that undercapitalization is one of the main causes of business failure, and should take measures to avoid this pitfall.

SALES TO NET WORTH

This ratio assesses the productivity of owner's equity in terms of the sales generated by the firm. A high ratio warns of inadequate capitalization by the owner and excessive debt financing, which results in what is known as a highly leveraged practice. A low ratio indicates that the practice is not utilizing its funds fully and the owner's equity is stagnating.

FUNDED DEBT TO WORKING CAPITAL

This ratio examines long-term financial obligations and provides information on the practice's ability to borrow. A low ratio indicates little reliance on funded debt for working capital and therefore places the practice in a good position to borrow.

FIXED ASSETS TO NET WORTH

This ratio shows the percentage of net worth that is tied up in fixed assets such as fixtures and equipment. A higher ratio, for example 75 percent, suggests that too much capital is tied up in fixed assets and reduces the flexibility of current operations. A low ratio may indicate that fixtures are obsolete and require replacement or that they have been depreciated to such a point that there should be sufficient funds in the depreciation account to replace them.

AVERAGE PAYABLE PERIOD

The average payable period, as mentioned earlier, indicates the number of days accounts payable are outstanding. Chapter 12 explained the rationale behind increasing the average payable period, where possible, to improve the pharmacy's cash position, and argued the wisdom of carefully evaluating whether benefits to the pharamacy are greater by extending the payable period or by taking advantage of cash discounts for prompt payment. This evaluation is critical for pharmacies that are reliant on debt capital. Regardless of the actual payable period, it should certainly be greater than its companion ration for the collection of accounts receivable (average collection period).

DEGREE OF NEWNESS OF FIXED ASSETS

The value of this ratio is to give some insight into the remaining "useful life" of the pharmacy's fixed assets. A ratio of under 50 percent might encourage the pharmacy to renovate or replace existing fixtures. The implications of this ratio should be discussed with the pharmacy's accountant, as they are largely relevant to the methods of depreciation employed.

The Profitability Equation

Some of the more critical ratios we have discussed are closely interrelated. One way to look at them is through a profitability equation that consists of a financial objective and a financial program.[3] The financial objective considers return on investment and the financial program considers profit, rate of asset turnover, and leverage. Two additional ratios are therefore involved, as follows:

$$\text{Asset turnover} = \frac{\text{Sales}}{\text{Total assets}}$$

and

$$\text{Leverage} = \frac{\text{Total assets}}{\text{Net worth (equity)}}$$

Asset turnover is a measure of the sales dollars generated by each dollar invested in the firm's total assets. Leverage measures the dollar value in total assets that is being acquired for each dollar of net worth or equity. By borrowing funds from banks or obtaining trade credit from suppliers, the pharmacy owner acquires assets that are worth more than the amount of capital invested in the business by the owner(s), thereby obtaining leverage for the firm.

With these ratios, we can proceed to the profitability equation, which is as follows:

$$\text{Return on investment} = \text{Profit} \times \text{Asset turnover} \times \text{Leverage}$$

or

$$\frac{\text{Profit}}{\text{Net worth}} = \frac{\text{Profit}}{\text{Sales}} \times \frac{\text{Sales}}{\text{Total assets}} \times \frac{\text{Total assets}}{\text{Net worth}}$$

or

$$\frac{\text{Profit}}{\text{Net worth}} = \frac{\text{Profit}}{\text{Sales}} \times \text{Asset turnover} \times \frac{\text{Total liabilities and Net worth}}{\text{Net worth}}$$

If this equation were expanded to take into account the income statement and balance sheet, it would appear as illustrated in Figure 18.1.

ANTICIPATING PERFORMANCE: BREAK-EVEN ANALYSIS

Break-even analysis is an important tool in financial planning, used to assess the relationship between sales and expenses. It anticipates future

[3] W.R. Davidson, D.J. Sweeney, and R.W. Stampfl, *Retailing Management*, 6th ed. (Toronto: John Wiley and Sons, 1988), p. 164.

Figure 18.1 PLANNING FOR PROFITS

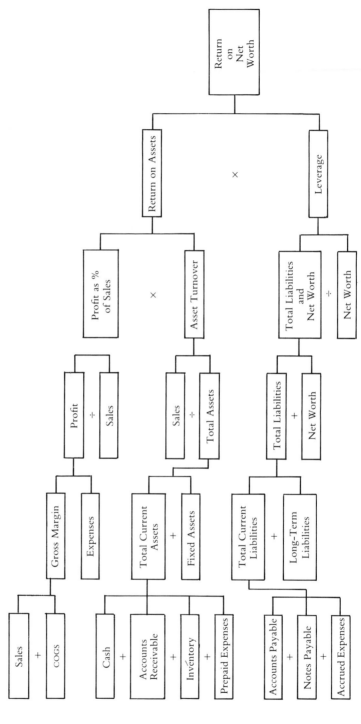

†Howard L. Hessler, "The DuPont Chart System for Appraising Operating Performance," in W.E. Thomas, Jr., ed., *Accounting, Budgeting, and Control*, 2nd ed. (South-Western Publishing Company, 1960). p. 799.

performance by predicting the effect that manipulating retail prices, cost of merchandise, expenses, and gross margin will have on profits. The calculation of a break-even point – the level of sales volume at which total revenue equals total costs – is a straightforward procedure consisting of five steps:

1. Categorize the expense items as fixed or variable expenses. Some expenses may be difficult to assign and a mix of common sense and good judgment is required."
2. Calculate the variable-expense ratio. This is simply the sum of the variable expenses expressed as a percentage of sales."
3. Calculate the gross-margin ratio. The income statement will provide the gross margin as a percentage of sales."
4. Calculate the marginal-income ratio. This is found by subtracting the variable-expense ratio from the gross-margin ratio. The marginal-income ratio is the percentage of sales dollars left to cover the fixed expenses and profit (if any)."
5. Calculate the break-even point. This is determined by dividing the fixed expenses by the marginal-income ratio. The answer is the sales volume required for the business to break even.

Expense items can be categorized as shown in Table 18.4. Once again, the figures used in our example are drawn from the Seventh Annual Survey of Community Pharmacy Operations for 1986. Refer back to Chapter 4 (Figure 4.1 on p. 34) for the complete income statement from which these expense figures are taken. Table 18.5 illustrates the break-even analysis calculations described above.

Table 18.4   FIXED AND VARIABLE EXPENSES

Fixed Expenses		Variable Expenses	
Owner/manager salary	$ 46,197	Employee wages	$141,327
Rent	30,150	Taxes and licences	5,505
Light, heat, power	5,725	Advertising	15,303
Acct., legal, professional		Bad debts	602
fees	5,516	Miscellaneous	39,749
Insurance	3,544	TOTAL	$202,486
Interest paid	7,805		
Repairs	5,041		
Delivery	4,951		
Depreciation	9,947		
Telephone	3,109		
TOTAL	$121,985		

Table 18.5   BREAK-EVEN ANALYSIS CALCULATIONS

Variable-expense ratio:	$\dfrac{\text{Variable expenses}}{\text{Total sales}} = \dfrac{202,486}{1,302,190} \times 100 = 15.6\%$
Gross-margin ratio:	$\dfrac{\text{Gross margin}}{\text{Total sales}} = \dfrac{387,051}{1,302,190} \times 100 = 29.7\%$
Marginal-income ratio:	Gross-margin ratio 29.7% − Variable-expense ratio 15.6% = 14.1%
Break-even point:	$\dfrac{\text{Fixed expenses}}{\text{Marginal-income ratio}} = \dfrac{121,985}{14.1\%} = \$865,142$ in sales
Break-even point in days:	$\dfrac{\text{Break-even point in sales}}{\text{Average daily sales}} = \dfrac{\$865,142}{\$1,302,190 \div 365\ \text{days}} = \dfrac{865,142}{3568} = 242$ days or appr. 8 months

The break-even point is interpreted as meaning that at a sales volume of $865,142 (as shown in Table 18.5), the marginal-income ratio of 14.1 percent produces a marginal income of $121,985 and that this amount is equal to the fixed expenses of the business. Sales above this volume begin to contribute to the profit at a rate of $0.141 for each dollar of sales beyond the break-even point.

The break-even point has other applications. It can be used as a basis for decisions on expansion, reducing margins through price discounting, or forecasting required sales volume for a predetermined profit.

Expansion plans must take into consideration any additional expenses incurred and determine whether these are fixed or variable expenses. For example, if additional space is obtained in order to store home health-care products, rent is going to increase by, let us say, $6000. What volume of sales will be required to break even?

1. Variable expenses are the same.
2. Fixed expenses increase to $127,985.
3. The variable-expense ratio remains the same.
4. The gross-margin ratio remains the same.
5. The marginal-income ratio would be the same.
6. Therefore, the break-even point would now be:

$$\frac{\text{Fixed expenses}}{\text{Marginal-income ratio}} = \frac{127,985}{14.1\%} = \$907,695.$$

Plans to discount prices and become more aggressive in promoting products could reduce the gross margin from 29.7 percent to, say, 26 percent. If all other factors remained the same, what would be the effect on the break-even point?

1. Fixed expenses are constant.
2. The variable-expense ratio is the same.

3. The gross-margin ratio is now 26 percent.
4. The marginal-income ratio becomes 26 − 15.6 = 10.4 percent.
5. The break-even point is now:

$$\frac{\text{Fixed expenses}}{\text{Marginal-income ratio}} = \frac{121,985}{10.4\%} = \$1,172.932.$$

If a predetermined profit of $65,000 is desired, what sales volume would be required under the existing circumstances? Here, profit can be considered a fixed amount that must be covered by the pharmacy's revenues to break even and is therefore added to fixed expenses.

1. Fixed expenses increase to $186,985.
2. Variable expenses are constant.
3. The gross-margin ratio is still 29.7 percent.
4. The marginal-income ratio remains 14.1 percent.
5. The sales volume required to break even would be:

$$\frac{\text{Fixed expenses}}{\text{Marginal-income ratio}} = \frac{186,985}{14.1\%} = \$1,326,135.$$

Break-even analysis is only a tool and must be used with care, as it has limitations. For example, the analysis uses forecasts of sales, margins, and expenses that are somewhat arbitrarily assigned into fixed and variable categories. If increased sales volume is achieved through price reductions and a corresponding gross-margin reduction, the projected profit relationship will change also.

Remember that the usefulness of this technique is limited: it can be applied without overall adjustments only in cases where a small increase in sales volume relative to forecasted expenses is under consideration. This is so because increasing sales beyond a certain level will also entail increases in fixed expenses to accommodate the greater sales volume – in terms of space (rent), labour (managerial salaries), and fixtures. Therefore, in such cases, new estimates must be made and a new break-even point calculated.

Hence, it is important to be wary of the faulty assumption that once the break-even point is passed, profit can be increased with consideration only for increasing variable expenses, because fixed expenses are presumed to have already been met. If sales increase substantially, fixed expenses will indeed grow and result in changing the cost structure relative to profit.

SUMMARY

Professional services cannot be provided successfully or securely, for any length of time, from a practice that is not financially sound. It is the pharmacist-owner's responsibility to predict and promptly correct any problems in the operation that could jeopardize its financial stability and growth. The analytic tools presented in this chapter will assist the pharmacist in effectively monitoring and assessing the health of the practice on an ongoing basis.

RECOMMENDED READING

Bank of Montreal. *Small Business Problem Solvers.* See especially Problem Solver No. 5; *Making Sense of Terms and Jargon*, and Problem Solver No. 7, *Measuring Performance*. Available at all branches of the Bank of Montreal.

Thomas, W.E. Jr., ed. *Readings in Cost Accounting, Budgeting, and Control.* 2nd ed. South-Western Publishing Company, 1960.

19

SECURITY

INTRODUCTION

"An ounce of prevention" is the best advice available when it comes to pharmacy-related crime. Ranging from armed robbery to shoplifting, from burglary to employee theft, and from prescription forgery to credit-card and cheque fraud, there is ample evidence to suggest that every pharmacy can expect to be victimized in one way or another.

The reality is that pharmacies are particularly vulnerable to criminal attack because of the attractive mix of desirable merchandise they contain – drugs and cash – and the additional feature of late hours of operation. Early closing, however, does not always reduce the risk.

Taking steps to prevent these crimes may seem to be an expensive proposition. However, when the possibility of physical injury and the likelihood of mental stress are factored into the cost equation, the "bottom line" will become more attractive. In fact, security should be looked upon as an essential part of the cost of doing business in today's world.

Many common crime-prevention techniques can be applied to protect pharmacists, staff members, customers, and property from injury or loss. Exterior security measures, interior security devices and internal procedures, and the minimizing of security risks are essential aspects of effective policies and systems.

SECURITY AGAINST EXTERNAL CRIME

Exterior Security Measures

Pharmacy premises are often located on busy, well-travelled streets or in malls. However, relatively isolated sites or areas with little pedestrian or vehicular traffic requires more inventive crime-prevention consider-ations, specifically with regard to exterior security measures.

An analysis of the streetscape, including the types and operating hours of neighbouring businesses, the current local crime rate, and the prog-nosis for the future, should be undertaken. A careful inspection of the business site itself – the interior walls, ceilings (especially in malls), and basement construction – can uncover weak links in the premises' security potential.

Properly placed exterior lighting will act as a deterrent and will also serve to enhance the physical appearance of the premises. It is best to illuminate the entire property, including the roof, entrances, and loading areas. Exterior lighting fixtures should be protected from vandalism, and bulbs should be replaced regularly.

A commercial timer should be installed to control the exterior light-ing, and the device can also be used to control other functions such as heating systems and window-display lighting. Photo-electric switches can also be used to automatically turn on the lighting system as darkness approaches.

Landscaping should be evaluated with a view to eliminating con-cealment and climbing facilities for a burglar. Shrubbery and trees should be trimmed to a maximum height of three to four feet above the ground to permit natural surveillance of the property. Debris, such as empty boxes and garbage containers, should be cleared away or situated so it does not provide a hiding place.

If fencing is required, chain-link fences are recommended because they do not restrict visibility for police officers and other observers.

It is important to ensure that the pharmacy address is displayed prom-inently on both the front and rear of the pharmacy to enable police to locate the pharmacy quickly in case of an emergency. Rear doors are often not labelled, which can cause confusion and delay when police officers need to respond to the rear exit as well as the front.

Doors, Windows, and Roof Openings

Exterior doors should be of 1 3/4 inch (4.5 cm) solid-wood core con-struction or 16-gauge steel or aluminum alloy. Doorframes should be of comparably solid construction as the door. A security strike installed in the doorframe will reinforce the strike area and prevent a burglar from spreading the doorframe with a pry bar and thereby defeating the lock.

Particular attention should be paid to hinges, ensuring that they are mounted on the inside of the frame or are the type with non-removable hinge pins. A locking pin can also be installed in an existing hinge plate.

On all exterior doors, a good-quality single-cylinder deadbolt lock with a minimum 1 inch (2.5 cm) extension into the frame should be used. Do not rely on key-in-the-knob locks. (It should be noted that the use of double-cylinder deadbolt locks is prohibited on public buildings by the National Building Code of Canada.)

Glass doors and glass-panelled wood doors should be fitted with unbreakable glass. Pivoting bolts can be replaced with hook bolts to provide extra protection. Thumbturn locks (sometimes used in mall locations) should be protected by a firmly attached metal plate to block access to the thumbturn; otherwise, the thumbturn lock should be replaced by a keyed cylinder.

Since sliding glass doors can be lifted from the tracks and set aside, additional security measures such as pins, shims, or commercial locks especially designed for sliding doors are recommended.

Bay or loading doors must be equipped with protective devices such as slide bolts, cast-iron keepers and pins, cylinder bolts, and / or padlocks.

It is recommended that padlocks include such features as hardened steel shackle, heel-and-toe locking, a minimum of five tumblers in the chamber, solid one-piece body, and a key-retaining feature. The chain or hasp must also be made of high-quality hardened steel.

Glass windows should be strengthened with unbreakable glass, and metal security bars should be installed. Seldom-used windows should be secured permanently with tamper-proof screws or bolted from the inside.

Roof openings, such as skylights and hatchways, require special attention. Skylights should be covered with iron bars or a securely fastened steel grill. All hatchway openings on the roof should be covered on the inside with 16-gauge sheet steel, secured from the inside with a slide bar or slide bolts, and equipped with non-removable pins on outside hinges.

Air ducts or air-vent openings exceeding 8 to 12 inches (20 to 30 cm) should be covered with iron bars or a steel grill. In high-risk areas, it may be necessary to protect these entry points with alarm-system installations. Regular inspections of all access points should be undertaken to ensure that security devices have not been tampered with.

Good key control is essential, and it is not costly. Establish policies to specify which employees are permitted to have keys to entry doors. Assign and record key distribution. Collect keys from employees who leave the business, and modify lock cylinders where the circumstances of leaving seem to warrant it.

SHOPPING MALLS AND DEPARTMENT STORES

Pharmacies located within shopping malls (enclosed or not) or department stores face a few special problems. Because of the relative insecurity of walls and ceilings, extra vigilance is required with regard to the installation of systems or equipment to help reduce the risk of break-in.

For example, in both strip malls and enclosed malls, the common ceiling area can be used to advantage by burglars. Incidents have been reported of thieves breaking into stores that were not securely protected. In one such case, a clothing store was burglarized and the thieves then climbed into the ceiling area and made their way over other premises until they reached the pharmacy, where they simply "dropped in." It is important that alarm systems on the premises be designed to anticipate this type of activity.

In department stores, the dispensary and prescription-drug storage area is particularly vulnerable to individuals who hide elsewhere in the store until closing time, then make their way into the dispensary. Again, a fortified and separate alarm system might be necessary, as well as a special barrier apparatus to prohibit access to the dispensary at closing time. Indeed, it is wise practice in any pharmacy to check all areas of the store before extinguishing lights and locking up.

Alarm systems

Despite the installation of security devices to reinforce doors, windows, and roof openings, the lure of drugs and cash often prompts burglars to penetrate a pharmacy's barriers by force. A store in which no alarm system is evident is especially vulnerable.

An alarm system for a pharmacy may include one or a combination of the following elements:

1. Contact devices to protect all doors, windows, and other access points.
2. Motion-detection or photo-electric beam devices that indicate when external security barriers have been breached.
3. Exterior and / or interior camera surveillance or closed-circuit television systems.
4. Vault protection by means of acoustic or vibration alarms or capacity (proximity) alarms.
5. Emergency signalling devices that permit a robbery or kidnapping victim to send a silent alarm signal.

Installation of an adequate alarm system will serve to deter burglars, detect undeterred burglars, and provide special protection for high-risk merchandise such as narcotics, controlled drugs, and currency.

Pharmacists are advised to consult with the crime-prevention officers of local law-enforcement agencies for advice specifically related to their particular locations. It is also advisable to obtain equipment recommendations and price quotations from two or three reputable security firms.

SECURITY PROCEDURES

The types of crimes to which pharmacies are vulnerable from outside elements include breaking and entering, robbery, prescription forgery, and shoplifting. In each case, there are a range of security measures that should be taken, from precautions and preventive procedures to appropriate conduct in face of such crimes that will reduce the potential for injury to staff members and customers. We shall discuss some of these precautions and procedures in this section.

Break-ins and Robberies

There are several important steps that should be taken upon the discovery of a break and entry into a pharmacy:

1. Do not interfere if the offence is in progress.
2. Notify the police.
3. Note the description and licence-plate number of any vehicles seen leaving the crime scene.
4. Do not touch or disturb any evidence.
5. Request that any other witnesses remain at the scene to assist police with the investigation.

As opposed to breaking and entering or burglary, robbery is defined as the theft of property under the threat of force (regardless of whether the robber actually has a weapon). Well-trained store personnel who follow robbery-protection steps can greatly reduce the threat of robbery.

Important measures to be taken include (1) ensuring adequate staffing, relative to store size, and having at least two employees present when the premises are closed for the day; (2) reducing the target size (making frequent bank deposits and taking regular inventory of narcotic and controlled drugs); (3) installing a surveillance camera; (4) reporting suspicious persons; and (5) varying the time at which night deposits are made and ensuring that two people are present. Such measures wil help "tell" potential robbers that robbery-prevention procedures have been taken.

One useful security measure is to store "marked" money in the cash register – a few identifiable bills to be given to a robber along with the remainder of the cash-register contents. Should the robber be apprehended with the money, the bills can be positively identified as the property of a particular store. One approach involves separating out a few bills and noting their serial numbers, then keeping them in the register in an envelope labelled, for example, "Christmas Fund." A similar measure that has proved helpful in obtaining convictions is the marking of merchandise and containers with special pens to assist in positive identification. Other marking techniques for money or merchandise can be obtained from the crime-prevention division of your local police force.

If a robbery occurs, remain calm. Observe the individual(s) as closely as possible in order to give police a clear description later on. Co-operate with the robber, but do not volunteer to do more than asked. Give the robber the marked money from the cash register. When the robber leaves, note the direction of travel, the vehicle description, and the licence-plate number. Call the police immediately, and be prepared to give a description of the robber and the getaway vehicle. Close and lock the pharmacy, and preserve the scene for evidence. Request all witnesses to remain at the scene and make written notes of descriptions and other important information.

Prescription Forgeries

Constant vigilance in detecting and intercepting prescription forgeries has a hidden payoff. The "street" intelligence network will spread the word that a certain pharmacy should be avoided when it comes to attempting this type of fraud.

When presented with a prescription, pharmacists and dispensing personnel should ask themselves the following questions:

1. Do I know this patient?
2. Do I know this prescriber?
3. Is this the right physician identity number?
4. Is this the prescriber's handwriting?
5. Is the prescription for a commonly abused drug?
6. Is this a usual quantity, dosage, and direction for use?
7. Are these the usual abbreviations?
8. Is this prescription written in one handwriting, using one pen?
9. Is this an original prescription blank, not a photocopy?
10. Am I sure that nothing about this prescription looks suspicious?
11. In provinces where the triplicate prescription form program[1] is in effect, is the prescription written on the appropriate form?

If the answer to any of the questions is "No" or "I don't know," the situation warrants some investigation. Remember, always call the pres-

[1] The triplicate prescription form program is a program designed to reduce "multidoctoring" and the abuse of narcotic and controlled drugs. At the time of writing, the program had proven successful in Alberta and was soon to be in place in other provinces.

criber at a telephone number from your files or from the official telephone directory. Don't accept the telephone number on the prescription form as valid.

Some provincial licensing organizations have established phone networks through which other pharmacies are notified of any reported attempts to pass forged prescriptions. Contact your provincial licensing body for further information (see the Directory at the end of this book).

Shoplifting

Because of the wide variety of products available, pharmacies are a favourite target for shoplifters. Unfortunately, many pharmacies are also easy targets.

Shoplifters, both professional and amateur, employ an amazing array of techniques to obtain their objectives. Among the most common are:

1. removing goods from a counter by covering an item with a shopping bag, coat or umbrella and sweeping it off the counter into another bag;
2. distracting a sales clerk's attention (by one member of a shoplifting team feigning illness, a seizure, or a fight inside or immediately outside store premises), while an accomplice removes the desired merchandise;
3. switching the contents of an expensive product into the box or container of a less expensive product;
4. placing small objects into coat linings, gloves, hats, or other items of clothing;
5. running from the premises with valuable items that have been removed by the clerk from secure display cases.

There are a number of simple procedures which can be applied to deter shoplifting.

One of the most important (and least expensive) steps is to make contact with each customer. "May I help you?" are words a potential thief does not want to hear. Sales clerks should be trained to be alert and observant while they are attending to routine tasks such as stocking shelves and taking inventory. In addition, larger pharmacies frequently employ security agencies to provide "floor walkers" during major sales or very busy seasons.

Store layout should ensure clear visibility, elimination of blind spots that might provide cover for a shoplifter, and location of the check-out counters near store entrances and exits. (It is also helpful to have only one entrance/exit whenever possible, requiring customers to pass through a check-out area on leaving the store.) The installation of convex mirrors and / or surveillance cameras will have a deterrent value.

Valuable inventory should be placed in locked display cases in view of the check-out counter, but not near entrances and exits.

Signs should be posted that warn against shoplifting and tell customers that shoplifters will be prosecuted. Consistent enforcement of this policy will also have a deterrent effect.

Section 449 of the Criminal Code of Canada allows any person to make a citizen's arrest and to deliver the offender to a police officer. Before making a citizen's arrest, however, be absolutely certain that an item was stolen. The citizen making the arrest must be an eyewitness to the theft. Know the nature of the item taken, and be certain that the item was not paid for. Maintain visual contact with the shoplifter.

It is not necessary for the shoplifter to have left the premises in order to be apprehended. However, chances of a successful prosecution are greatly enhanced if the shoplifter is apprehended outside the store. The person who witnessed the act of shoplifting can say to the shoplifter, "I want you to come back to the store. You have something you have not paid for." Do not use force. Notify the police department and request assistance.

SECURITY AGAINST INTERNAL CRIME

According to security experts for retail businesses, theft by employees accounts for a much larger percentage of total losses from theft than shoplifting or other external crimes. Inventory shrinkage through internal thefts by employees accounts for as much as 80 percent of a store's losses.

Internal theft can occur within any division of a business – cash, purchasing, receiving, inventory, or shipping. The key to preventing losses of this nature lies in good supervision. The active involvement of the proprietor or supervisor will create obstacles to internal theft.

The first step in controlling internal losses is to hire honest and dependable employees. Application forms should request information which the employer intends to verify. Length and dates of employment are the two things most often falsified on applications, and this information should always be verified.

The second step in an effective internal security program is to establish good merchandise and money controls, combined with unscheduled audits and inspections to ensure that the controls are enforced.

There are two basic principles to follow when setting up control systems:

1. Reduce employee access to both money and merchandise so that access is restricted on the basis of need.

2. Separate responsibility between employees, so that the handling of money or merchandise is entrusted to one employee, while independent accountability and record keeping are assigned to another employee.

The majority of reported thefts involve cash. There are a number of basic safeguards that can be helpful in discouraging stealing. Recording of sales, bookkeeping, and bank deposits should be undertaken by different people. Frequent bank deposits and minimum cash in the register reduce the opportunity to manipulate cash receipts.

Cash registers should be audited without prior notification. A register reading is taken, the opening reading and starting cash are subtracted, and the resulting figure is compared to the cash on hand (which should be counted in the cashier's presence). Voids and refunds are then subtracted.

Too much money in the register may indicate that the cashier has not rung in each sale (but has rather accepted money from customers, failed to record it, and waited for a chance to remove the excess cash). This simple, obvious, and hard-to-detect method is employed by almost all employees who steal from the cash register.

A cash shortage could also indicate an employee theft. Cashiers may extract cash by preparing false refund forms or creating void purchase slips and pocketing the equivalent amount in cash. Approval for each of these transactions should therefore be required from a supervisor.

Repeated errors may indicate that a clerk does not have the ability to handle money and make change. In short, out-of-balance registers point to the need for questioning and close attention to individual employees, as well as enforcement of basic security and audit functions.

Many merchants employ a commercial shopping service to evaluate their store's retail sales practices. Random visits to the business by idividuals or teams of "shoppers" making a series of test purchases from each employee will result in reports detailing any dishonest practices, in addition to such problems as poor service and discourtesy. (On the other hand, extremely good service would also be noted).

Bank statement reconciliations should be completed each month by a person other than the one who prepares the bank deposits. Periodic record audits will act as a further deterrent.

It is also important to ensure that safeguards are in effect in all purchasing and receiving procedures. Centralized purchasing, using prenumbered purchase orders on which all details have been noted and approved (including unit price, number of units ordered, and name of employee who ordered the merchandise), allows for easier supervision.

It is also wise to insist that every purchase or expense be accompanied by an invoice or other documentation before it is paid. Responsibility for purchasing, receiving, and paying bills should, if possible be assigned to different individuals.

It is important to establish a central receiving area and require accountability. An employee should be appointed to receive and sign for all incoming merchandise, using shipping receipt forms. Require that each shipment be checked, counted, and compared with the invoice, as well as the purchase order.

It is not surprising that, of all the merchandise carried by pharmacies, dispensary inventory presents a special temptation for employee theft. Such theft can involve either large or small quantities of desirable drugs. Continuous supervision of the dispensary is highly recommended, and it is wise to restrict access to the area to authorized dispensary personnel only and to enforce this policy strictly. The development of rigorous inventory-control methods, including frequent periodic reconciliations, may be necessary to prevent or detect shortages.

Finally, staff purchases are known to present another area of opportunity for internal theft. All sales to employees should consequently be handled by an approved supervisor. An employee other than the purchaser should be involved in wrapping and shipping the merchandise and the purchaser should only be allowed to pick the merchandise up from a secure collection area at the end of the work shift. It may be necessary, in larger operations particularly, to restrict staff-purchasing activities to times when the premises are not open for business.

While many business owners feel that employees are less likely to steal if they are given a substantial employee discount on purchases, others believe this to be too costly a deterrent, noting that some employees take undue advantage of the privilege, buying items not only for themselves but also for friends and relatives.

FIRE SECURITY

Protection against fire damage is another area that pharmacists and their store planners need to consider. Because fire-protection regulations vary from one jurisdiction to another, pharmacists are advised to consult local authorities to determine the prevailing requirements. Exits, sprinkler systems, and fire extinguishers, as well as the safe storage of flammable chemicals, are a few of the areas that must be considered.

Fire extinguishers are designed for use during the early stages of a fire. They should be located in several areas of the store (dispensary, stockroom, and front-store area). It is essential to have extinguishers serviced periodically to ensure that they are in good operating condition.

The installation of sprinkler systems should be considered in order to help prevent extensive damage by fire to pharmacy premises. It must, however, be remembered that, even if drug inventory bears no obvious signs of heat damage (scorch marks, smoke deposits) after a fire, the pharmacist must consider the possibility of invisible damage by heat, toxic fumes, or smoke penetration of containers, which would necessitate the disposal of the entire drug inventory.

If a fire erupts during business hours, the plan of action should include locating the fire, getting staff and customers out of the premises, and calling the fire department.

CONCLUSION

Pharmacy owners and managers will find it useful to review the following Security Checklist in order to ensure that they have taken into consideration all the security measures necessary for the protection of their operations.

A high number of negative responses to the questions in the checklist would indicate a need to enhance the security of the premises and the store operation. Improving security will not necessarily ensure that pharmacy crime will be eliminated, but it will discourage intruders and other criminals, who will usually choose the least secure target as their object.

SECURITY CHECKLIST

1. Are all entrances and exits well lighted?
2. Is the address prominently displayed on the front and rear of the premises?
3. Have areas of concealment for burglars been eliminated?
4. Are good key-control procedures practised?
5. Are all exterior wood doors of solid core construction?
6. Are the doorframes reinforced at the strike area?
7. Are the exterior doors hinged on the inside?
8. Are the exterior doors equipped with a deadbolt lock?
9. Have glass panels been replaced with unbreakable glass or covered by a mesh grill or bars?
10. Are double glass doors equipped with a cylinder deadbolt?
11. Have glass windows and sliding glass doors been equipped with additional security devices?
12. Have all access points (skylights, hatchways, air ducts, loading bays) been considered and have all outside walls been secured by the installation of vibration alarms?
13. Are routine maintenance checks performed to ensure that security arrangements are intact and alarm systems functional?
14. Is the interior of the pharmacy well lighted to ensure visibility both in and out?
15. Are windows free of display cards and advertising clutter?
16. Are narcotic and controlled-drug inventories and reconciliations being performed regularly?
17. Are cash-handling functions divided among several employees?
18. Is a commercial shopping service employed to evaluate employees' retail-sales practices?

19. Are strict purchasing and receiving accountability procedures being enforced?
20. Does the proprietor or a designated individual take an active supervisory role?
21. Are employees trained to prevent and respond to shoplifting attempts?
22. Have all staff members received training in what to do if an armed robbery occurs?
23. Are dispensary staff members instructed on how to detect and intercept prescription forgeries?
24. Are crime-prevention-program decals and posters displayed in the dispensary and front-store area?
25. Has liaison been established with local law enforcement agencies?
26. Does the pharmacy have a good insurance policy?

Recommended Reading

B.C. Police Commission. *Business Crime Prevention Seminar*, Vancouver, 1978.

B.C. Police Commission and Ministry of the Solicitor General of Canada. *Business Watch,* Vancouver, 1979.

Brown, L.J., and Stewart, T.J., eds. *Pharmacy Security Guide.* Vancouver: College of Pharmacists of British Columbia and British Columbia Police Commission, 1981.

Carson, C.R. *Managing Employee Honesty.* Los Angeles: Security World Publishing Co., Inc., 1977.

Hemphill, C.F. *Modern Security Methods.* Englewood Cliffs, N.J.: Prentice-Hall, Inc., 1979.

Hughes, M.M. *Successful Retail Security.* Los Angeles: Security World Publishing Co., Inc., 1978.

Lipman, A. *How to Protect Yourself from Crime.* New York: Avon Books, 1975.

Rawlins, S/Sgt. V. *Business Security Manual.* Ottawa: Ministry of the Solicitor General of Canada, 1978.

Robbery Prevention Kit. Solicitor General of Canada (available from R.C.M.P. units).

Saby, Cst. G.R., and Cole, Corp. R.S. *Program Against Drug Diversion.* R.C.M.P., Manitoba Pharmaceutical Association, Bureau of Dangerous Drugs (Prairie Region), 1983.

Sawers, J.W. *Protecting Your Home Against Burglary.* Ottawa: Canada Mortgage and Housing Corporation, 1981.

Weber, T.L. *Pharmacy Security Manual.* Smith, Kline and French Laboratories, 1976.

20

COMPUTERS IN PHARMACY PRACTICE

INTRODUCTION

In Canada, pharmacists were among the first professionals to become interested in using computers. They were quick to see the computer as a useful tool that would provide freedom from the many repetitive technical and clerical tasks involved in pharmacy practice. From the early 1970s, the most enterprising of pharmacists were starting to use either stand-alone minicomputers or the services of a central computer, provided by firms specializing in this area.

Enthusiasm grew with the advent of microcomputers and, today, most pharmacists are convinced of the benefits of computerization. On the other hand, they now face a much wider range of options in stand-alone equipment, software packages designed for pharmacy practice, and computer services that specialize in pharmacy practice. Pharmacy owners must educate themselves in order to make the proper choice of equipment and systems.

To start, the computer must be demystified: it is a tool capable of storing large amounts of information and executing thousands of commands per second, but it has no intelligence of its own and will not produce useful results unless properly programmed and supplied with appropriate, and accurate, data. The usefulness of a computer system is therefore proportional to the skills and knowledge applied by the analysts and programmers who initially design its software programming.

Computer systems consist of two elements – hardware (the physical equipment) and software (the programs that instruct the hardware to perform various functions). The hardware includes the following essential components: a central processing unit (CPU), storage devices (hard or floppy disks or magnetic tape), one or more cathode-ray tubes (CRT – commonly referred to as monitors), keyboards, one or more printers, and, optionally, a modem – the device that translates electronic messages for transmittal over telephone lines. Software, that is, the necessary set of electronic instructions that the hardware executes, is currently available for a range of applications in pharmacy practice, including patient profiling, drug-interaction detection, prescription processing, nursing-home programming, third-party billing, automatic price updating, general ledger, accounts payable and accounts receivable, inventory control, durable-medical-equipment control, word processing, payroll processing, and various other applications depending on the needs of the pharmacy.[1]

Important decisions must certainly be made about the hardware component of a pharmacy computer system – for example, whether it has sufficient storage capacity, the speed of the processor, the number of terminals it can accommodate and whether it is up to date and lends itself to upgrading. However, the most critical decisions for the pharmacist will relate to the software packages offered: are the programs designed in a way that will properly meet the pharmacy's needs, and how well do those programs perform?

Most pharmacy-system suppliers currently offer "bundled" or "turnkey" computer systems, meaning simply that the hardware and software are sold together as a complete system by a single supplier. The advantage of purchasing a turnkey system rests in dealing with only one supplier, who will become familiar with all the pharmacy's needs and applications and will accept responsibility for servicing both components of the system. Also, it should be noted that current pharmacy systems are available with integrated software, meaning that professional functions can be tied to business-management functions – for example, to automatically generate prescription-refill reminder letters to patients.[2]

The pharmacist must explore the various available systems and select the one that will best satisfy present needs and be capable of adapting to future needs. In addition, decisions must be made with regard to the suppliers of the system, to determine the extent of service and support offered and whether it will continue for a reasonable period after the purchase of the system.

Choosing the supplier of the system is extremely important. The prospective purchaser should check to see how long the supplier has been

[1] Laura Lang, "Why Should Pharmacists Computerize?" *Pharmacy West* (May 1987), p. 29.
[2] Lang, "Why Should Pharmacists Computerize?" pp. 28, 29.

Table 20.1.   COMPUTER SYSTEM APPLICATIONS IN PHARMACY
PRACTICE

Input (by programmer and/or pharmacist)	System Function	Output (to meet pharmacy's needs)
Patient information (name, address, date of birth, allergies, consumption patterns, etc.)	File search Product search Pricing Data verification Billing	Complete patient files Labels and receipts Insurance claims Nursing-home reports Inventory control reports Accounting and financial reports Sales analysis Purchasing reports
Product information (name, contents, formulation, dosage form, instructions for use, cost and fee, etc.)		
Laws and regulations (operative details of narcotic and controlled drug laws and of provincial licensing body regulations)		
Third-party payer information (account forms, terms)		

in business and the resources of the supplier in terms of support personnel. A very good practice is to request a list of customers served by the supplier and then to check with some of these customers to determine their satisfaction. Suppliers may offer supposedly good systems at very competitive prices but be gone from the business within a year or so.

Every system yields a product (output) that satisfies the needs of its users as expressed by the programmed instructions and by the entry of relevant data (input). Some examples of this process in the context of pharmacy practice are shown in Table 20.1.

The system chosen must be capable of fulfilling the needs and requirements of the pharmacist, both as a health professional acting in accordance with the regulations of provincial regulatory bodies and government authorities and the requirements of insurers, and as a manager who must ensure that the pharmacy is profitable. The first step for the pharmacy owner or manager in choosing a system for a pharmacy, then, is to *define needs clearly*, in order to know what to look for in the systems offered.

In community-pharmacy practice, day-to-day computing needs are known to change constantly. It is therefore critical that the package selected be flexible and adaptable to modification over time. As mentioned earlier, it should be possible to upgrade the equipment in order to increase system and storage capacity and to integrate the software improvements that are likely to develop in the future.

In this chapter, we shall focus largely on professional and managerial needs relating to the dispensary. Front-store management needs were addressed in our discussion of POS systems in Chapter 11 (pp. 158-160); here, we shall give only an overview of those requirements, toward the end of the chapter. Although it is true that the smaller, more clinically oriented pharmacy may not find it cost-effective to invest in front-store computerization (at the outset, at any rate), we would nevertheless recommend that, in selecting a computer system for the dispensary, all pharmacy owners at least consider the system's potential for integration with front-store systems in the future.

PROFESSIONAL NEEDS

Professional needs are in part dictated by the requirements of the provincial licensing bodies and government authorities that regulate the operation of a pharmacy. These include requirements for maintaining patient files, rules for labelling, and laws governing the handling of narcotic and controlled drugs.

Patient Files

The patient file is the cornerstone of the pharmacy computing system. The software chosen should be designed to accommodate all the information normally maintained in manual patient-medication records. (Some provincial regulatory agencies have established precise guidelines for the design of computerized patient files and the information that they must contain.) All the information that pertains to the maintenance of patient profiles, as well as basic information identifying the patient (including surname, given name, date of birth, and address), should be recorded in the file. In addition, allergies, chronic illnesses, the general condition of the patient, and any other relevant health-related characteristics can be entered. It is important to verify that a system's patient file has been designed to provide sufficient space for information which is essential for the pharmacist in properly conducting patient-profile analysis. Finally, with systems that have an accounts-receivable capacity, the patient file should contain the necessary information for billing the patient's personal account and, to facilitate third-party billing, all relevant data on the particular drug plan as well as the patient's assigned eligibility number.

The computer system selected should make patient files easily and quickly accessible and, in order to prevent duplication of files, it must also allow for multiple access to each file. The most common method of access to a computerized patient file is alphabetical by surname and first name, but access should also be possible using other unique identifiers, such as the patient's middle initial, maiden name, or birth date. For patients with insurance coverage, it may also be possible to access the file using the eligibility number assigned by the particular insurer. Finally, access should be possible using any of the prescription numbers on medication dispensed to the particular patient.

Since the information in the patient file will change continually over time, the system should feature simplicity and speed in its updating capability. The updating of existing information and the addition of new data should be controlled by a system of passwords that permit specific categories of changes. This way, the security of patient files can be protected by informing only authorized personnel of the passwords. For example, while a change of address might be entered by any employee of the pharmacy, only the pharmacist would have the means to insert a notation indicating that a patient no longer suffers from a particular allergy.

Prescription Processing

Each time a prescription is dispensed, it must be entered into the patient's individual file. Federal law requires that original prescriptions, initialled by the dispensing pharmacist, be kept on record by the pharmacy for at least two years. Original prescriptions entered into computerized patient files must similarly be retained for this length of time. (Note that, in certain provinces, the life of a prescription is limited to one year, at which time a renewal prescription must be initiated.) The computer system selected should have sufficient storage space in the patient files to allow for a minimum of two, and preferably three, years' medication history for each patient. Knowing both the number of new prescriptions dispensed daily and the desired retention period will enable the pharmacist to calculate the total number of prescriptions that the system must be able to store. This figure will allow the supplier to determine the total storage space required. It is wise, however, to allow for a little more space than is immediately necessary, to accommodate possible increases in the daily number of prescriptions dispensed. A prescription should only be deleted from the system once the retention period has lapsed. Each prescription should be identified by a unique number, which the system will protect against duplication.

All information from the original prescription and any renewals must be accessible to the pharmacist at all times. Whether a prescription is received verbally or in writing, the following information should be entered into the file: the original date of dispensing; indications as to whether an alternative brand of the drug was used rather than the brand prescribed; product information (name, formulation, dosage form, manufacturer); the quantity prescribed, the dosage, and the prescribing physician and dispensing pharmacist. For each renewal, the system registers the date dispensed, the quantity dispensed, and the name of the dispensing pharmacist, together with any other information that has changed – without altering data pertaining to previous transactions that already exist in the file. A system that complies with these requirements will allow the pharmacist, when dispensing a new prescription, to recall each of the previous transactions in order to review the medication that the patient has received to date. The system allows stored information to be changed, but only by means of a specific password. If access to a particular prescription is required, it is normally achieved by entering the unique prescription number. If, on the other hand, the prescription number is not known, the system should be able to display all the prescriptions stored in any selected patient file, accessible by the patient's name.

Many computer systems available today have the capability of detecting drug interactions. The products in the drug file are coded in such a manner as to produce a warning when an interaction between two drugs takes place. Some systems even indicate the significance of the interaction by stating levels, the first level being the most significant, the second level not as significant. It is extremely important that the pharmacist not rely totally on the computer interaction programmes. It is possible a drug will not be coded or a new drug coming on the market will not be included in the programme. The pharmacist's professional knowledge is the criteria for establishing drug interactions. Computer drug interaction programmes are an aid to the pharmacist in the course of analyzing patient profiles. For example, the computer will search past prescriptions (and non-prescription drugs) in the patient file when a new prescription is entered, and will issue a warning on the screen if any potential drug-interaction problems are detected.[3] The pharmacist must then assess the clinical importance of the interaction, and proceed accordingly.

Product Files

Most pharmacy computer systems supply product or drug files that contain essential identifying and descriptive information on a fairly comprehensive list of products that are available on the market or at least carried by a major wholesaler in the area. Product files may vary from one area of the country to another and from one pharmacy to another, and may have to be customized by the individual pharmacy to more

---

[3] See Chapter 22 for further discussion of drug-interaction detection systems, available data banks on adverse drug reactions, and computer-related innovations that could have a profound effect on patient profiling and prescription processing.

accurately reflect its inventory. The product description in the system's drug file should be thorough and complete in order to avoid any ambiguity, containing information such as the DIN (Drug Identification Number), brand and generic name, drug formulation, dosage form, price, and manufacturer, as well as codes indicating the drug's classification under federal law Interaction and Counselling Codes and whether it is reportable or non-reportable. Similarly, information should be accessible by DIN or by an alphabetical search using the brand or generic name of the product. Pharmacy computer systems are normally programmed to search drug files by content and manufacturer as well. In general, the more information the pharmacist can provide, the faster and more precise the search will be.

To enable the pharmacist to better advise the patient when dispensing medication, many systems also provide a certain amount of supplementary information on the product, which is accessible using a designated code. This information is for reference only, however, and should always be adapted to the prescription at hand. The manufacturer's recommended dosage, any relevant warnings or precautions to be taken, side effects or adverse effects, and possible interactions with other drugs or with foods may be included. Pharmacists usually supplement the drug information provided in the system files with other available patient-counselling aids, which we shall discuss in a later section.

System or software suppliers periodically generate updates to product files (reflecting new products or price changes), which they supply to client pharmacies on diskette, or, where applicable, transmit electronically (by modem) to the pharmacy computer.

PRICE CALCULATION

The system should also be able to calculate prescription prices based on cost-price and professional-fee information that is stored in the product file. Again, individual pharmacies normally find it necessary to customize the costs included in the system's product files, and, of course, to update them as necessary. They must also input the appropriate professional fee.

Pharmacies now sign agreements with provincial governments and private insurers to provide prescribed drugs at negotiated prices under the respective drug plans. Despite efforts to maintain uniformity of prices to paying patients and third-party payers, differing prices often occur. Consequently, cost as a component of the selling price may differ under the different plans. This situation requires a computer system that will apply the appropriate data depending on the nature of the patient's coverage (or lack of coverage).

All changes or updates in costs or professional fees that are entered into the system should be reflected in the prices that it calculates for all new prescriptions and prescription renewals. The system selected should enable price updates to be made easily and swiftly. Some pharmacy-system suppliers provide product-file diskettes with price updates every January and July in response to formulary changes.

Physician Files

The system should contain a file on the prescribing physicians in the area, with all the information necessary to identify the doctor and to prepare reports: surnames and given names, complete addresses and telephone numbers, and, in provinces that require it, the physician's licence number. The file should contain space for notes to be added by the pharmacist regarding the current status of physicians listed and other relevant information, derived either from personal experience or by notification from the provincial licensing body (for example, that a physician has closed his or her practice or is no longer licensed to prescribe narcotic and controlled drugs). It is even helpful to record any reports of theft of a physician's personalized prescription forms. The availability of such information in the system can protect the pharmacist from dispensing drugs on fraudulent or forged prescriptions.

Labelling of Prescription Drugs

The labelling of prescription drugs is governed by the regulations of each of the provincial licensing bodies. The information required to appear on labels normally includes identification of the pharmacy, the patient, and the prescribing physician and the name and dosage form of the product prescribed, as well as the quantity dispensed and directions for use. The price paid by the patient, broken down to show product cost and professional fee, is also required by some provinces. In addition, the computer system might be programmed to print, on a detachable part of the label, any precautions that might apply to the use of the medication. The pharmacist can then decide whether or not to give this information to the patient.

Patient Counselling Aids

As you will recall from Chapter 17, patient-counselling aids are available from a number of sources, either in the form of print materials or on diskettes that can be integrated with many of the currently available pharmacy computer systems (see pp. 279-80). A computerized version is now offered by the USP-DI, but other organizations are likely to computerize their products in the near future as well (for example, PAL and SIM). These aids are not intended to replace the pharmacist's recommendations, but to reinforce them and act as a reminder for the patient. While the printed information sheets have been valuable as aids in advising and instructing patients, their computerized counterpart overcomes one significant drawback: the pharmacist is now able to adapt the information to more precisely address the particular patient's case. This is important in that, previously, patients were exposed to generalized, comprehensive information pertaining to all possible cases, and could become needlessly perturbed or confused by warnings or instructions that were not necessarily relevant to them.

Each of the patient-counselling-aid files is coded by product and, on generating a new or renewal prescription, the computer will indicate the code of the file to be given to the patient. If a printout is generated by the system for an individual customer, the computer can be programmed to add the patient's name, the prescription number, date of service, and name of the prescribing physician. The pharmacist should then be able to adapt the text that is contained in the file, tailoring it to the needs and circumstances of the particular patient. In some cases, of course, the pharmacist may decide that the information does not require adjustment. Nonetheless, it is of the utmost importance that the system allow the pharmacist the choice, by having the capacity to adapt the text of the files.

Nursing-Home Applications

Pharmacies holding contracts to service old-age or nursing homes can now avail themselves of special computer software programs designed specifically to address the pharmaceutical and patient-counselling needs of the elderly in an institutional setting. Various types of reports can be generaged to assist nursing-home staff in administering their patients' often complex therapeutic drug treatments. For example, each prescription in the system, whether to be taken once or four times daily, will bear the appropriate hour at which the drug should be administered, and a report can be generated for each patient in the form of a daily drug-administration schedule or timetable. Relevant patient information, including diagnosis and allergies, can be programmed to print on each report. "Physician-order" reports can also be generated, listing all medication and ancillary orders, including diets, treatments, and lab orders. Companies offering such programs provide preprinted, multi-part forms designed for printing several reports at one time. Among the other reports available through nursing-home systems are drug-interaction screening reports, departmental nursing-home reports, and shipping reports that allow verification of the drugs delivered by the pharmacy to the home. In addition, accounts receivable functions can be integrated to provide a comprehensive management tool for the pharmacy's involvement with the nursing home.

To facilitate the management of patient and prescription files, the pharmacy computer system should ideally be a flexible one, which can amalgamate duplicate files when they occur; display patients' prescription profiles on the screen for the pharmacist to identify any possible interactions, assess the consistency of treatment, or detect excessive consumption; reprint labels or files; and print out patient files.

One of the most obvious, and perhaps most significant, advantages of computerization in the area of professional services is the time that it makes available for the pharmacist to spend with patients. A computer system that is properly designed for the pharmacy's needs and properly used by well-trained, reliable staff will cut down immensely on the steps formerly involved in filling a prescription and the time formerly spent on related paperwork.

ADMINISTRATIVE NEEDS

The pharmacy owner or manager requires a system that can perform a range of administrative tasks to facilitate the smooth operation of the pharmacy.

Billing and Accounts Receivable

The system selected should have the ability to prepare claims for reimbursement from the various prescription-plan insurers. This process involves more than just the printing of reports.

The system must check eligibility numbers, verify that the product is covered by the insurance plan, calculate the amount of the claim and, where appropriate, the amount payable by the patient. The terms and requirements of each government and private insurer that provides coverage for the pharmacy's patients must be programmed in the system. Each time prescription information is entered, the system should be able to draw on insurer identification stored in the patient file and cost information stored in the product file, selecting the appropriate cost price, adding the professional fee, and automatically generating a claim to the appropriate third party, specifying, where applicable, the deductible amount payable by the patient. The system should be equipped to transmit claims by whatever means and in whatever form each agency requires. There are several possibilities for submitting claims: as hard copy, on diskette, or by electronic transmission over telephone lines, using a modem. Some systems offer a program that displays the account formats used by each insurer.

The insurer will return the pharmacy's statements of account, in print, electronically or on disk, and the computer can then easily compare claims and produce lists of any outstanding claims, which must be checked and resubmitted for payment.

The system must of course have the ability to generate receipts for patients paying a deductible amount or, where no insurance coverage is involved, the full amount of the prescription. Most systems available today print the receipt, the label, the prescription itself, and a counselling message on a single, perforated form. (Some pharmacies still find it less expensive to have two printers, one for labels and the other for receipts, and to print receipts only as they are required.)

Pharmacies using third-party billing systems and transmitting claims directly to insurers find that their claims are not only paid sooner, but that significantly fewer claims are rejected (the latter will of course depend on the accuracy of information that is entered into the computer). In general, integrated accounting and pharmacy software will facilitate the management of the full scope of accounts receivable for insurers, co-paying patients, and self-paying patients. A second CRT and an additional printer are often added to permit both pharmacy and accounting functions to be used simultaneously.

HEALTH-SERVICES CARDS AND THIRD-PARTY BILLING

A very recent development that may further enhance speed and accuracy in third-party billing should be noted here as well. At the time of writing, a plastic health-services card that allows pharmacists to make paperless claims had just been introduced in Saskatchewan. These cards, issued by the health ministry to all patients insured under the provincial drug-benefit plan, bear a magnetic identity strip that can be read by a special pharmacy device similar to those used to validate charge cards with an on-line link to the drug plan's central computer. The pharmacist simply enters the quantity dispensed and the unit cost, and the central computer calculates the total price and the co-pay amount. At the present time this device is not linked to the pharmacy's computer and it is necessary to enter the information twice. Future developments will enable information to be transmitted automatically to the drug plan's computer when the pharmacist enters the prescription. It also prepares weekly billings for each pharmacy and reimburses the pharmacies by cheque. Among the benefits of this innovation are the "immediate and automatic adjudication of a claim and calculation of costs; direct billing; and flagging of double-doctoring and other abuses."[4] Health-services cards may be the wave of the future, with a dramatic impact on pharmacy computer users.

[4]"Newsfront: Paperless Claims for Saskatchewan," *Drug Merchandising* 70, no. 2 (February 1989):14.

Administrative Reports

After a pharmacy computer system has been in place for several months, a wealth of information about patients and their prescriptions will have been gathered and stored in the computer. It should be possible for the system to sort this information in ways that will enable the pharmacist to produce all the reports and analyses necessary for proper management. Examples of such reports and analyses include the following:

1 Print-out of patient file, to be supplied to a patient that is moving out of the area or to an attending doctor, either on demand or as a courtesy, in the event of a patient's hospitalization.
2. An alphabetical listing of patients, to check for possible duplication or to use as a mailing list.
3. A list of patients by the products dispensed to them, in the event of a manufacturer's recall of a drug product.
4. A list of patients who have not renewed their prescriptions within the required time period, to ensure continuity of treatment and patient compliance.
5. A daily summary of prescriptions by specified third-party payers, to check amounts being claimed from each agency and amounts to be received in cash from patients.
6. A monthly breakdown of sales by individual product to facilitate inventory control and purchasing; in alphabetical order by product, manufacturer, or generic name.
7. A monthly analysis of sales by payment category (cash or third party) to create an accurate record of accounts receivable.
8. A monthly analysis comparing sales this month with sales in the same month last year and/or year-to-date sales for the current year and the same period last year.
9. An analysis of the number of prescriptions dispensed per hour through the course of a given day to aid in establishing an appropriate work schedule for personnel.

MANAGEMENT NEEDS IN THE DISPENSARY AND FRONT STORE

Inventory Control

In our discussion of inventory control in Chapter 11, we described the functions performed (and the benefits to be gained) by a computer system programmed for perpetual inventory control for the dispensary (see pp. 157-58). We also described the more sophisticated and far-reaching capabilities of point-of-sale systems, originally designed for use in the front store. The reader is urged to review the material in Chapter 11 in light of our present discussion. Here, we shall point out only a few further considerations for the pharmacy owner embarking on computerization in his or her store.

The benefits of computerized perpetual inventory control are indisputable. The choice of system will depend, however, on the nature of the pharmacy and its volume of business. The owner of a small pharmacy oriented toward professional services and located in a medical clinic, for example, may find it unnecessary and certainly far too costly to consider a POS system – a pharmacy system programmed for perpetual inventory control would be sufficient. This pharmacy owner may even choose not to purchase a perpetual inventory-control system at the very outset, but one that will generate separate sales reports for each product, since this may be sufficient, at least initially, for stock control. (Product sales lists would allow the pharmacy owner to identify best sellers and to calculate required order quantities, as well as to detect products that are not selling.) But, since dispensary management needs are numerous, even the owner of the small, clinically oriented pharmacy should be aware of existing possibilities and choose a system flexible enough to accommodate those future needs.

At the other extreme is the large, merchandise-oriented pharmacy. In this case, the owner, on assessing the needs of the pharmacy and calculating the costs and benefits involved, will probably find that investment in a POS system is well justified. POS systems may be offered by the supplier of the pharmacy's dispensary system or by other suppliers, and may either be integrated with that system or operated separately. Also, you will recall from Chapter 11 that one of the outstanding benefits of currently available POS systems is their capacity for automatic reordering and accounts-payable management – that is, their value for efficiency and control not only in inventory management but also in the full range of purchasing activities. Finally, the potential for electronic ordering through a direct link to suppliers' computer systems was discussed in Chapter 11, and is something worth considering for the larger pharmacy.

Regardless of the inventory-control system selected, its efficiency and usefulness for management decisions will depend to a great extent on the absolute precision and accuracy of information entered into the system by pharmacy staff. Similarly, while computer systems will provide accurate data on inventory levels, regular and properly timed physical counts continue to be necessary to identify and control any existing shrinkage problems.

Front-Store Management Needs

As discussed in Chapter 11, POS systems with fully integrated accounting systems will address a range of management needs, assist in managerial decision making, and – assuming the choice of the proper system as well as effective training of staff and full support services – improve the pharmacy's productivity and profitability. The following list will serve to recap the range of functions available:

1. *Price look-up and control*: In addition to its ability to set and control prices and effect price changes during sales promotions, the POS system can provide, through its systems-report generator, a record of all products sold during the sale period, calculate the gross margins and assess the overall effect on the pharmacy's gross margin. The price-control feature will also alert management when cashiers override prices in the system, thus preventing unauthorized discount prices to be provided. Cashiers are identified with all transactions.
2. *Business reports*: Reports include daily-transaction reports, regular gross-margin reports, product movement by department, purchasing reports, reports that track sales by time to assist in determining the hours at which additional staff are required, customer lists with complete demographic data, and lists of suppliers with their prices, terms, and any minimum-order requirements. Customized reports are also possible, depending on the pharmacy's requirements.
3. *Accounting packages*: This feature offers the benefit of reducing repetition in entries. When merchandise is received, entries are made in the appropriate accounting ledgers or journals; when merchandise is sold and charged to customers, these entries are recorded appropriately. Files contain information on when accounts are due for payment. The system can also group accounts receivable by age (that is, the period past the due date) and generate invoices, statements, and letters as required. It will alert staff about the status of customer accounts. If properly set up, the system can calculate various financial ratios, including the pharmacy's average collection period (and average payable period).

System Control Measures

The pharmacy computer system selected should be precise and self-validating. For example, it should be programmed to accept the use of alphabetical characters only in fields such as patient name, and numerical characters only in fields such as product number, physician's licence number, and quantity; it should also be programmed to validate all fields that have a specific identification number (for example, eligibility numbers and DINs).

Strict precision in data input will ensure the accuracy of data output and of all reports produced, resulting in fewer claim refusals and more accurate data for management decisions.

Creating backup files of data entered into the system is one of the most important aspects of computer use – it offers the only protection one has against potential system crashes and other problems. The pharmacy owner purchasing a computer system should discuss backup procedures in detail with the system vendor.

Password Systems

Various pharmacy personnel will be called upon at one time or another to use the computer system. It is therefore essential that a security system be in place to control and limit access to informaton to authorized personnel only. To this end, information and operations must be divided into three or four categories accessible only with the appropriate passwords. Such a classification method could be conceived as follows:

> *Level 1*: Allows for creation of files, preparation of prescriptions, and printing of labels and receipts. Allows for correction of data on same-day transactions only.
> *Level 2*: Allows for correction of information on files and prescriptions entered previously.
> *Level 3*: Allows access to medical, product, cost-price, and price-grid files to make appropriate changes.
> *Level 4*: Allows access to reports and management lists.

It is critical that the pharmacy's computer system allow for several levels of passwords in order to protect the professional integrity of the pharmacist and the confidentiality of the data. Passwords should be chosen by the pharmacy owner or manager, then assigned to the appropriate personnel. The pharmacist should be at liberty to change passwords as often as is deemed necessary to protect stored information.

SERVICING THE COMPUTER SYSTEM

As mentioned earlier, it is important that the computer system selected be adaptable to new developments in both hardware and software. While there is certainly a limit to such flexibility, the pharmacy owner or manager should at least ensure that the supplier involved can guarantee continuing service and maintenance of both the hardware and software components.

Pre-installation surveys to assess functional needs and storage-capacity needs, as well as to determine any preparations to be undertaken by the pharmacy, are very important and offered by most vendors of pharmacy systems.

Centralized Systems

Before in-house pharmacy systems achieved their current sophistication and more affordable prices, pharmacists often opted for "central-system" services provided by computer firms. This meant essentially contracting for full service and transferring the responsibility for management reporting to the computer service company. Many pharmacies today use central-system services for particular functions (for example, processing of accounts receivable) by linking their in-house systems to the computer firm's mainframe processor. The monthly cost is higher, but the pharmacist is freed of most tasks involving the regular evaluation and maintenance of such files for managerial purposes.

When full centralized services were more commonly employed, the pharmacist would switch on his terminal when the pharmacy opened, dispense prescriptions and enter appropriate data into the files through the course of the day, then switch the terminal off at closing time. During the night, the service company would generate all required daily reports, make up and transmit claims to the various insurance companies, create backup files, and update product and physician files as necessary. The computer service would also produce a claims report in order for the pharmacist to check accounts receivable. At the end of the month, sales reports, product profiles, and pharmacy activity reports were prepared and sent to the pharmacist.

Some pharmacies still do engage full centralized services. Their contracts can normally be terminated on sixty or ninety days' notice. If the supplier fails to take advantage of improvements in available software or reduces levels of service, the pharmacist can stop payment and cancel the contract. As such computer services depend on monthly revenue from their clients, they generally try to ensure client satisfaction.

Purchasing a Stand-Alone System

In choosing a stand-alone system, the pharmacy owner normally purchases a microcomputer and the rights to a software package. The pharmacist must first ensure that the hardware is produced by an established and reliable manufacturer. Various brands of microcomputers exist on the market today, but not all of them are of high quality. Given that the pharmacist will own and use the equipment for a number of years, he will want to be sure that the manufacturer is well established and that the equipment will not soon become outdated. The availability of replacement parts must be explored. The pharmacy owner would also be well advised to research the performance records of the particular make and model of microcomputer under consideration as well as the financial security of the manufacturer. It is very risky to purchase from the type of company that assembles microcomputers using parts manufactured by other companies. While a top-line microcomputer will inevitably be higher priced, it is a much better, safer, and longer-term investment.

When it comes to choosing a software company, caution is the rule. Since the pharmacist does not own the software, but only buys the right to use it, all modifications and improvements are the responsibility of the supplier. There are independent programmers who create software for use in pharmacies, but unless they offer continuous service, it is probably better to avoid them. Software and hardware maintenance service should be supplied by the same company. If a problem arises, the pharmacy owner then simply contacts the supplier, who is under contract to accept responsibility for service or replacement of the software.

With a stand-alone system, the pharmacy owner must be prepared to invest the time required to bring files up to date, record new products and update physicians' files (as necessary, prior to receipt of software updates from suppliers); create reports; prepare claims to insurance companies; and ensure that backup files are run daily. With both stand-alone systems and systems linked to central computers, it must be possible to contact the supplier's customer-service department during the pharmacy's business hours. However, there are various types of support agreements and they provide different levels of service for different charges. The pharmacy owner must assess affordability without jeopardizing the security and proper functioning of the system, which could lead to serious losses. The types of support agreements are as follows:

1. Take-in service (applies to hardware only). The pharmacy takes the unserviceable equipment to a service centre and is provided with a replacement until his equipment is repaired. (Lowest charge)
2. On-site service, 9 a.m.-5 p.m., five days per week. This is the most commonly used service.
3. Extended hours after 5 p.m., weekends and holidays; on-site service. (Highest charge)

The quality of the professional services extended to patients will depend on the comprehensiveness, accuracy, and flexibility of the pharmacy's computer system. Hence, the pharmacist must be assured of the system's complete and effective support. When making the final choice, ask suppliers for a list of their clients and contact several of them to determine their level of satisfaction with the system. See the Checklist at the end of this chapter for a sampling of the types of questions to ask suppliers in your search for the system and supplier that are best suited to your needs.

Conclusion

Today's pharmacy owner or manager cannot afford to ignore computers. The use of the computer is accepted within the profession, and regardless of the practice setting in which the pharmacist works, he or she will certainly encounter some form of computerization.

This does not imply that the pharmacist must become a computer expert. The computer will always be a tool in pharmacy practice, and should be viewed as such. The pharmacist has therefore only to ensure that the tool fulfills present needs, that it can be upgraded to meet future needs, and that the supplier offers a complete service for both components of the system – the hardware and the software.

The implementation of a pharmacy computer system requires considerable planning and preparation, as well as the full co-operation of the entire staff. Pharmacy owners or managers should advise their staff members of the benefits that the system will bear for them. Care should be taken to address any concerns that they may have regarding continuing employment; reassurances should be given that each staff member assigned to the system will be properly trained, gaining increased skills and the ability to contribute more effectively to the operation. Also, the staff should be advised that they can share in the benefits of a business which shows improved profitability resulting from proper use of the system.

Finally, all pharmacist-owners embarking on computerization are urged to enlist the aid of their accountants in a careful assessment of the relative costs and benefits of this significant investment in the pharmacy's future.

Pharmacy Computer System Checklist

How long has this system been on the market?
What is its on-line storage capacity? In bits per disk? In Rs per disc? In months?
Will the system – as demonstrated – accommodate 3 years of information?
Is the screen large enough to see all of a record at once?
How many terminals can be used at once on the system?
Can operators at different terminals be doing different tasks (multi-task feature)?
Is the keyboard easy to read and teach?
Is a modem included?
Does the vendor supply a complete user's manual?
What about expandability? Can I add more than one screen or printer? At what cost?
How many steps/info are required to enter a new R?
How many steps/info are required to enter a new patient?
How many steps/info are required to process a renewal R?
What are the shortest and longest response times to expect?
How is a drug name entered?
Is there a fast way to get a price quote without processing the R?
Does the computer automatically calculate the R price?
Can different pricing schedules (for different drugs and different patient groups) be accommodated?
Are price-update diskettes available for my area? How long after Jan. 1, July 1?
Is there a way to put custom messages on the prescription label?
Does the system warn of possible drug interaction and allergy problems?
Will the system print a current patient record as needed?
Does the system keep track of (and signal) specific third-party plan requirements?
Does it prepare third-party claims? Are printouts accepted by all third parties?
Does the system produce the following:
    Daily, monthly, and year-to-date cost, revenue, and margin summary?
    Daily, monthly, and year-to-date R dispensed summary?
    Product usage and movement reports?
    Plan-specific third-party daily, monthly and year-to-date summaries?
    Controlled substances inventory and usage report?
How long will it take to train staff to be proficient in using the system?
How often is the software updated? Are there any costs for updates?
How long has the vendor been in the pharmacy system business?
Will vendor supply a list of adopters in my area (rather than a few selected names)?
Is all necessary hardware included in the price?
Is all necessary software included in the price?
What supply costs should I expect? At first? Thereafter each month?
Does the vendor sell computer system supplies (paper, ribbon, diskettes)?
Is preventive maintenance included in the service contract?
What types of service contracts are available?
Does the vendor provide a "loaner" if equipment has to be removed to be repaired?
Will enhancements be available to me?

Source: Adapted from *Pharmacy Computer System Analyzer,* a pamphlet published by the American Pharmaceutical Association, 1984, and from "Things to Consider Prior to Buying a Pharmacy Computer," a list distributed to its members by the Nova Scotia Pharmaceutical Society.

RECOMMENDED READING:

College of Pharmacists of British Columbia. "Guidelines for the Selection of a Pharmacy Computer." *B.C. Pharmacist* (June 1985), pp. 1-8.

"The Decision to Automate." *Journal of the National Association of Retail Drug Stores* (August 1985), pp. 50-56.

"Electronic Claims: A Revolution in Progress." *ComputerTalk for the Pharmacist* (September/October 1988), pp. 15-26.

Fassett, William E., and Christensen, Dale B., eds. *Computer Applications in Pharmacy*. Philadelphia: Lea & Febiger, 1986.

Israel, Florence. "Your Guide to Scanners." *Drug Merchandising* (June 1985), pp. 33-37.

Lang, Laura. "Why Should Pharmacists Computerize?" *Pharmacy West* (May 1987), pp. 21-32.

Lauer, Judith E. *Computers for Pharmacy*. The American Pharmaceutical Association, 1978.

Nelson, Arthur A. "Computers in Community Pharmacy Practice: Will They Affect Your Practice?" *Lilly Digest* 1986, pp. 5-10.

Pharmacy Computer System Analyzer. Pamphlet published by the American Pharmaceutical Association, 1984.

Reiman, Tyrus. "Automating the Front Store." *Drug Merchandising* (June 1985), pp. 29-32.

"Your Next Computer." *Drug Merchandising* (September 1986), pp. 62-71.

The journal *ComputerTalk for the Pharmacist* (published by ComputerTalk Associates Inc., Whetpain Office Campus, 1750 Walton Rd., Blue Bell, Pa. 19422, U.S.A.) would be a valuable subscription for pharmacy owners interested in staying up to date on developments in computer systems for pharmacy practice.

21

INTERPROFESSIONAL RELATIONS

INTRODUCTION

Recent changes in both the health-care environment and the practice of pharmacy itself have intensified the focus on the concept of the "health-care team" and, consequently, on the importance of interprofessional relationships. Technological advances have produced an explosion of drug products and drug-delivery systems. As a result, pharmacists can expect to share more responsibility with physicians and other health-care professionals for rational selecting, administering, and monitoring of medications, as well as for more adequate education of the patients who use medications.

As health-care costs skyrocket and the population ages, more emphasis is being placed on self-care and on the use of non-prescription medications.[1] The pharmacist's key location in the community and important role of monitoring the use of both prescription and non-prescription medications affords an opportunity to capitalize on this unique position within the health-care team.

The growing emphasis on preventive health care will affect the roles of health-care professionals and the ways in which they interact. With the relative oversupply of physicians in some areas, the increased number of medical specialists, and the appearance of the "emergicentre" and

---

[1] M. Hetherington, "Seniors and Self-Medication: Synergistic Impact on Pharmacy in the 80's and 90's," *Canadian Pharmaceutical Journal* (August 1984), pp. 377–79.

"medi-malls,"[2] competition for patients has increased. Also, it is less common today for an individual to be cared for exclusively by one physician over the course of a lifetime. Such changes underlie the importance of a team approach to the provision of health care.

The profession of pharmacy has also undergone significant changes in the last several decades: it has shifted from a primarily product-based enterprise to a more service-oriented endeavour, as reflected in activities such as patient counselling and monitoring medication use with patient medication profiles. With the introduction of provincial drug plans and generic drug products, drug-product selection and drug-use review activities have gained importance. Also, as in the medical profession, it is less likely today for an individual to patronize only one pharmacy over the course of a lifetime. Pharmacy now faces increased competition, new types of pharmacy operations, and a manpower shortage. Such changes within the profession, together with the new directions evident in the health-care environment, shape the role of the pharmacist within the health-care team as well as the nature and significance of interprofessional relations.

When considering interprofessional relationships, it is important to focus on other health-care professionals' perceptions and expectations of the pharmacist. Generally, other health-care professionals appreciate the pharmacist's ability to contribute to the care of the patient and to the efficiency of the team's efforts in providing the best possible care. As the number and complexity of therapies increase and providers become more specialized, the need for a co-ordinated effort among providers becomes imperative. From the pharmacy perspective, it is only through co-operation and communication that the pharmacist's knowledge can be utilized for rational drug therapy and drug-use control. It is under such conditions that the patient will receive the best possible care.

If the pharmacist is passive or works independently of other health-care professionals, both the patient and other health-care providers will be deprived of the pharmacist's knowledge. One author reports that American pharmacy students may be more apprehensive about communication than are similar members of the general population. He also suggests that quiet people may not be seen as competent and intelligent and that other health-care professionals may not respond to the quieter members of a health-care team.[3] Pharmacists must be aware of such dynamics, and must also recognize that communication apprehension may be overcome in a number of ways, including relaxation therapy and assertiveness training. In addition to the perhaps natural tendencies of

[2] N. Regush, Canada's Health-Care System: Condition Critical (Toronto: Macmillan of Canada, 1987).

[3] J.B. Kitching, "Communication, Counselling and Co-operation: Communication and the Community Pharmacist," The Pharmaceutical Journal (October, 1986), pp. 449–52.

pharmacists to be quiet or apprehensive about communication, they often practise in community settings where it may be easy to become isolated from the rest of the health-care team. Given such factors, it is important to remember that without some conscious personal effort, the pharmacist may jeopardize making a meaningful contribution to the team.

A pharmacist can contribute meaningfully to the health-care team's effort by providing information about new and existing drug products; drug–drug, drug–food, and drug–allergy interactions; misuse of medications; compliance; appropriate drug therapy; adverse drug reactions; and the proper handling and storage of medications. In order to contribute effectively to the team effort, the pharmacist must gain recognition as the authoritative provider of such important information. Pharmacists must take the initiative to keep other health-care professionals aware of pharmacy's potential contribution. Goods or services that are not actively marketed seldom enjoy a demand.

INITIATION AND MAINTENANCE OF INTERPROFESSIONAL RELATIONSHIPS

Within the community-pharmacy practice setting, the primary interprofessional relationship is between the pharmacist and the physician. There is less contact between community pharmacists and certain medical specialists (such as podiatrists), nurses, dentists, physiotherapists, occupational therapists, chiropractors, optometrists, nutritionists, diagnostic laboratory technicians, veterinarians, and social workers. This can be explained to some extent by the fact that many of these professionals are not extensively involved in drug-use control and because the typical patient encountered in community-pharmacy practice seldom uses their services. However, it is important to recognize the potential for interprofessional relationships with all of these groups. Many of the principles that will be discussed with respect to the pharmacist–physician relationship may be applied to other health-care professionals as well.

Physicians

> Medicine and pharmacy have a shared history over the centuries . . . [but both have] emerged as true professions. Both are based on disciplines that generate systematic knowledge grounded in theory; both apply their knowledge and skills in service to the public; and, most importantly, both are self-regulating by setting and upholding high standards of practice.[4]

[4]P.J. Sanazaro, "Medicine and Pharmacy: Our Once and Future Status as Professions," *American Journal of Hospital Pharmacy* (March 1987): pp. 521–22.

Although it is important to recognize the common history of these two professions, it is also important to realize that in a changing health-care environment, the roles and responsibilities of each also change and the interrelationship between the two professions is not static. At one time, pharmacists were primarily compounders of concoctions that were intended to remain mysterious; hence, the pharmacist was encouraged not to discuss medications with patients or anyone else. The emphasis on compounding has declined over the years and patient-oriented services, such as counselling and monitoring patient profiles, have become more important.

With the introduction of Medicare, governments increasingly influenced the professional activities of pharmacists and other health-care professionals. Provincial drug plans, with accompanying formularies, made pharmacists responsible for selecting the drug product to be dispensed (when a choice existed) and for conducting drug-utilization reviews to ensure rational drug therapy. When drug costs are borne primarily by a government drug plan, both physicians and consumers may be less likely to consider the cost of prescription medications. When consumers must pay for prescription medications at the time of dispensing, however, both physicians and patients become more concerned with the issue of cost in relation to the benefit of the drug. Pharmacists can play an important role in helping physicians assess the cost–benefit ratio of drug products in specific situations.

The development of interprofessional relationships depends largely upon successful initiation. While initiation may be the most difficult step, it is perhaps the most important one. Nothing can replace the value of personal contact with an individual physician. This contact provides both parties with the opportunity to associate a face with the individual's name. Personal recognition between pharmacists and physicians may begin during college years if students make an effort to meet socially and work together toward common goals.

There are many ways in which a pharmacist can create opportunities to initiate professional relationships with physicians. For example, pharmacists may attend or organize educational seminars and use such opportunities to meet local physicians. A visit to the physician's office may be appropriate if specific drug information is to be delivered. Social activities ranging from coffee to golf, as well as community events, provide valuable opportunities. Pharmacists should make every effort to become personally acquainted with local physicians.

A look at physicians' perceptions of pharmacists might be a useful starting point for considering some of the important issues involved in developing and maintaining the pharmacist–physician relationship. Two recent studies explored physicians' perceptions of pharmacists. In 1984, the Schering Corporation conducted a study of 300 physicians and 225 pharmacists in the United States.[5] In 1986, the Upjohn Company of Canada conducted an in-depth interview with ten general practitioners and then surveyed 100 more throughout Canada.[6]

The Schering survey suggested the following strategies for an improved pharmacist–physician relationship: (1) providing more drug information to meet the growing needs of physicians; (2) installing a private, unlisted telephone line exclusively for physician communication; and (3) continuing to perform the four pharmacy services identified as most important by the survey group: identifying potential drug misuse or abuse situations, alerting physicians of possible prescribing errors, identifying potential drug interactions, and maintaining patient profiles.

The Upjohn survey provides a fairly recent view of Canadian general practitioners' perceptions of the community pharmacist. Particularly important to the issue of interprofessional relationships are the aspects of image, services, interactions with physicians, and recommendations for improvement.

Upjohn's survey found that more physicians perceive pharmacists as "more business-oriented" than as either "more health-care–oriented" or "equal" in business and health-care orientation. The survey's criteria for a health-care orientation included the pharmacist's position as a member of the medical team, a public-service role, concern for the welfare of patients, and a lack of concern for money. The business orientation was defined as reflecting primarily financial priorities and an emphasis on selling non-pharmaceutical products. Figure 21.1 and Table 21.1 summarize the results of this inquiry into the physician's perception of the image of community pharmacists.

Physicians surveyed in the Upjohn study rated the following services provided by the community pharmacist as most important: (1) correctly reading prescriptions; (2) including full instructions on labels; (3) identifying double-doctoring; (4) identifying prescription errors; (5) identifying duplicate prescriptions; (6) ensuring compliance; and (7) checking for forged prescriptions. Of these services, ensuring compliance was considered the area in greatest need of improvement. Table 21.2 summarizes these results.

Two aspects of pharmacist–physician interaction were explored by the Upjohn survey: filling of repeat prescriptions and physicians' information needs. More than two-thirds of the physicians surveyed agreed that pharmacists should be able to provide patients with refills on prescriptions in cases of acute need or if the physician could not be reached.

[5] "1984 Schering Report Explores Pharmacist–Physician Relationships," *American Pharmacy* NS 24, no. 10: (October 1984) pp. 13–14.
[6] Upjohn Company of Canada, *Canadian Community Pharmacy Services, 1986 Study* (Don Mills: Upjohn Company of Canada, 1986).

Figure 21.1 PHYSICIANS' PERCEPTIONS OF PHARMACISTS:
IMAGE CLASSIFICATION

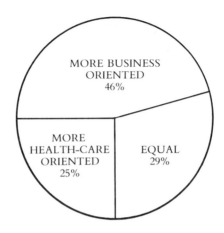

Source: Upjohn Company of Canada, *Canadian Community Pharmacy Services, 1986 Study.*

Table 21.1 PHYSICIANS' IMAGE OF COMMUNITY PHARMACISTS,
BY REGION

	Total	B.C.	Prairies	Ontario	Quebec	Atlantic
Business	46%	43%	41%	44%	56%	40%
Health care	25%	14%	35%	18%	28%	40%
Equal	29%	43%	24%	38%	16%	20%

Source: Upjohn Company of Canada, *Canadian Community Pharmacy Services, 1986 Study.*

This practice was not seen as viable in minor or non-life-threatening situations. Surveyed physicians indicated they would contact a pharmacist for the following information: (1) details about new drugs; (2) drug information that is difficult to locate; (3) details of patient-medication records; and (4) international drug names.

One-third of the physicians surveyed felt that pharmacists needed to improve their services most in the area of patient counselling. The next most significant area for improvement was identified as that of communication between the physician and pharmacist. One-third of the physicians felt that no improvements were necessary.

Table 21.2   FUNCTIONS OF COMMUNITY PHARMACISTS
CONSIDERED OF GREATEST IMPORTANCE BY PHYSICIANS

Functions Performed Well

	Scale 1-7
• Reading ℞ correctly	6.05
• Checking with M.D. before filling repeat prescription	6.00
• Labelling	5.92
• Correct number of pills	5.85
• Checking for forgeries	5.75
• Catching ℞/dosage errors	5.73

Functions Not Performed Well

	Rating 1-7
• Noting drug interactions/allergies, contraindications	4.89
• Monitoring patients	4.84
• Verbal instructions	4.82
• Ensuring compliance	4.28

Source: Upjohn Company of Canada, Canadian Community Pharmacy Services, 1986 Study.

Several situations that commonly arise in community-pharmacy practice require pharmacist–physician interaction. These are related primarily to the prescription process – for example, providing drug information, influencing prescribing behaviour, obtaining refill authorizations, identifying and communicating prescription errors, counselling patients, and preventing drug misuse and abuse. Other such situations may be related to specialized services, such as hospice care or the compounding of dermatological preparations.

A recent survey of American general practitioners and internists showed that the type of information commonly sought by physicians from community pharmacists included medication costs, dosage forms, generic products, drug identification, drug interactions, brand-name products, dosage and toxicity, side effects, contraindications, and patients' allergies. Physicians also expressed appreciation for pharmacists who informed them of potential interactions between medications prescribed by two or more physicians.[7]

As in any relationship, areas of conflict can strain the relationship between pharmacist and physician. Potential problems that may arise when physicians request information include: (1) inconveniences associated with telephone communication; (2) third-party intervention in the

[7] E.M. McCormick, "What Drug Information Do Doctors Seek From Retail Pharmacists?" Pharmacy Times (March 1986), pp. 23–25.

communication process, for example, by pharmacy technicians, front-store staff, or physicians' receptionists or nurses; and (3) inappropriate handling of drug-information requests by the pharmacist. The pharmacist may avoid these potential communication problems by:

1. having an exclusive physician telephone line, with an unlisted number, answered only by the pharmacist to avoid unnecessary delays;
2. personally phoning physicians, and doing so only when necessary;
3. keeping professional communications focussed on the issues at hand and avoiding unnecessary apologies for intrusion – if the issue is important enough to warrant a telephone call, there is no need to apologize;
4. keeping a pencil and writing pad available next to the telephone;
5. instructing third parties to immediately commit to writing all drug-information requests and to check the spelling of technical terms and drug names;
6. if a request for drug information cannot be answered immediately, providing the information as quickly as possible;
7. providing a written follow-up, detailing the requested information and reference sources.

Physicians appreciate being informed about unusual or adverse effects experienced by their patients as a result of using prescribed medications. In this regard, the same guidelines as suggested for handling drug-information requests should be followed to prevent potential communication problems.

Although some physicians may not be in favour of pharmacists recommending specific drug products,[8] it has been shown that pharmacists *can* influence prescribing habits and thereby contribute to rational, as well as cost-effective, drug therapy.[9] Attempts to influence physicians' prescribing habits may be problematic if physicians perceive them to be an infringement on their authority. This, however, is not likely to be the case if pharmacists are viewed by physicians as non-threatening allies. Some ways in which pharmacists can encourage this sense of alliance include:

1. making recommendations *with* physicians, not *for* them;
2. anticipating potential prescribing problems and implementing intervention strategies to avert them;

[8] "1984 Schering Report Explores Pharmacist–Physician Relationships," *American Pharmacy* NS 24, no. 10 (October 1984): 13–14.

[9] K. Warrian and J. Irvine-Meek, "Pharmacists' Interventions on Physician Prescribing and Drug Costs in Selected Areas of General Medicine and Orthopaedic Surgery," study conducted at the Toronto General Hospital, 1987.

Table 21.3 SHOULD PHYSICIAN HAVE TO TALK TO THE
PHARMACIST PERSONALLY ABOUT REPEAT
PRESCRIPTIONS THAT REQUIRE AUTHORIZATION?

	Total	B.C.	Prairies	Ontario	Quebec	Atlantic
Yes	71%	36%	88%	59%	96%	70%
No	27%	64%	12%	35%	4%	30%
Don't know	2%			6%		

Source: Upjohn Company of Canada, *Canadian Community Pharmacy Services, 1986 Study.*

3. identifying influential opinion leaders among physicians to support
   pharmacy recommendations;
4. identifying physicians' valued outcomes of drug therapy and dem-
   onstrating how pharmacy-recommended prescribing changes can help
   to achieve these;
5. making recommendations in a private and professional manner.

One situation that commonly requires pharmacist–physician interaction is the request for prescription-repeat authorization. The most common problem related to this situation occurs when a nurse or receptionist
(rather than the physician) attempts to provide authorization.[10] According
to pharmacy regulations, the pharmacist may insist on speaking directly
to the physician about repeat authorizations. As shown in Table 21.3,
the majority of physicians support pharmacists' insistence in this matter.
The best way to alleviate this problem is to remain professional in both
attitude and manner when dealing with physicians and their agents. Steps
that may be taken in this direction include:

1. gaining the support of physicians who agree with the need for direct
   communication;
2. impressing upon both physicians and their staff the implications for
   liability associated with authorizing prescription repeats;
3. ensuring that all pharmacists and staff abide by the regulations; and
4. encouraging a unified stand within the pharmacy profession on this
   issue.

An American survey showed that, on average, a pharmacist corrects
two or more prescriber errors per day.[11] The most common error is the
omission of a dosage strength and the second is the failure to provide
proper directions for taking the medication. Most physicians appreciate

[10] For a specific example of this problem, see "Pharmacists Fight Manitoba RNs over ℞
'Communication'," *Drug Merchandising* (December 1986), p. 10.
[11] J. D'Agese, "Prescribing Errors Abound, New Pharmacist Poll Finds," *Drug Topics* 128,
no. 14 (16 July 1984): 14-16.

being informed of prescribing errors and believe that the responsibility for detecting them is shared by the physician and the pharmacist. Prescription errors seem to occur most often with verbal prescriptions and with prescriptions for a drug whose name may sound similar to that of another drug. Pharmacists may be able to avert prescribing errors by:

1. checking any questionable or missing component of the prescription with the prescriber (diplomacy and tact are of the utmost importance in such situations);
2. connecting a tape recorder to the telephone to record all prescriptions for verification purposes; and
3. checking patient profiles for allergic conditions and potential interactions before filling prescriptions.

The misuse and abuse of prescription medications is another area in which the interprofessional relationship between physician and pharmacist provides an important service to society. Problems associated with prescription-drug abuse include double-doctoring, forgeries, and unauthorized sale or distribution of prescribed medications. Prescription-medication misuse may include overuse or underuse of these agents, as well as inappropriate use. Pharmacists may follow several techniques to deal with problems of prescription-drug abuse and misuse:

1. participate in a phoning tree or fan-out information network to ensure that everyone concerned is aware of a specific case of abuse or potential abuse;
2. inform physicians about confirmed or suspected cases of abuse or misuse;
3. monitor patient profiles for frequency of refills on medications that have a potential for misuse and inform physicians of such instances;
4. participate in programs designed to reduce prescription-drug misuse or abuse, such as the triplicate prescription program.

The primary recommendation that Canadian physicians made for pharmacists, as outlined in the 1986 Upjohn study, was to improve patient counselling. Inadequate patient counselling may adversely affect patient compliance, reduce opportunities to detect potential therapeutic interactions, and reduce the effectiveness of prescribed medications. Pharmacists should counsel patients regarding prescription medications on a regular basis and in an effective manner.

On the other hand, with regard to patient counselling about over-the-counter drugs, pharmacists must be careful to recognize the limitations of non-prescription products and ensure that conditions being treated with such drugs are indeed self-limiting. Inappropriate patient counselling regarding non-prescription use may result in exacerbation of the patient's condition. Consequently, the condition may not be treated effectively, and may in the end require more extensive therapy than would normally have been necessary. Patients with potentially serious conditions should be referred to a physician. Also, a referral should be made if the OTC medication does not provide relief within a reasonable length of time.

In addition to the situations outlined above, a number of other issues that can cause pharmacist–physician conflict have been identified: differences in age and gender between the physician and the pharmacist; the compounding of specialized products for terminally ill patients or dermatology patients; and occurrences (reported in the United States) of physicians dispensing drugs and pharmacists prescribing them.[12] In a rapidly changing health-care environment there will always be new areas of potential conflict between professional groups. It is important to try to anticipate and recognize such areas in order to defuse conflicts with calm, rational discussion before they arise.

Dentists

> The day is long gone when any one professional is solely responsible for the patient. For this reason, the dentist should include information about the patient's pharmacist in the patient's medical history file; the pharmacist should include the name of the patient's dentist in the patient's medication file.[13]

It has been suggested that all dentists cultivate a professional relationship with a pharmacist to ensure access to a consultant regarding drug-related problems and an information source regarding new drug products.

Although dentists prescribe infrequently and from a relatively limited group of drugs (primarily antibiotics and analgesics), it is important for the community pharmacist to have a good working relationship with local dentists. Again, in establishing a professional relationship, there is no substitute for personal contact. This may be accomplished by providing continuing-education lectures for dentists on the role of OTC and prescription medications in managing the dental patient, or by providing a catalogue of the oral-hygiene products available in the pharmacy.

Pharmacists may improve the pharmacist–dentist relationship by:

1. referring patients to dentists when appropriate;
2. having well-stocked dental-hygiene and denture-care sections in the pharmacy;

[12] R.L. Rundle, "Doctors Stir Controversy by Selling Drugs Directly to their Patients. . .While Pharmacists Seek Bigger Role in Health Care," *Wall Street Journal*, 29 September 1986.

[13] *The Dentist and the Pharmacist* (American Dental Association and American Pharmaceutical Association, 1983).

3. being well informed to counsel patients in the use of dental products;
4. providing the dentist with prescribing information;
5. focussing on target groups such as preschoolers, disabled patients, the elderly, pregnant women, diabetics, cancer patients, and people with AIDS;
6. exchanging educational pamphlets with dentists;
7. monitoring patient profiles for drug effects that might relate to dental concerns;
8. notifying dentists of patient allergies or potential interactions with existing patient medication regimens;
9. in certain cases, compounding preparations for use in the dental office;
10. providing updates for new forms of therapy, possibly in the form of a newsletter.

The pharmacist's unique position in the community provides an important opportunity for front-line detection of potential dental problems in patients. For this reason, it is important to establish and maintain the pharmacist–dentist relationship.

Nurses

The pharmacist–nurse relationship is generally more pronounced in the hospital setting than in the community-pharmacy setting. In hospitals and nursing homes, the nurse often replaces the patient in taking responsibility for administering medications. Hence, in these settings, the pharmacist–nurse relationship is as important for ensuring proper use of medications as is the unmediated pharmacist–patient relationship in the community-pharmacy practice setting.

It should be noted, however, that many pharmacies today provide pharmaceutical services, on contract, to nursing homes. The interaction between nurses and pharmacists in these situations is extensive. The head nurse is usually responsible for ensuring that the home's standards for pharmacy services are being met. The pharmacists providing such services, in addition to dispensing prescriptions for residents, are usually required to serve on the home's drugs and therapeutics committee and to participate in patient-medication reviews along with nurses and physicians. The responsibilities of the pharmacist may include the provision of seminars on drug information to nurses and other personnel employed in the nursing home. Once a rapport is established, nurses come to rely on the pharmacist for information relating to drug interactions and adverse drug reactions, as well as for advice on alternate dosage forms of medication for patients.

Within the community-pharmacy setting, there has been a development in recent years that affords another opportunity for pharmacist–

nurse interaction, and that is the introduction of home health-care centres in community pharmacies. These centres offer for sale and/or rent many products necessary for the care and rehabilitation of patients in a home setting, including canes, crutches, walkers, commode chairs, wheel chairs, hospital beds, surgical stockings, surgical garments, braces, respiratory aids, diabetes testing equipment, supplies and appliances for ostomates, and devices for monitoring blood pressure. These centres employ, in addition to pharmacists, certified orthotic technicians and, in some cases, nurses.

As an example, a chain of pharmacies in Nova Scotia that offered home health-care services in some of its outlets employed a registered nurse to supervise these departments in their stores. In addition to her supervisory responsibilities, the nurse co-ordinated purchasing for the departments and, along with the pharmacist, promoted the concept of the home health-care centre among physicians in the region. The working relationship between the nurse and the physicians did much to enhance the emerging contacts between physicians and pharmacy staff. The nurse was also very helpful in teaching customers how to derive maximum benefits from blood-pressure devices, diabetes testing equipment, and ostomy supplies and equipment. Another option that one independent pharmacy found successful was to employ a registered nurse on a part-time basis to conduct clinics for its customers on subjects such as hypertension screening, diabetes screening, and immunization.

Beyond the examples described, the opportunities for pharmacist–nurse interaction in the community are still quite limited, since nurses, outside the hospital, are largely employed only in nursing homes and physicians' offices or as community-health nurses. The most common need for interaction is to provide nurses with drug information, either on an ad hoc basis or in formal continuing-education settings. The pharmacist may also be called upon in various situations to support nurses' efforts in educating patients to ensure medication compliance.

Nursing education in Canada has recently begun to focus more on the prevention of illness and on adaptation to disease than on the treatment of illness. With the rapidly increasing proportion of elderly people in the Canadian population, nursing is preparing to engage more actively in the community-service arena. As evidenced by our example of the home health-care centre, these shifts suggest an increasing opportunity for community pharmacists to work closely with nurses.

Others

Although the community pharmacist typically has limited contact with health-care professionals other than those described above, it is important to realize the opportunity that exists for interprofessional relationships with groups such as physiotherapists, occupational therapists, chiropractors, podiatrists, optometrists, nutritionists, diagnostic laboratory technicians, and social-service workers. The primary interactions with these health-care professionals involve provision of information about the effects of medications and perhaps referral of patients to the appropriate professional for help.

Drug therapy may affect laboratory test results or cause drug-food interactions that would be of interest to the laboratory technician and nutritionist, respectively. In certain instances, nutrition may be a tool in illness prevention and treatment. Ambulatory patients may require total parenteral nutrition solutions to be provided outside institutional settings. These are examples of situations in which the community pharmacist may work closely with a clinical nutritionist. The nursing-home setting affords opportunities to work more closely with social workers by providing information on sources of drug-payment assistance or supplying drug information. As an exercise, form a group with five to eight of your colleagues to brainstorm and create examples of situations in which the community pharmacist may have an opportunity to interact with the other health-care professionals listed above.

PROFESSIONAL COURTESIES

At one time professional courtesies between pharmacists and other health-care providers consisted mainly of offering discounts on office supplies. Today, with the current emphasis on the health-care team, professional courtesies extend to include the following:

1. focussing on the well-being of the patient rather than competing for the patient's business;
2. maintaining open lines of communication with other professionals to notify them of pharmacy-related changes that may affect their practice;
3. supplying information to the patient in such a manner that it will not be interpreted as contradicting another professional's judgment;
4. exercising caution and tact when notifying other professionals of potential medication-related errors, especially by ensuring that such communication does not occur in the presence of patients;
5. referring patients to other health-care professionals when appropriate;
6. remembering that each profession has a role to play in the management of a patient's condition and that a team effort will benefit the patient much more than a disjointed approach to health care.

PROFESSIONAL ASSOCIATIONS

> Every man owes some of his time to the upbuilding of the profession to which he belongs.
>
> Theodore Roosevelt

Professional associations provide an opportunity for each member of the profession to lend a hand in building the profession. Furthermore, the involvement in professional associations lends credibility to both the individual member and to the association.

Interprofessional issues are often best handled by the professional associations representing those who will be directly affected. This approach minimizes confusion and can strengthen the position of a profession in negotiations on issues of potential interprofessional conflict. The professional association can also provide stability within the profession as well as a strong voice when professional interests must be brought to the attention of health-care policy makers. The professional code of ethics ensures that the expectations of patients and payers of professional services will be met and that the patient's interests will be served.

Members of the profession benefit individually and as a group from public support. Professional associations can further the interests of the profession by undertaking public-relations campaigns to garner this support and confidence. Associations may also work to strengthen interprofessional relationships by promoting the concept of a team approach to patient care. An example of this is the Canadian Pharmaceutical Association's (CPhA) advertising campaign directed toward physicians, addressing common concerns about compliance and prescription repeats (Figure 21.2). Similarly, the Canadian Dental Association (CDA) recently placed an advertisement in the *Canadian Pharmaceutical Journal* to encourage interprofessional awareness (Figure 21.3).

Interprofessional relationships are strengthened when individuals make an effort to establish and maintain relationships on a personal basis and when professional associations work together to co-ordinate interprofessional programs and activities.

NEW OPPORTUNITIES

An opportunity for interprofessional liaison also exists through various interprofessional committees at both the provincial and federal levels. These include Drug and Therapeutics committees and Drug Utilization Review committees. Such committees often have representation from pharmacy, medicine, and dentistry and, sometimes, from nursing. Some federal committees of the Health Protection Branch also make provision for interprofessional membership.

Figure 21.2   CPhA ADVERTISING CAMPAIGN

Source: Canadian Medical Association Journal, Vol. 134, No. 7 (April 1986): 17.

Figure 21.3   CANADIAN DENTAL ASSOCIATION ADVERTISEMENT
APPEARING IN THE CANADIAN PHARMACEUTICAL
JOURNAL

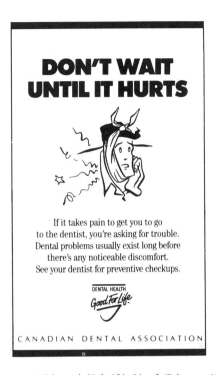

Source: Canadian Pharmaceutical Journal, Vol. 121, No. 2 (February 1988): 143.

RECOMMENDED READING

Cotner, J. "'Marriage' of Pharmacy and Nursing Offers One-Stop Health Care." *Pharmacy Times* (August 1986), pp. 49–52.

The Dentist and the Pharmacist. American Dental Association and American Pharmaceutical Association, 1983.

Manners, S. "The Physician Talks to the Pharmacist." *Canadian Pharmaceutical Journal*, 119 (August 1986): 440–42.

McCormick, E.M. "What Drug Information Do Doctors Seek from Retail Pharmacists?" *Pharmacy Times* (March 1986), pp. 23–25.

"1984 Shering Report Explores Pharmacist–Physician Relationships." *American Pharmacy* NS24, no. 10 (October 1984): 13–14.

Propper, T.A. "Why Communication Between Dentists and Pharmacists is Really an ℞ for Success." *Pharmacy Times* (July 1987), pp. 48–50.

Regush, N. *Canada's Health-Care System: Condition Critical.* Toronto: Macmillan of Canada, 1987.

Schoepp, G. "Marketing Physician Consultations." *Drug Merchandising* (November 1987), pp. 19–24.

Smith, M.C., and Knapp, D.A. *Pharmacy, Drugs and Medical Care.* 3rd ed. Baltimore: Williams and Wilkins, 1981. pp. 2274–2776.

Tindall, William N.; Beardsley, Robert S.; and Curtiss, Frederic R. *Communication in Pharmacy Practice.* Philadelphia: Lea & Febiger, 1984.

Upjohn Company of Canada. *Canadian Community Pharmacy Services, 1986 Study.* Don Mills: Upjohn Company of Canada, 1986.

22

INNOVATION AND TECHNOLOGY

INTRODUCTION

Our society is undergoing profound changes in this post-industrial era of information and services. Pharmacy cannot avoid being affected by these changes and pharmacists must acquire the modern tools that will enable them to fully and efficiently perform their professional duties.

Pharmacy has always been characterized by its dual aspect of offering both products and professional services. In the information age, pharmacists must continue to play the dual role entrusted to them in the most complete and efficient manner possible, while at the same time complying with the socio-economic requirements imposed on them by governments and other third-party insurers. Consequently, pharmacists will have to define their services more precisely, increase the range of services they provide, and evaluate their costs more accurately. They will be called upon to free themselves from routine and technical tasks in order to devote more time to informing and advising the public and other health professionals about pharmaceuticals and related issues. These information and counselling functions will assume a greater importance as pharmacotherapy becomes more complex and medication more specific, efficient, and personalized in nature.

361

In its 1986 report on pharmacy, a committee of inquiry created by the Nuffield Foundation in Britain concluded that the dispensing of medication would continue to be an important activity of pharmacists, but that their professional role should be construed in terms of increased collaboration with other health professionals and increased interaction with the public. This would be accomplished chiefly through participation in public health-education programs and the provision of pertinent information to consumers about the proper use of prescription and non-prescription drugs.[1] Several Canadian studies in recent years have also emphasized the need for pharmacists to inform, advise, and teach the public about drug-related matters.[2]

The object of this chapter is not to speculate on the future of the community pharmacy, but rather to show how recent innovations and technology can help pharmacists play their part to the fullest, both as dispensers of medication and providers of information. We shall not attempt to describe and analyze each of the existing (or potential) new technologies in detail, but will focus on their application and usefulness for the pharmacist.

AUTOMATION OF TECHNICAL FUNCTIONS

One of the pharmacist's fundamental tasks is to prepare and dispense both prescription and non-prescription drugs to members of the community. In its practice guide, published in 1981, Quebec's Order of Pharmacists described each of the functions and tasks involved in preparing and dispensing a prescription.[3] A study performed at Auburn University established that 39 successive actions were involved in filling a prescription, from the moment the prescription was received to the moment the medication was dispensed to the patient.[4] Many of these actions can be performed by technical personnel, but some can even be automated.

[1] *Pharmacy*, Report of the Committee of Inquiry Appointed by the Nuffield Foundation (London: The Nuffield Foundation, 1986).
[2] See the *National Omnibus Gallup Poll*, The Upjohn Company of Canada, 1982; *Canadian Pharmacy Services Study, 1984*, The Upjohn Company of Canada; and "G.P.'s Attitudes to the Community Pharmacist," *Canadian Community Pharmacy Services Study, 1986*, The Upjohn Company of Canada.
[3] Ordre des Pharmaciens du Québec, *Guide de pratique*, September, 1981.
[4] *Autocount: The Baker Cell System* (Dorval, Que.: Automated Prescription Service Canada, 1985).

Automated Tablet- and Capsule-Counting Systems

Automatic systems for counting tablets or capsules have been available commercially in Canada for a number of years. One such system is called the "Autocount" Baker Cell System.[5] It consists essentially of cells grouped together in a cabinet, each containing a single product. Each cell is connected to a control module that governs that cell's counting operation. By a simple touch of the appropriate keys, technical personnel can obtain the exact count of the medication prescribed. Such a system is able to deal out 100 capsules in 10 seconds.

Analysis has shown that automated counting systems can reduce the number of actions involved in preparing and dispensing a prescription by half. The time saved this way is valuable, because it relieves the pharmacist of largely mechanical tasks and allows him to devote more time to professional activities, such as patient counselling. It has also been shown that such systems can be used profitably for about 60 to 70 percent of all prescriptions requiring tablets or capsules. The obvious limitation of automated counting systems is that they cannot be used for liquids or semi-solids.

An automatic counting system can be linked to a computer that will control its operation and trigger the tablet or capsule counter. In addition, software programs are available that facilitate the automation of an even larger number of the tasks involved in filling a prescription. For example, it is now possible for the pharmacist to simply enter a prescription into a computerized patient file to activate a series of operations, from counting out the medication to printing the label and receipt. All that remains to be done is to put the medication into a suitable vial and attach the label.[6]

The Swedish System

Swedish pharmacy has always been considered a forerunner where operational aspects of drug dispensing are concerned. Taking a very pragmatic approach, Apoteksbolaget, the state-run company that owns all

---

[5] For more information on this system, see "The Electronic Counter: a little marvel of speed and accuracy which relieves the pharmacist from purely technical tasks," *Le Pharmacien* (October 1985), p. 39; and "Robot in the Pharmacy: Automated prescription system for 48 most-prescribed Rxs, counts 100 capsules in 10 seconds," *Drug Merchandising* (April 1984), pp. 16-18.

[6] An excellent study of such a system is John Nazzaro's "Looking at a Computerized Pharmacy in the Military Sector," *Computers in Hospitals* (September/October, 1980).

pharmacies in Sweden, has conducted numerous studies to develop model equipment that will improve health-care efficiency and make high-quality pharmaceutical services available at the lowest possible cost. One of the results of these efforts is an entirely automated module that processes prescriptions from the point of writing to that of dispensing the medication to the patient. The system comprises a terminal in the physician's office into which the physician enters a prescription that is then relayed through an electronic network to a terminal at the patient's pharmacy. The pharmacy's computer prepares the medication, prints the label and the receipts, and updates the patient file.[7]

All the technology required to operate similar systems now exists in Canada, but widespread implementation is still problematic because of the diversity of existing pharmacy computer systems. Such obstacles, however, are likely to be overcome within the next few years. Prescriptions are already being electronically transmitted to some community pharmacies. These new systems will not only prove time-saving, but will also reduce the number of errors that occur in the process of reading and transcribing prescriptions and selecting products. In addition, they will increase efficiency in the preparation and dispensing of prescriptions, thereby freeing the pharmacist from routine and technical tasks.

Mail-Order Dispensing Services

A certain phenomenon that has taken root in the United States might prompt Canadian community pharmacists to re-evaluate their own performance in dispensing drugs. In the course of the last few years, several private companies have capitalized on an idea that originated in government, specifically the U.S. Veterans' Administration, some 20 years ago, and offered mail-order drug dispensing services to the general public. Approximately three percent of all prescriptions filled in the United States are now dispensed through such systems. The number of mail-order services in operation is growing rapidly and their volume of business is estimated to increase from $720 million (U.S.) in 1987 to over $3.8 billion (U.S.) by the end of the 1980s and over $8.8 billion (U.S.) by 1995.[8]

Generally speaking, these mail-order services enable members of organizations such as the American Association of Retired Persons (AARP), trade unions, and war veterans' groups to obtain medication at lower cost. The use of highly automated procedures, computerization, technical personnel, volume-purchase discounts, and provision of long-term drug

---

[7] Swedish Pharmaceutical Society, personal communication, June 1988.
[8] "Mail-order Drug Delivery," *Industry Report*, Eberstadt Fleming Inc., 9 January 1987.

supply to their customers have enabled these companies to dispense drugs at lower cost, which has resulted in substantial savings for the patients.[9] User organizations and companies also benefit from decreased administrative costs for group programs. The companies operating such services claim that they are the consumer's answer to the current high cost of prescription drugs.

Over and above monetary savings, organizations that purchase from mail-order dispensing services also gain access to data banks with information on the use and cost of the drugs prescribed to their members or employees. The mail-order companies also offer employers and other user organizations a management system for their drug-insurance plans. In addition, they provide detailed and complete information on product selection, physicians' prescribing patterns, savings for contributing organizations and their beneficiaries, a drug utilization review (by drug and by therapeutic class) for each plan, and a list of potential drug abusers. Finally, such services take extensive precautions to prevent fraud and abuse.

Mail-order services have some obvious limitations: they cannot offer the convenience of same-day prescription service and are appropriate only for chronic-care drug therapies; they cannot provide personal services nor the continuity afforded by community-pharmacy practice. However, they do give evidence that it is possible to fill prescriptions in a safe and efficient manner at what appear to be reasonable costs. Automation, computerization, and skilled technical personnel are highly instrumental in achieving that goal.

Community pharmacists would be well advised to analyze such operations and to automate and computerize as many technical tasks in their own pharmacies as possible. They would then have more time to devote to other professional tasks, such as personalized services and counselling for their patients. As the president of one mail-order company said, "The best way to fight mail-order is for the pharmacist to sell his personality to the customer; if the pharmacist is liked, he (she) has the edge."[10] It would perhaps even be advisable for community pharmacists to create (or re-introduce) co-operatives as a means of facilitating the development of joint automation projects, thereby lowering costs. It seems evident that, in the near future, in face of the considerable increase in demand for medication in our society – especially among the growing proportions

[9] Sharon Murphy Enright, "Mail-order Pharmaceuticals," *American Journal of Hospital Pharmacy* 44 (1987), pp. 1870-73; Martha Glaser, "Mail-order Rs: Separating facts from fiction," *Drug Topics* (6 February 1984), pp. 42-48.
[10] Glaser, "Mail-order Rs: Separating facts from fiction," p. 46.

of senior citizens – governments and other third-party insurers will put considerable pressure on pharmacists to contain the costs generated by prescription-drug use.

COMPUTERIZATION

As we saw in Chapter 20, computerization is probably the technology that has in recent years had the greatest impact on the community pharmacist's daily practice, and will continue to do so in the near future. The computer systems and software currently available allow pharmacists to free themselves from technical and routine tasks and to focus their attention on professional duties. Numerous data banks now exist containing extensive information on the effectiveness of drug products, adverse effects, directions for use, precautions to be taken, contraindications, clinical indications, possible interactions with other medication or with food, and advice that should be given to patients. In the very near future, with the help of computers and peripheral systems, pharmacists will be able to control the use of medication much more closely than has ever been possible before.

Patient-File Analysis

In addition to preparing and dispensing drugs, pharmacists are responsible for monitoring drug use and helping patients to understand their drug treatments. The computerized patient file has given pharmacists a valuable tool to assist in performing this function. The pharmacist's professional activity is based on the patient file, the study of which enables him or her to provide patients with optimal pharmacotherapy. Chapter 20 described how to set up a computerized patient file for easy access to the data that is essential for profile analysis. We shall now explore further some of the factors of which pharmacists should be aware in their use of computer systems for such analysis.

DETECTION OF DRUG INTERACTIONS

Computerized drug-interaction data banks, compiled from the existing literature on the subject, have been on the market for some time now. Although they are an invaluable aid, these data banks have often been found to be incomplete or dated due to the rapid development of scientific knowledge and the considerable delay between the publication of new research in the literature and its incorporation into the data banks. A number of software companies have attempted to address this problem by regularly updating their data banks to reflect recently published clinical information. An example is *Hansten's Drug Interaction*, which is available on diskette and can be integrated with most pharmacy systems, and whose purchasers are provided with updating services.

Care must be taken in the choice and maintenance of a drug-interaction detection system.[11] Good systems are characterized by exact and complete data and an adequate means of identifying drugs, the products that contain them, and their therapeutic class. The system must also require pharmacists to keep complete and up-to-date files on each patient's drug history. Above all, a good drug-interaction detection system should generate precise, relevant information, without a lot of unnecessary or unimportant detail, which could cause the pharmacist to mistrust the system and hence ignore its messages.

Such detection systems are not intended to replace the pharmacist. With their great operating speed, however, they are an excellent tool to help the pharmacist make professional decisions and assume more fully his or her responsibilities in the area of patient care.

DETECTION OF ADVERSE EFFECTS

The detection and prevention of adverse effects associated with drug products is another field to which modern pharmacotherapy pays particular attention. Systems that monitor such effects have been in existence in Canada and elsewhere for some years now. Such systems are, as a rule, based on two main sources of information. The first consists of the results of compulsory clinical tests designed to determine any adverse reactions caused by new drugs, which are conducted by pharmaceutical companies seeking authorization to release those drugs commercially. The incidence of reactions documented this way is bound to represent only a partial measurement, since only a limited number of individuals are exposed to the new drug during clinical trials. The second source of information comprises, in large part, statements volunteered by health professionals to government bodies such as the Health Protection Branch of Health and Welfare Canada, which is responsible for public health protection and drug-release authorization. The two main sources are supplemented by data from certain other countries, such as Great Britain, where such information is collected in a more systematic manner.

It stands to reason that computerization of the results of clinical research, together with a systematic monitoring of patients, will yield much more dependable data about the actual incidence and seriousness of ad-

[11] Jeffrey R. Koup, "Therapeutic drug monitoring and other clinical applications," in William E. Fassett and Dale B. Christensen, eds., *Computer Applications in Pharmacy* (Philadelphia: Lea & Febiger, 1986), pp. 133-34.

verse reactions to drugs and will assist in developing more complete and more reliable data banks. Until that time, Canadian pharmacists can nevertheless benefit greatly from currently available data in their efforts to detect and prevent the occurrence of adverse drug reactions among their patients.

Pharmacists in Canada will certainly benefit from the Canadian Pharmaceutical Association's undertaking to computerize the *Compendium of Pharmaceuticals and Specialties* (CPS). Pharmacists will be able to integrate the CPS into their computer systems and draw on it to detect any adverse reactions that their patients might experience. The computerized *Compendium* will also represent an invaluable data bank from which pharmacists will derive assistance in their other professional tasks, such as informing and counselling patients. The *United States Pharmacopoeia – Drug Information* (USPDI), also available in electronic form, should similarly prove to be an invaluable source of information for pharmacists.[12]

It will probably take a few more years, however, before computerized programs capable of systematically detecting adverse drug reactions are available on the market. Present-day technology would permit it, but adequate information-gathering systems are still lacking. As drug specialists, pharmacists must avail themselves of all the currently existing tools, which are essential to acquiring the requisite knowledge of drug products.

Finally, it is interesting to note that, according to one study, the Canadian public is quite willing to pay a fee to pharmacists for the advice or recommendations they provide.[13] This is an important issue that Canadian pharmacists must consider carefully in order to arrive at an appropriate response.

PATIENT COMPLIANCE

Failure among patients to comply with prescribed drug treatments constitutes a major problem in pharmacotherapy – one that community pharmacists can help resolve. Being the last health professional in contact with patients before they take their medication, the pharmacist can intervene to make them aware of the importance of adhering faithfully to the treatment prescribed. In this regard, the computerized patient file

---

[12] For an excellent description of these and many other existing data banks that relate to drugs and therapeutic drug treatment, refer to Patrick M. Malone, "Drug Information Retrieval and Storage," in William E. Fassett and Dale B. Christensen, eds., *Computer Applications in Pharmacy* (Philadelphia: Lea & Febiger, 1986), pp. 140-57.
[13] *Canadian Pharmacy Services Study, 1984*, The Upjohn Company of Canada.

gives pharmacists a powerful tool in identifying patients who are not compliant, and enables them to remind those patients regularly about their drug treatment.[14]

Smart Cards

A very recent development – still in the experimental stage – that could revolutionize the processing and dispensing of prescriptions is the "smart card." The size of a credit card and containing a computer chip, the smart card can carry large amounts of information regarding its bearer, for example, the person's complete medical and drug history. Early testing of smart cards in Canada has had physicians encoding prescriptions onto a patient's card, and pharmacists decoding them, with the help of special equipment that "reads" the cards. The implications are clearly immense – an entirely paperless process from the physician's order to the dispensing of medication and, combined with existing computer-system capabilities as well as the health-services cards that we described in Chapter 20, the billing of third parties. Furthermore, theoretically at least, smart cards could make in-house patient-profiling systems obsolete. They would also allow patients even greater flexibility in their choice of both physicians and pharmacists, while simultaneously permitting immediate detection of any attempt on the patient's part to engage in double-doctoring. They would, in general, reduce the possibility of fraud, duplication, and error.

Smart cards at present have significant limitations. One that will probably be overcome in time is the current inability of the card to hold a sufficient number of prescriptions. Serious ethical issues – protection of privacy being the most obvious – will have to be debated and resolved before smart cards gain authorization and widespread acceptance. Pharmacists should, however, be watchful of developments in the near future.

Computer-Assisted Self-Care

Self-diagnosis and self-medication have been known to exist from time immemorial, and there is little doubt that self-medication will increase considerably in the years to come. Confronted by the growing costs of

---

[14] The results of a Canadian survey showing that community pharmacists can contribute considerably to solving this problem are reported in Colin Heard, Jim L. Blackburn, Mark S. Thompson, and Sylvia M. Wallace, "Evaluation of a Computer-Assisted Medication Refill Reminder System for Improving Patient Compliance," *Canadian Pharmaceutical Journal* (October 1984), pp. 473-77.

health programs, governments are likely to encourage this trend. A first step will soon be taken in this direction when government authorities permit the sale, without prescription, of certain products containing hydrocortisone and of some Ibuprofen preparations. In this regard, the Canadian government is following the lead of the United States, which has already authorized the change in status of several drugs, thus aiming at limiting government spending since most non-prescription drugs are not reimbursed by drug-benefit plans.

Consumers at large, as well as general practitioners, trust and seek out pharmacists' advice on drugs, especially those sold without prescription. As a result, there is a general expectation that community pharmacists will assume this increased responsibility as the trend toward self-medication grows, and take an even more active role in patient counselling.

In a recently published article, William McGhan describes some interesting instances in which community pharmacists used computers and peripheral systems to support their interventions with patients in the area of self-care.[15] In fact, some pharmacists have even assisted patients in establishing their own diagnoses with the help of a computer. The Montreal Clinical Research Institute has recently developed one such computer-assisted self-care program, and others are now available in Canada as well. These are very powerful, interactive, and inexpensive support tools that may be complemented by drug information provided by the pharmacist. Opportunities exist here to combine the use of self-care programs and drug-information data banks for patient counselling.

Further technological developments, such as artificial intelligence and human-interface capacity, will certainly render self-care services even more attractive in the future.

CONCLUSION

In Chapters 20 and 23, various applications of the new technologies, ranging from inventory control to diagnostic equipment, are discussed. Here, we have attempted to outline briefly the opportunities that technology, and especially computer systems, offer community pharmacists in helping them pursue their professional responsibilities. Assisted by modern technology, pharmacists can noticeably diminish their technical tasks, and devote the time saved to the performance of their professional duties. Computerization can also help them in their professional tasks by providing easy access to impressive quantities of stored information. It is imperative that community pharmacists make the most of these modern tools, both in their own interests and in the interests of the patients they serve.

[15] William F. McGhan, "Computer-Assisted Self-Care: Meeting the Challenge," *Merck Minutes* 5, no. 1 (February 1988): 1-6.

RECOMMENDED READING

Bezold, Clement; Halperin, Jerome A.; Binkley, Howard L.; and Ashbaugh, Richard R., eds. *Pharmacy in the 21st Century: Planning for an Uncertain Future*. Washington, D.C.: Institute for Alternative Futures and Project Hope, American Association of Colleges of Pharmacy, 1985.

"Directions for Clinical Practice in Pharmacy." Proceedings of an invitational conference conducted buy the ASHP Research Education Foundation and the American Society of Hospital Pharmacists, Hilton Head, South Carolina. *American Journal of Hospital Pharmacy* 42 (1985): 1287-1342.

Fassett, William E., and Christensen, Dale B., eds. *Computer Applications in Pharmacy*. Philadelphia: Lea & Febiger, 1986.

23

NEW SERVICE OPPORTUNITIES

INTRODUCTION: A CHANGING ENVIRONMENT

Important studies, conference proceedings, books, and papers have been published in various countries on the contemporary and future role and responsibilities of the pharmacist. To mention a few, the "Pharmaceuticals in the year 2000" conference, the "Directions for Clinical Practice in Pharmacy" conference, and the International Seminar on Management of Pharmaceutical Services have stimulated interesting reflection.[1] "Pharmacy in the 21st Century," a strategic-planning conference for the professional pharmacy community, concluded that "health care in the twenty-first century will differ substantially from what it is today and the effects of these changes will be profound and will affect the basic fabric of pharmacy."[2] In England, the report of a committee of inquiry appointed by the Nuffield Foundation has analyzed the present and future structures of pharmacy in its several branches, as well as its potential contribution

[1] C. Bezold, *Pharmaceuticals in the Year 2000* (Alexandria, Va.: Institute for Alternative Futures, 1983); American Society of Hospital Pharmacists, "Directions for Clinical Practice in Pharmacy," *American Journal of Hospital Pharmacy* 42 (June 1985): 1287-1339; Proceedings of the International Seminar on Management of Pharmaceutical Services (Stockholm: The Swedish Pharmaceutical Society, January 1985).
[2] C. Bezold, J.A. Halperin, H.L. Binkley, and R.R. Ashbaugh, *Pharmacy in the 21st Century* (Alexandria, Va.: Institute for Alternative Futures, 1985), p.291.

to health care, in a very innovative way.[3] Changing pharmacies from production-distribution-oriented operations to market-oriented service operations was the topic of a most interesting study conducted in Denmark.[4] In Canada, the 1971 report of the Commission on Pharmaceutical Services, entitled "Pharmacy in a New Age," made recommendations that are still valid and appropriate today.[5] In addition, surveys conducted by pharmaceutical organizations and pharmaceutical manufacturers have documented the appreciation that the majority of people in the United States and Canada have for pharmacists and their services.[6]

Pharmacy faces many problems, mainly because the profession has not precisely addressed all the aspects of its mission in today's health-care environment. But more than ever, pharmacists are being given opportunities to make unique contributions within the health-care systems of their countries in the years to come. This is true for Canada as well: the need for innovation in pharmacy practice and in the marketing strategies pharmacists will have to adopt has never been greater. New drugs, new products, new devices, and new types of service will offer pharmacists the opportunity to expand their role – and increase their sales – by promoting effective means of distribution and use of the new products and services both in pharmacies and in patients' homes.

The trends and forces that we can identify today and that already affect the delivery of health care and the practice of pharmacy are many. This chapter shall explore these growing trends and the impact they will have on health conditions, drug therapy and the drug market, patient care, health maintenance and disease prevention, wellness and health promotion, health-related products, and pharmacy services. A new demand for health programs and services is developing and will increase the opportunity for community pharmacists to provide a variety of appropriate, cost-effective services and products, resulting ultimately in increased sales and profits.

What Are the Prospects for Health?

Neither the causes of death and disability nor their determinants are likely to change appreciably over the next decade. Chronic diseases are now

[3] *Pharmacy*, Report of the Committee of Inquiry Appointed by the Nuffield Foundation (London: The Nuffield Foundation, 1986).

[4] P.J. Kielgast, "Changing pharmacies from production distribution oriented operations to market oriented service operations" (unpublished paper, 1985).

[5] *Pharmacy in a New Age*, Report of the Commission on Pharmaceutical Services (Toronto: The Canadian Pharmaceutical Association, 1971).

[6] *The Schering Reports*, I–VIII (Kenilwork, N.J.: Schering Laboratories, 1978–86); The Upjohn Surveys on Pharmaceutical Services in Canada (Toronto: The Upjohn Company of Canada, 1982–88).

the primary cause of death and disability; also, the Canadian population is growing older rapidly. Both factors will place a greater demand on the health-care system. Epidemics such as AIDS will have an increasing impact and will continue to require expensive therapy in the foreseeable future.

Morbidity and Mortality

During the last fifty years, mortality rates have declined considerably and life expectancy has increased, as have morbidity rates. These trends are expected to continue, resulting in an older, but less healthy, population.

A concept known as "disability-free life expectancy" (DFLE) has been developed to provide a conceptual framework for targeting health strategies and interventions in relation to morbidity. DFLE is an index of mean length of healthy life (see Table 23.1). If, over time, DFLE increases more slowly than life expectancy, then the number of years of disability experienced will increase; if both increase at the same rate, an equilibrium will be maintained; and if DFLE increases more rapidly than life expectancy, the number of years of disability will be reduced, achieving what is called a "compression of morbidity." This is the goal toward which the health professions aspire, but it will not be an easy challenge to meet.

Table 23.1   LIFE EXPECTANCY AND DFLE IN CANADA

Year	Male 1978	2000	Female 1978	2000
Life expectancy	70.8 (+1.6 years)	72.4	78.3 (+3.1 years)	81.4
Disability-free life expectancy (DFLE)	59.2	——	62.8	——
Years of disability	11.6 (16%)	——	15.5 (20%)	——

Source: R. Wilkins and O.B. Adam, "Health Expectancy in Canada, Late 1970s: Demographic, Regional, and Social Dimensions," American Journal of Public Health 73, no. 9 (September 1983): 1073.

The degenerative diseases are expected to remain the major cause of death and disability in the foreseeable future. The health threat facing the Western countries in the year 2000 is expected to consist mainly of the following diseases:

1. Cardiovascular diseases
2. Age-related health problems

3. Cancer
4. Lifestyle-related health problems
5. AIDS, sexual diseases[7]

The new environmental threats, including new air and water pollutants, chemical carcinogens, pesticides, herbicides, food additives, cosmetics, excessive radiation, extreme urbanization, and accidents, have replaced the traditional physical and bacterial dangers, with predictable effects on our needs for health care. Behavioural patterns are also increasing the risk of illness. In fact, there is no longer a clear boundary between environmental and behavioural factors as threats to health. Cancer can result either (or both) from smoke-contaminated workplaces or from individual smoking. The risk, however, is greatly increased when both factors are present.

Caring for the Elderly

The population of Canada is growing older rapidly. By the year 2000, there will be more than 3.5 million Canadians aged 65 or older, and more than 8 million aged 50 or older. This changing mix of our population, together with the projected longer life expectancy, will focus pharmacy on ambulatory patients afflicted with chronic diseases, who can be treated and maintained by drug therapy.

The 1981 Canada Health Survey showed that 70 percent of persons aged 65 or older used some kind of prescribed drugs. In this group, 13 percent of the males and 25 percent of the females were taking three or more prescribed drugs. The survey also indicated that, in a random sample of outpatients over 60 years of age, 34.4 percent were taking cardiovascular drugs or diuretics; 15.6 percent, tranquillizers or hypnotics; and 20.9 percent, analgesic and anti-inflammatory drugs.[8] The Gerontology Research Council of Ontario prepared a background paper to the survey for its national conference on drug use among the elderly, which was summarized in the *Canadian Pharmaceutical Journal* as follows:

> Use, misuse, or abuse of drugs in the elderly severe enough to cause hospitalization can be classified in two broad categories:
>
> – Adverse effects such as drug toxicity from excessive dose, drug accumulation, drug interactions, product quality, altered biological response due to aging or disease, and predictable side-effect and allergic responses; and

---

[7] *Medicine in the Next Century*, The Bristol-Myers Report
[8] Canada, Health and Welfare Canada, *The Health of Canadians*, Report of the Canadian Health Survey (Ottawa: Supply and Services Canada, 1981), p.163.

– Sub-therapeutic responses that may be due to insufficient dose, decreased bioavailability, drug interactions, faulty product, and non-compliance by the patient.

Either of these two problems can result in hospital admissions that could have been avoided. They may originate from at least six sources. . . .[9]

Of the six sources identified, it is interesting for our purposes to note what the report had to say with regard to medical doctors, pharmacists, nurses, and the patient:

Physicians may contribute to the problem by unnecessary over-prescribing, inappropriate dosing or drug selection, insufficient professional counselling, inadequate reporting or follow-up on adverse drug reaction, and insufficient drug specificity in prescribing.

The pharmacist may also contribute to therapeutic problems in the elderly through inappropriate dispensing or labelling, insufficient patient counselling or provision of information, inadequate patient profile system, warning, reporting, and following up adverse reactions, and drug product substitution without prior knowledge of the patient or physician.

The nurse or other health care provider may be inattentive in the administration of drugs as a result of inadequate patient counselling, monitoring, and reporting.

The patient may be responsible for problems through non-compliance, multiple concurrent use of doctors and pharmacies, and inadvertent or intentional drug misuse or abuse.

The council made interesting recommendations to help meet the problems of use, misuse, and abuse of drugs among the elderly. One is of particular interest to pharmacists:

The pharmacist should be used by the patient more frequently as a source of information. A 1984 study showed that only 20 percent of patients talked with the pharmacist when they got their prescriptions filled. On the other hand, a 1985 survey showed a 39 percent decrease in one year in medication problems after intermittent pharmacist consultation in senior citizens' apartments.

Since chronic diseases have become the dominant cause of death and disability, and since chronic patients and the elderly are high users of

---

[9]D. McIntosh, "Aging and Drugs," *Canadian Pharmaceutical Journal* 121, no. 4 (April 1988): 246. (All excerpts quoted in this section are attributable to this source.)

care and drugs, pharmacists have a significant opportunity to promote and monitor good and rational therapy through appropriate and effective services.

Drug Therapy in the Future

It is clear that the future will bring a need and an opportunity for community pharmacists to expand the clinical dimensions of pharmacy practice. Good management of comprehensive pharmaceutical services should strive to create a closer fit between the services offered and the needs of the public. The management and marketing of pharmacy services should involve the sort of concepts and principles that can be used to manage health and pharmacy services in a more equitable, appropriate, and efficient way.

NEW DRUGS AND NEW DELIVERY SYSTEMS

New drugs and new technologies and devices for administering drugs will soon emerge from the major efforts in basic and clinical research currently being undertaken in universities, hospitals, research institutes, and industrial laboratories. Antiviral agents, anticancer agents, immunomodulators, endorphins, and new mood-altering drugs, among others, will bring important benefits to society. Gene-replacement therapy and the ability to prepare monoclonal antibodies create new therapeutic possibilities. While these dramatic advances in the number and sophistication of pharmacotherapeutic agents will bring enormous benefits to our society, they will also carry significant risks. It is generally recognized that if drugs are not adequately monitored, the costs associated with these risks will be much higher than the costs of the new products. Consequently, there will be a crucial need for more effective drug-use control, evaluation, and information. With the advent of new methods of drug administration, pharmacists will be called upon to assist or instruct patients in the use of the new dosage forms that would be involved. For example, reservoirs of medication implanted in the patient's body would have to be refilled periodically. The materials for refilling would be obtained at the pharmacy, and the pharmacist would provide information on the proper refilling techniques and use of the medication. Some medicinal products and devices that involve self-administration would be obtainable from the pharmacist, who would then be responsible for providing all the necessary instructions for proper use.

PHARMACEUTICAL SERVICES, COST CONTAINMENT, AND QUALITY OF LIFE

The cost of drugs and pharmaceutical services is too often evaluated in terms of the cost of the products themselves and the traditional dispensing and distribution costs. The major improvements that are now required in the cost-effectiveness of drugs are not likely to come from saving a few dollars when buying stock, or keeping inventory low, or not exceeding a price ceiling. These measures help control some components of the direct costs of a treatment, but do not address the indirect and intangible costs to the health-care system and to society, which are related to the overall *effectiveness* of a drug – that is, the degree of benefit that can be achieved for a patient (or a group of patients) under usual conditions of care. The determination of effectiveness requires the measurement of both the desirable effects and the undesirable effects (that is, adverse reactions). In the case of a drug therapy, when non-compliance occurs, closer monitoring by the pharmacist, together with patient education, would reduce not only the direct costs of treatment, but also the indirect costs (productivity losses, high morbidity and mortality rates) and the intangible costs (pain and other psychosocial costs). For example, medication that does not interfere with a person's ability to perform social roles or with his or her emotional or cognitive functioning lowers both indirect and intangible costs. Such medication therefore improves the *quality of life*. Adverse effects could include those that prevent patients from working, diminish their performance, or, in the case of elderly people, limit their autonomy and lead to premature admission to nursing homes – all of which detracts from quality of life.[10]

More attention should be given by pharmacists, third-party payers, and patients to the ability to maintain or improve these aspects of effectiveness and quality of life in the course of managing a disease. These concepts are important not only for professional satisfaction and the social good: they are economically relevant in terms of optimizing the impact of pharmaceutical services on the cost and quality of health care and in terms of creating more equitable reimbursement systems for pharmacists.

The pressures to reduce drug costs are so strong that pharmacists have even reduced their fees for some categories of drugs. The dispensing of the birth control pill at a very low fee is an example of this. Consider, however, how important the possible drug interactions from contraceptives are and how pharmacists must be aware of all the options for managing these interactions when making recommendations for individual patients.[11] Should such a service be worth less?

[10] A. Archambault, "Cost-Effectiveness in Health Care: Complexity of the Equation," *Journal of the Canadian Dietetic Association* 49, no. 2 (Spring 1988): 80.

[11] G.L. Plosker and E.M. Hawes, "Oral Contraceptive Drug Interactions: A Clinical Perspective," *Canadian Pharmaceutical Journal* 119, no. 12 (December 1986): 688.

POST-MARKETING SURVEILLANCE

Post-marketing surveillance (the monitoring of new drugs) offers a challenging opportunity to all Canadian pharmacists. It is a subject that has been debated over the last several decades, and pharmacists may now wish to exercise a more visible role in the drug monitoring research of the coming decade. Patients, medical doctors, and firms will be exerting pressure on the government to accelerate the approval time for certain drugs. We can already envisage new methods of drug introduction involving restricted use by specific population groups and specific medical specialties – those, for example, that deal with sexual diseases, AIDS, and cancer. Government, in close co-operation with pharmaceutical firms, medical doctors, and pharmacists, would be in a position to create such surveillance mechanisms to better identify the risks, the benefits, and the complications of a new drug. Some pharmaceutical firms have already accepted their responsibilities in this domain by initiating major post-marketing surveillance programs in Canada. Orphan drugs will be increasing in number and they will require specialized methods of handling. Where small populations are involved in a surveillance, pharmacies may inherit the specialized function of dispensing these drugs to the patients and monitoring the therapy effectively. Pharmacists, because of their unique position in the health-care environment, could play a very important role in such surveillance studies and provide an ideal environment for patient liaison and counselling.

Wellness and Health Promotion

> There are increasing health expectations as well as shifts in individuals' perceptions of health and illness, including wellness programs, self-care, health promotion, and disease prevention.[12]

It is expected that an increasing demand for wellness and health-promotion products and services will emerge as groups of consumers and innovative health-care professionals place a greater emphasis on disease prevention, changes in lifestyle, and health promotion. A variety of products and kits are currently on the market.

Health promotion and disease prevention have become national goals that may help to re-establish the pharmacy as the source of health-related products and services. In November 1974, a federal publication entitled *A New Perspective on the Health of Canadians* put forward the view that people's health was influenced by a broad range of factors, such as human

---

[12] American Pharmaceutical Association, *The Final Report of the Task Force on Pharmacy Education* 1984, p. 17.

biology, lifestyle, the organization of health care, and the social and physical environments in which people live.[13] Health policies and practices have since been developed within this broad context. *Achieving Health for All: A Framework for Health Promotion* was published by the federal government in 1986. It describes the nature of the health challenges facing Canadians and reinforces the message of the 1974 publication by emphasizing health promotion as "a process of enabling people to increase control over, and to improve their health."[14] Self-care, which refers to the decisions taken and the practices adopted by an individual specifically for the preservation of his or her health, is viewed as one of the mechanisms intrinsic to health promotion. These new directions will certainly provide Canadian pharmacists with new opportunities to expand their role and services.

Self-Care

Several factors have been responsible for the growing interest in self-care during the past few decades. Among the most important are the demystification of primary medical care, the "consumerist" movement and the anti-technology movement, and a greater involvement on the part of the public in health care and related issues. The demand for self-care has also been stimulated by greater access to technological information and by rising levels of education, which have resulted in a greater tendency among members of the community to exercise personal judgment. The public has also become more assertive in its concern about perceived abuses and poor standards and quality in health care. Finally, increasing health-care costs have caused people to turn to the option of self-care.

One study defines self-care as "a process whereby a layperson functions on his / her own behalf in health promotion and prevention and in disease detection and treatment at the level of the primary health resource in the health-care system."[15] Four roles are identified for self-care: health maintenance, disease prevention, self-diagnosis, and self-medication and self-treatment. The study observes that "self-care can also be viewed as a decision-making process which involves self-observation, symptom perception and labelling, judgment of severity, and choice and assessment of treatment options."[16] The results of several

[13] M. Lalonde, *A New Perspective on the Health of Canadians* (Ottawa: Government of Canada, April 1974).

[14] J. Epp, *Achieving Health for All: A Framework for Health Promotion* (Ottawa: Supply Services Canada, 1986).

[15] L.S. Levin, A.H. Katz, and E. Holst, *Self-care: Lay Initiatives in Health* (New York: Prodist, 1976).

[16] Levin et al., *Self-care*.

studies suggest that approximately 75 percent of all health care is undertaken without professional intervention, and also indicate that a large majority of symptoms of illness or injury are treated through self-care and non-prescription medications. Furthermore, in a study published in 1972, more than half the physicians surveyed felt that at least 25 percent of their consultations were for conditions that the patient could have self-treated.[17] Self-care opens up various new possibilities for pharmacists. Let us return to the four identified roles that comprise self-care and see how pharmacists can expand their function and their services in this new context.

HEALTH MAINTENANCE AND DISEASE PREVENTION

Technology and new scientific discoveries are unlikely to alter morbidity and mortality rates appreciably in the next ten to fifteen years, and socio-economic factors could even reduce the potential gains. In this context, improvements in health status are most likely to result from healthier lifestyles and an improved environment, as well as from a new approach to health priorities and to policy decision making – one that encourages resource allocation according to cost-effectiveness considerations. The health and pharmacy industries may want to consider giving priority to developing new drugs, manufacturing new devices to prevent or reduce disability, and organizing and offering a full range of products and services to promote health and wellness. People will need assistance in adopting healthier lifestyles – through education, information, and audio-visual aids – and in managing their treatments better – particularly those administered at home. Pharmacists might well be in the best possible position to market new lines of products and services and to participate in what has been described as "the changing ownership of information."[18]

As pharmacists, we try to motivate patients to maintain good health practices through patient education in the form of health information and medical facts, and, particularly, effective and adequate information on diseases and the drugs used for their treatments. But patient education is more than this: "It involves motivating the patient to take action to stay healthy by avoiding harmful activities and by forming behavioural habits."[19] Because of this, educating patients requires behavioural interventions that can be very time-consuming. Computers can be helpful in reducing the time involved and even in increasing the effectiveness of the pharmacist's intervention. Several computer programs for patient education are already available in North America, covering subjects such

[17] K. Dunnell and A. Cartwright, *Medicine Takers, Prescribers and Hoarders* (London: Routledge and Kegan Paul, 1972).

[18] Bezold et al., *Pharmacy in the 21st Century*, p. 97.

[19] W.F. McGhan, "Computer-Assisted Self-Care: Meeting the Challenge," *Merck Minutes: A Publication for Pharmacists* 5, no. 1 (February 1988):1.

as smoking, diet, exercise, substance abuse, communicable diseases, early detection of disease and self-management, and prescription compliance.

The question of the incentives for pharmacists to perform preventive health-care roles is a complex one.[20] Much of the economic incentive is indirect, and preventive health-care involvement therefore continues to be perceived as an altruistic endeavour by community pharmacists. However, certain areas of preventive health care can have a strong economic incentive. A few of them are listed in Table 23.2.

Table 23.2   PREVENTIVE HEALTH-CARE ACTIVITIES AND
PHARMACISTS' ECONOMIC INCENTIVE

Preventive Health-Care Activity	Pharmacists' Economic Incentive
1. Hypertension detection and prevention	High
2. Diabetes screening and counselling	High
3. Antismoking programs	Very low
4. Cancer and sunlight	Intermediate
5. Non-prescription drug counselling	High

Source: P.J. Bush, *The Pharmacist's Role in Disease Prevention and Health Promotion* (Washington, D.C. : ASHP Research and Education Foundation Inc., 1983), p.28.

The public interest in products of natural origin should not be overlooked. It has resulted in the rapid growth of the so-called health-food store. The pharmacist's knowledge of natural products and the appropriate use of such compounds affords a significant opportunity for selling natural products with medicinal properties in pharmacies.

Electronic instruments represent another important opportunity for pharmacists. This equipment can be used for monitoring body functions and biofeedback, as well as for health education. The rapid growth of microelectronics has spawned a large number of health applications, with which pharmacists should become familiar to broaden the scope of their services.

The areas of nutrition and drug therapy are becoming more closely linked, with nutrition products selling alongside pharmaceuticals. Pharmacists have traditionally entered this field when new food products became available that grocery stores were not prepared to sell. For example, it is not generally known that pablum was developed as an infant formula and, initially, sold only through pharmacies in Canada. Simi-

[20] For more information on incentives to perform preventive health roles, see P.J. Bush, *The Pharmacist's Role in Disease Prevention and Health Promotion* (Washington, D.C.: ASHP Research and Education Foundation Inc., 1983).

larly, Metracal was sold in pharmacies. A wide range of infant products and special diet products continue to be sold in pharmacies and this will be a growth area as pharmacists add to their offerings in the food area.

SELF-DIAGNOSIS AND TEST KITS

More than fifty diagnostic kits are now available in the United States. Ovulation test kits, colorectal cancer screening kits, blood glucose monitors, a test for strep throat, and the usual forms of urine and blood tests are only few examples. A new generation of tests to monitor for a host of diseases and medical conditions will be available in the near future. The market for diagnostic kits is expanding rapidly in the United States: it is now estimated at $515 million (U.S.) and, according to a New York-based consulting firm called Packaged Facts, is expected to hit $1.4 billion (U.S.) at retail by 1992. Among U.S. retail pharmacists, 49 percent agree that test kits will be one of the highest-selling products in 1988, and the market is expected to grow at a rate of 31 percent.[21] It should not take long before a similar situation develops in Canada. When one considers the current pace of research and development in the United States into tests kits "for everything from sexually transmitted diseases to drug use,"[22] it is clear that Canadian pharmacists will soon be asked to make shelf space available for more and more diagnostic products. Some of these kits are designed for use at home by the patient; others must be used in laboratories – for example, in community-pharmacy dispensaries and in physicians' offices.

The companies that market diagnostic tests to be used at home also provide the users with free information available on a direct telephone line. What role, then, can pharmacists play? First, not only can they participate in the distribution and sale of the kits, but they can also provide direct and adequate information – in a more effective way – about using the kits and interpreting the results obtained. They can also promote the use of laboratory tests to be conducted by professional pharmacy staff and interpreted for the patients. Tests realized under a pharmacist's advice or supervision would be more reliable and more cost-effective for the patients: the cost to the consumer would be less than the cost of a kit, the tests would be performed safely and properly, misinterpretation of results would be minimized, and results could be recorded in the patient profile for future reference. The pharmacist could refer the patient to a physician or other health professional when such a course was indicated. If reimbursement programs were to be established to pay for prescriptions for these kits, pharmacists, in close co-operation with physicians and

---

[21] Tina Kyriakos, "Every Home a Mini-lab," *Drug Merchandising* 69, no. 3 (March 1988): 40–49.

[22] Kyriakos, "Every Home a Mini-Lab," p. 40.

other health professionals, could assume an important role and derive professional as well as financial rewards. Of course, pharmacists would have to exercise caution in this new role with respect to federal and provincial public-health laws and regulations. Take, for example, the case of the electronic glucose meter. As the executive director of the Canadian Pharmaceutical Association said, "If pharmacists cannot sell them, who is going to be the outlet? Only medical, licensed dealers? And how many of them are around? Does the public normally go to these places?"[23] It seems clear that the public's best interest will not be served if these devices are prevented by law from being sold in pharmacies. While the profession may have to lobby for the right to sell diagnostic kits, electronic glucose meters, and similar products, the opportunity is there and it should be taken, in order to establish this as one dimension of the practice of pharmacy.

SELF-MEDICATION AND SELF-TREATMENT

Since 1960, a number of important studies on self-medication have been conducted in Canada, the United States, Argentina, Britain, Europe, and Australia. Some of the major conclusions of those studies are as follows:

1. Illness is extremely common; 75 percent of the population will feel ill at some time in any given month.
2. The vast majority of symptoms do not receive medical attention; more than 80 percent of all illnesses are not seen by physicians.
3. Only about half of all illnesses receive any kind of treatment at all.
4. About 60 percent of the people whose illnesses are treated at all use non-prescribed products; this means that about 30 percent of all ill people self-medicate with non-prescription drugs.

The 1981 Canada Health Survey revealed similar trends in the occurrence of self-medication. People with at least one health problem took one or more selected actions to treat their symptoms: 48 percent chose to use medications, while the remaining 52 percent chose to rest in bed, limit their activities, or consult a health professional.[24] It was also found that of the 48 percent who chose to use medication, 60 percent reported taking at least one drug on the doctor's advice.[25] This means that 29 percent of all patients surveyed were treating their symptoms with non-prescription drugs.

[23] D. McKie, "Electronic Glucose Meters," *Canadian Pharmaceutical Journal* 119, no. 8 (August 1986): 436.
[24] Canada, Health and Welfare Canada, *The Health of Canadians*, p. 163.
[25] J. Ableson et al., *Perspectives on Health* (Ottawa: Supply and Services Canada, 1983), p. 35.

Comparisons among Canada, the United States, Australia, and France reveal that non-prescription drugs are increasingly viewed as an effective and inexpensive way to manage particular symptoms. It is true that controls on non-prescription-drug distribution differ among these countries. (For example, there is a "third class" of non-prescription drugs in Canada that only pharmacists may sell.) But it seems that governments in many countries now view pharmaceutical products from a different perspective with regard to their safety and the risk-benefit ratio involved. They now see self-medication as an essential element in helping to prevent the costs of medical care from becoming unacceptably high. Some prescription drugs have been reclassified after being on the market for a certain number of years, and more are expected to acquire non-prescription-drug status in the future. The non-prescription-drug market will continue to expand rapidly. In 1982, the most significant switch from prescription to non-prescription product classification in the United States was for 0.5 percent hydrocortisone topical ointment. Total sales for the prescribed product were $12 million (U.S.) in 1981; in 1982, sales reached $56 million (U.S.) – $18 million from prescription sales and $38 million from non-prescription sales. It is even predicted that non-prescription drugs will make up about 50 percent of all drug sales by the year 2000.[26]

Self-medication is becoming a way of life for consumers of all ages, with the exception of young children, for whom parents prefer to get a physician's advice and prescription medication. People are becoming more knowledgeable about minor ailments and the related drugs, and they feel they do not need to see a medical doctor to manage "small risks." Many of those who self-medicate do not have budgetary constraints, but may indeed have time constraints due to the demands of their professions; they see self-medication with drugs obtained from a pharmacist as an "easier access to care." This growing trend toward self-medication was documented during the sixth general assembly of the World Federation of Proprietary Medicine Manufacturers held in Ottawa in 1984, which took as its theme the role of self-medication in achieving the World Health Organization's goal of "health for all by the year 2000." Canadian-government thinking on self-medication was confirmed by federal Health Minister Monique Bégin in her speech to the Canadian Pharmaceutical Association Conference in May 1983. She said: "Canadians wish to play an active part in those decisions which have an impact on their health. Self-medication is an important part of this concept."[27] The pharmacist can play a key role in keeping drug profiles, educating

[26] *Trends and Forecasts, 1984–1986* (Reston, Va.: The National Pharmaceutical Council, 1986), p. 22. See also L.E. Fryklof and R. Westerling, *Self-medication* (Stockholm: Swedish Pharmaceutical Press, 1984).

[27] M. Bégin, "Address to the Canadian Pharmaceutical Association," *Canadian Pharmaceutical Journal* (1983), p. 314.

and counselling patients, preventing misuses, and referring patients to other health professionals. Rather than being a barrier between the self-medicating patient and the acquisition of a drug, the pharmacist will become a necessary and final source of help.

SOME CURRENT CONCERNS

The general interest in a healthier lifestyle has also resulted in more people becoming physically active and taking part in sporting and physical activities. This increase in activity has generated more sports-related injuries that require treatment. Pharmacists are now playing an important role in the initial assessment and treatment of minor injuries.[28]

Another current phenomenon affecting pharmacy is the rapid increase in substance abuse, which will call for continuous treatment programs for a large number of people over the next few decades. These treatment programs will require very strict monitoring of drug use by patients and, in some cases, daily or weekly provision of medication. More intensive attention to the use of prescription medication by this group of patients will be required, and pharmacists might provide it as a specialized service. It is expected that they would be reimbursed for this monitoring and counselling function.

HOME CARE

Home care is the provision of health-care services and products to people in their homes. The following services may be available on demand or on medical referral: nursing care; physiotherapy; occupational therapy; speech therapy; medical services; social-work services; nutritional counselling; drugs, dressings and medical supplies; diagnostic laboratory services; hospital and sick-room equipment; transportation; and meals-on-wheels. More than 13 percent of the Canadian population will be over 65 by the year 2000 and, as the population ages, consumer spending on medical supplies will increase. A Nova Scotia pharmacy executive summarized the situation this way: "One of the most important growth areas in the future will be home health care. . . . This is about the only area left where drugstores aren't likely to get competition from supermarkets and mass merchandisers. It is predicted that by 1995 'sales of home health-care products will reach $3 billion in Canada.' Pharmacists will have to be educated to take on more of the health care responsibilities in their stores and possibly in their patients' homes and it'll mean constant marketing to the home health-care community."[29]

---

[28] See Chapter 24 for more information on sports-related injuries.

[29] As quoted in Tina Kyriakos, "Checks Latest Trends," *Drug Merchandising* 69, no. 3 (March 1988): 10.

Thus, the dispensing of home health care, mainly in the form of drugs and a variety of health-related products, will become a very important dimension of pharmacy practice in the future. You will learn more about the practical aspects of introducing home health-care products and services in Chapter 24. Among the more radical changes that can be envisioned are the following:

1. House calls and a greater role in providing and prescribing home health care.
2. Monitoring and dispensing drugs through an electronic medicine cabinet in the patient's home. A wholesaler or pharmacist would stock the cabinet with drugs in "video cassette-type packages," which, when inserted into the cabinet, would program the machine for automated dispensing and documentation. A panel in the pharmacy, connected by telephone lines, would monitor the electronic cabinet in the patient's home.[30]

SUMMARY

Pharmacists will be given the opportunity to assume more and more responsibility for patient care, especially within the elderly population. New drugs and new dosage-form technology based on a better understanding of biological phenomena at the molecular level will result in a crucial need for more effective drug control, evaluation, and information. Post-marketing surveillance creates an opportunity for pharmacists to exercise a more visible role in drug monitoring.

Greater emphasis will be placed on health maintenance, disease prevention, health promotion, changes in lifestyles, self-diagnosis, self-medication, self-treatment, patient information, and education. Pharmacists have two options in relation to this new demand. They can either limit their practices to the traditional distributive role, leaving to other types of firms and to other health professionals the role of filling new patient needs and demands, or they can seize the new opportunities to expand the clinical dimensions of their profession, and become fully engaged in the delivery of a variety of health-related products and services in pharmacies and in patients' homes. To keep up with a health-care world that will focus on the "compression of morbidity" is the current challenge facing Canadian pharmacists. They are in a good position to provide appropriate and cost-effective services and products to satisfy this new demand, and stand to gain increased sales, profits, and professionalism.

[30] K.N. Barker and R.E. Pearson, "Designs of the Future: Dispensing in the 21st Century," *American Journal of Pharmaceutical Education* 50 (Winter 1986): 362; A. Archambault, "Why Clinical Path Leads to Year 2000?" *Drug Merchandising* 68, no. 12 (December 1987): 30.

RECOMMENDED READING

Bezold, C. *Pharmaceuticals in the Year 2000.* Alexandria, Va.: Institute for Alternative Futures, 1983.

Bezold, C.; Halperin, J.A.; Binkley, H.L.; and Ashbaugh, R.R. *Pharmacy in the 21st Century.* Alexandria Va.: Institute for Alternative Futures, 1985.

Levin, L.S.; Katz, A.H.; and Holst, E. *Self-care: Lay Initiatives in Health.* New York: Prodist, 1976.

Fryklof, L.E., and Westerling, R. *Self-medication.* Stockholm: Swedish Pharmaceutical Press, 1984.

Norman, R. *Service Management: Strategy and Leadership in Service Business.* New York: John Wiley and Sons, 1984.

24

UNDERSTANDING THE
ENVIRONMENT

Identifying Your Environment

To operate a pharmacy successfully, every owner or manager must be able to identify the factors that make up the business and professional environments. The political and economic climates, pertinent demographics, Canadians' health-care perceptions, and changing lifestyles must all be taken into account. How will each of these key factors affect your business?

Political Climate

In recent years, federal and provincial politicians have frequently been heard to refer to policies and concepts such as government restraint, privatization, free trade, and tax reform. How significant are these public policies to a pharmacist's environment?

In this section, we shall explore some of the trends and policies that currently govern the political environment. It is certainly advantageous, if not essential, for every profession and industry to take full stock of existing influences, as well as to try to foresee their implications for the future. For example, while it is too early to assess the implications of the 1988 Free-Trade Agreement with the United States for our health care and pharmaceutical industries, it is nonetheless a political development that could have important effects and therefore demands our attention. We can speculate that high-tech products like the recombinant form of tissue plasminogen activator (Activase®) might be more readily available from the best U.S. manufacturing facilities with a free-trade agreement. Will some of the multinational companies set a North American price for a product, rather than distinct Canadian and American prices? Will Canadian generic companies expand aggressively into the U.S. market? We can only speculate on these issues at the moment, but we should be watchful of developments as they occur.

GOVERNMENT-SPENDING RESTRAINT

From 1940 to 1980, the public sector in Canada grew steadily, initially as a result of the war effort and the need to develop social programs. But by the late 1970s, Canada came under severe criticism from other Western industrialized countries for having too large a public-sector program and a correspondingly excessive public debt.

Faced with burgeoning deficits, the various levels of government were obliged to introduce considerable fiscal restraints in the early 1980s. Provincial and federal governments alike found it politic to respond to taxpayer demands for real decreases in government spending, even if it meant a marked diminution in service levels. The majority of the public continues to favour a closer management of tax dollars. The consequent changes in fiscal policy have already caused changes in the delivery of health-care services, and will undoubtedly lead to more.

PRIVATIZATION

To providers who always put compassion before cost, treating health care as a commodity would be unthinkable. But as the universal applicability of economic laws pressed home and costs rose through the roof, politicians had to look at even more specific administrative remedies.

Consequently, government restraint has evolved into the policy of privatization, defined as the act of reducing the role of government or increasing the role of the private sector in an activity or in the ownership of assets. Privatization has come to symbolize a new way of looking at society's needs and represents a rethinking of the role of government in fulfilling them. It means relying more on private business and less on government to satisfy citizens' demands. Proponents of privatization envision the government providing the proper political environment, while small businesses carry out transactions on the public's behalf. So, in essence, privatization is more a political than an economic act.[1]

[1] E.S. Savas, *Privatization: The Key to Better Government* (Chatham, N.J.: Chatham House Publishers, Inc., 1987), p.233.

The concept of privatization is, however, nothing new. Urban dwellers who volunteered for their fire department or "meals on wheels" were, in essence, practising a form of privatization. Privatization was first proposed as a deliberate public policy to improve government performance in 1969.[2] Since then, there has been a worldwide political push in this direction. Why?

Much of the work performed by government employees consists of routine commercial activities that are in no way unique to government. An even more fundamental point bears mentioning: typically, administrative complexity in the public sector slows down productivity. Despite attempted remedies, such as centralization, decentralization, computerization, labour-management committees, and budget limits, the overall improvement in government efficiency and cost-effectiveness has been modest at best.

When it comes to the ability to get things done, the North American public considers the private sector superior to political institutions.[3] People believe that the long-term well-being of society will be maximized if economic decisions are left mostly to the marketplace. The argument is that competition within the private sector produces pressure for greater efficiency. And everyone approves of efficiency because it produces a higher standard of living.

Privatization, then, is a strategic approach to improving the productivity of government agencies, thereby giving people more for their tax dollars. Table 24.1 summarizes the forces at play and the reasoning behind privatization.

The federal and provincial governments have begun to implement privatization in earnest through various approaches. After the 1984 election, the Mulroney government dismantled the Liberals' National Energy Program and privatized the oil and gas industries. And in April 1988, our federal government announced it was selling Air Canada shares to the private sector.

During the 1980s, Ottawa reduced its subsidization of certain services, like those offered by Canada Post (this is referred to as "load shedding"). In British Columbia, Vander Zalm's Social Credit party made privatization a political priority.

But when individuals are deprived of certain benefits, the party in power generally pays a high political price. This makes it very difficult to roll back established programs, particularly those with a high profile, like health-care programs.

Political leaders have historically found the notion of eliminating user charges and providing services "free" to their constituents irresistible. But a more informed public is not as susceptible to such manipulation.

[2] P.F. Drucker, *The Age of Discontinuity* (New York: Harper and Row, 1969).
[3] S.M. Lipset and W. Schneider, *The Confidence Gap* (New York: Free Press, 1983), p. 75.

Table 24.1. THE FORCES BEHIND PRIVATIZATION

Force	Goal	Reasoning
Pragmatic	Better government	More cost-effective public services
Ideological	Less government	Government is too powerful; its decisions are inherently less trustworthy than free-market decisions.
Commercial	More business	Government spending is a large part of the economy; more of it should be directed toward private firms.
Populist	Better society	People should have a choice in public services; people should rely more on their community and less on distant bureaucratic services.

Source: Adapted from E.S. Savas, *Privatization: The Key to Better Government* (Chatham, N.J.: Chatham House Publishers, Inc., 1987), p.5.

Consequently, a key privatization strategy of provincial governments is to impose user fees or co-payments wherever practicable or to link spending programs directly to taxes levied for that purpose. The fundamental objectives of a user charge are to cut costs by decreasing utilization or to reveal fully the true cost of service, thereby stimulating consumers to shop around for the best deal. In British Columbia in 1987, for instance, the user fee was set at 75 percent of the pharmacist's professional fee for patients over 65 years of age.

What is the likelihood that user charges will become more common? Very good, indeed. While many Canadian pharmacists have been directly affected by these policies, physicians' user fees may soon be a reality as well, despite the Canada Health Act, which was passed in 1984 to protect universal access to medical care by allowing the federal government to withhold transfer payments to provinces that permitted direct fees.

When governments promote the philosophy of privatization, it means that they too would like to utilize competition to the fullest possible extent. They would like to let the marketplace determine price and increase bidding wars within government as well.

Privatization is both a means and an end, but it is not a political fad. Its successes in capitalist countries (and, recently, in some communist countries as well) are too evident for it to fade away quickly. The debate about whether public or private provision of services is in the best public interest will be going on in Western countries, including Canada, for years to come. In the end, the challenge in privatization will be to achieve a better division of responsibilities and functions between government and the private sector in order to take advantage of the strengths of each and overcome the limitations of the other.

BILL C-22

Since 1969, it had been federal government policy to keep the prices of prescription drugs down by encouraging competition from generic drug companies through a system of compulsory licensing. Under this scheme, established as an amendment to the Patent Act, a Canadian company could obtain a licence to import and sell a patent drug if it paid a royalty of four percent of revenues from the sale of the drug to the patent holder. While the mandate of increasing price competition was largely achieved, Canada was spending less than most Western countries on research and development (R&D), prompting a number of industry pundits, politicians, and consumers to say the system had become too one-sided in favour of the generic drug houses. In addition, there was considerable pressure from outside and within our borders to head in a new legislative direction. Compulsory licensing in Canada had jeopardized larger foreign-trade arrangements, and small Canadian firms emerging in the biotechnology area were looking for patent protection to get their feet on the ground.

Federal legislation that would strengthen R&D and bring the country more exceptional new drugs like enalapril (Vasotec®) or nifedipine (Adalat®) was deemed by the Mulroney government of the late 1980s to be in the public interest.

Bill C-22 (an act to amend the Patent Act), was drafted to provide some new incentives for innovative companies and was passed by the Conservatives in November 1987, after being held up for several months by the Senate. The controversial bill, which some felt was tied into the free-trade agreement with the United States, provided for a ten-year patent-protection period for Canadian-made drugs, and a seven-year protection period for imported drugs.

The bill also established a Drug Prices Review Board (DPRB), headed by Dr. Harry Eastman of the University of Toronto, which will have independent power to remove the exemption of a drug from compulsory licensing if the board judges that price increases are not justified. Moreover, the board will have the ability to invoke an extra penalty by removing protection from one additional drug produced by the same company. Under Bill C-22, R&D pharmaceutical companies have promised to spend $1.4 billion on research in the ten-year period ending in 1997. DPRB will collect and publish information documenting how much the innovative manufacturers actually spend on research during that period.

Bill C-22 will certainly have an effect on the environment in which pharmacists work, since they are intimately involved in every aspect of the drug-manufacturing process. They are employed in manufacturing firms, hospitals, governments, faculties of pharmacy, and in the community. But the magnitude of the effect is not clear. Pharmacists, along with other Canadians, will have to wait until the next decade to see what the real effects of Bill C-22 will be on the dynamics of the marketplace. In all likelihood, there will be an overall increase in the number of products coming onto the market, a decrease in the rate at which generic drugs will be introduced, and an increase in the number of clinical trials being conducted on drugs in Canada.

A full parliamentary review will be held after the bill has been in operation for nine years.

Economic Climate

GOVERNMENTS AS PAYERS

Without question, the most significant change to occur in the economics of pharmacy practice in the last 20 years has been the increasing involvement of third-party agencies – mainly provincial governments – as payers.

Each provincial government's prescription-drug plan possesses unique features that directly influence its resident pharmacies' professional, business, and economic climate. The Canadian Pharmaceutical Association's Community Pharmacy Affairs committee monitors the various negotiated agreements. In 1987, pharmacists in British Columbia, Prince Edward Island, Nova Scotia, Quebec, Saskatchewan, and Alberta could product select, but, in the other provinces, pharmacists were obliged to observe rules of mandatory substitution of generic products. Similarly, the number of days' supply that it was legal to dispense varied across the country, as did the amount of the deductible. Some provinces, such as Alberta and Newfoundland, allowed pharmacies to mark up drugs before applying their professional fees, while others permitted their pharmacies to charge a "purchasing advantage" in addition to their professional fee. Still others, including British Columbia, Saskatchewan, Prince Edward Island, New Brunswick, Manitoba, and Alberta, imposed a consumer co-payment or, more aptly, a user fee, in line with the privatization strategy mentioned earlier. (Contact the relevant provincial government or pharmacy association for the latest information; terms are constantly being negotiated.)

While it is useful to compare the general aspects of the various drug plans (see the Directory section of this book for a complete comparative chart of the provincial drug plans), let's contrast two high-profile schemes – namely, Ontario's best available price (BAP) and British Columbia's actual acquisition cost (AAC) schemes – to get a feel for the realities of an economic environment.

According to the Ontario Drug Benefit Act (Bill 55), passed in 1986, "best available price" means the lowest price, calculated per gram, millilitre, capsule, or tablet, for which that dosage form or strength can be purchased in Canada for wholesale or retail sale in Ontario. In other words, BAP involves real acquisition cost (best volume price) plus a negotiated purchasing advantage (currently 10 percent) to encourage efficient purchasing. The purpose of the purchasing advantage is to protect pharmacies that cannot purchase the product at the discounted price that is available to large-volume operations. The only allowable discounts for community pharmacies are prompt-payment discounts not exceeding 2%/30 days or dating not exceeding 120 days.

There is a clause in Bill 55 that allows the minister of health to estimate the best available price when a manufacturer fails to provide the Ontario government with sufficient pricing information on a product. This has been a sore point with the Ontario Pharmacists' Association because, when the government's estimates have come in below known market prices, the pharmacies of the province have had to absorb the difference between what they paid and what the government decided they should have paid. In addition, R&D manufacturers have been frustrated by having to compete almost exclusively on the basis of price. (The provincial government issues formularies, that is, benefit lists of pharmaceutical products that attempt to promote the use of less costly or more therapeutically rational treatments. Formularies tend to intensify competition among manufacturers, who are often forced to submit tenders for a drug product based predominantly on price. By the same token, manufacturers must often make their case for inclusion of their product in a specific therapeutic category of a formulary, for example, anti-ulcer drugs.)

On the other hand, "actual acquisition cost" (AAC) is the cost actually paid by a British Columbia pharmacist, after discounts and rebates, for a product that is dispensed. To improve their cash flow and maximize return on investment, pharmacists working under AAC rules prefer deals

Table 24.2.   A COMPARISON OF TWO METHODS OF PRESCRIPTION PRICING

Actual Acquisition Cost (AAC)	Best Available Price (BAP)
1. Manufacturers compete on services/incentives	1. Manufacturers compete on price
2. Ministry reimburses pharmacies at different levels of cost	2. Ministry treats all pharmacies equally
3. Gives pharmacies no incentive to buy efficiently	3. Induces pharmacies to buy efficiently
4. Favours consumers located near high-volume pharmacies	4. Gives all customers equal access to low prices regardless of location

Source: Adapted from V. Meere, "Waiting for the Axe," Drug Merchandising 67, no. 3 (March 1986): 35.

with manufacturers or wholesalers that provide invoice dating as a primary feature. In contrast to the BAP scheme, manufacturers are not required to supply price information to provincial governments employing plans based on AAC.

As you can see from Table 24.2, each area of the country has its own problems and concerns and must work in a unique economic environment.

Generally speaking, during the 1980s, provincial governments have been more hard-nosed in their negotiations with health-care professionals. In many instances, pharmacists have had to turn to products other than pharmaceuticals or market their professional services more aggressively in order to operate a profitable business. The development of the home health-care industry, which will be discussed in more detail later in this chapter, has been a natural outgrowth of these new environmental conditions.

INSURANCE COMPANIES AS PAYERS

Like their counterparts in government, private insurance companies have been seeking less expensive health-care alternatives. London Life, for instance, has been considering the implementation of a capitation reimbursement scheme. While capitation (claiming a fixed fee per patient for a specified time, regardless of the amount of care required) works well for long-term-care facilities, it makes little business sense with respect to ambulatory patients. Capitation rates could be exploited by both consumers and private payers. On the one hand, patients would soon recognize they would get a better economic deal if they saw their pharmacist more often. On the other hand, third parties could attempt to set remuneration at levels that did not relate to the costs of providing service, or they might direct clients to specific pharmacies. All these market factors would fundamentally change the pharmacist's business environment and for that matter, the standards of professional practice. In their own best economic and professional interest, pharmacists should say no to capitation schemes, except in hospital contracts.

TAX REFORM

The federal government's commitment to tax reform has already had some impact on pharmacies. As of July 1, 1988, the general corporate tax rate fell to 28 percent from 36 percent. But whatever the federal government is able to give in the way of marginal increases in disposable income, the provincial governments seem quite willing to take away through income surtaxes. The net effect of tax reform will likely be less dramatic than the politicians would have us believe.

As part of the tax reform, the federal government cut back the capital-cost allowance program that permits businesses to deduct the depreciation of assets from their income. Companies are now obliged to write off depreciation of assets at a slower rate. Instead of the original 50 percent write-off that was allowed in the first two years of the investment, only 15 percent is now deductible in the first year, followed by 30 percent of the balance of the investment in subsequent years. This policy will surely numb the entrepreneurial spirit in our country. In addition, the lifetime exemption for capital gains was reduced to $100,000 from $500,000, except for gains in small business. The tax reform has directly affected deductions available for meals and entertainment, as well as for company cars. In January 1988, a federal sales tax was imposed on all long-distance telephone calls, as well as on local calls made by businesses.

More dramatic economic effects will be seen when the much-debated "business transfer tax" is implemented by Ottawa. Needing the co-operation of the provinces to make it work, this "value-added tax" would apply to every transaction that occurs, from the primary producer to the consumer. At each stage, the seller would compute the difference between the amount of tax he collected from his customers and the amount of tax he paid to his suppliers. He would then remit that difference to the federal government. Alternatively, Ottawa could unilaterally impose a federal goods and services tax on every transaction. Either multi-stage taxation scheme will be politically precarious, and the federal government's tax-reform options will be limited by the vast annual deficit of approximately $30 billion. The federal government's fiscal maneuverability will be restricted because of its need for income, the political expediency of maintaining its high level of government spending, and its desire to encourage confidence in domestic and foreign investment by preventing growth of the deficit.

The value-added tax will have an effect on the pharmacist's business environment, especially during its early stages. The cost of inventory will rise because the wholesaler or manufacturer will add the federal-government tax to the cost of the goods. As a result, some pharmacies will probably experience cash-flow difficulties. Similarly, there will be some consumer resistance to paying more for prescriptions, the price of which will be further increased by the pharmacist's value-added tax contribution.

In the end, the federal government's tax reform of the late 1980s largely amounts to another way of pursuing the load-shedding approach mentioned earlier in this chapter (p.393). The political *modus operandi* is "make the user pay."

Health-Care Perceptions

PUBLIC PERCEPTION OF HEALTH-CARE PROFESSIONALS

The public's level of confidence in pharmacists seems to have risen during the 1980s and consumers now seem to be happier with the professional services being rendered by pharmacists. The Canadian Pharmacy Services Study, 1988, entitled "What Your Customers Think of You," which was commissioned by the CPhA and sponsored by the Upjohn Company of Canada, found that 79 percent of Canadians had either "a great deal" or "quite a lot" of confidence in pharmacists. Our profession clearly outscored nurses (73 percent), dentists (72 percent), and physicians (67 percent) in the area of patient confidence.

In making future business plans, pharmacists should realize that they play a key – and positive – role in their environment, that is, in the communities in which they work.

CHANGING ROLES OF HEALTH-CARE PROFESSIONALS

The roles of the various players in the health-care system are constantly changing. As discussed in Chapter 21, pharmacists are in some instances working more closely with physicians. Physician-oriented pharmacy practice occurs when pharmacists are encouraged, through the specific management policies of the pharmacy, to develop their judgmental skills for the purpose of counselling physicians in the optimal use of drugs. (The introduction of a drug-information hot-line for physicians is one example of such management policy.) Environments suitable for the development of physician-oriented practice include pharmacies in clinics or medical buildings, pharmacies in small communities, and pharmacy departments in hospitals – in other words, environments that foster one-to-one personal contact between the physician and the pharmacist. Also, the role of nurses has changed within the health-care environment to the extent that they have taken on the role of patient advocate and, in the public debate concerning health care (including the provision of pharmaceutical services), speak on behalf of the patient.

HOME HEALTH CARE

Between 1960 and 1980, Canada's hospital expenditures grew at an average annual rate of 15 percent. About two-thirds of that growth was attributed to wage and price inflation, and the remaining one third to population growth and more intensive hospital services.[4]

[4]L. Auer, *Canadian Hospital Costs and Productivity*. A Study Prepared by the Economic Council of Canada (Ottawa: Ministry of Supply and Services, Catalogue #EC22-138/1987E, 1987), p.55.

In line with their privatization strategies and need for austerity, governments have begun to encourage home health care, as described in Chapter 23. One example of a program developed with this concept in mind is Hospice, which is designed to provide a caring environment for the physical and emotional needs of the terminally ill. Palliative care offered by hospitals is intertwined with care of the patient in the home by members of the immediate family.

"WALK-IN" MEDICAL CLINICS

For the sake of convenience, people living in urban areas tend to shop in large shopping centres. Walk-in medical clinics have sprung up in these malls to supply fast medical care without the need of an appointment. Some provincial medical associations, concerned about lack of continuity in medical services, have frowned on such operations. They believe that the important role of the family physician could be jeopardized. Governments have had some reservations about the so-called "McDonald's of medicine" outlets as well: they argue that making medical care more easily accessible will only increase health-care costs.

Despite these objections, consumers seem to like walk-in medical clinics, and a number of innovative pharmacists have taken advantage of the trend by establishing dispensaries at nearby sites.

ALTERNATIVE FORMS OF HEALTH CARE

Chapter 23 discussed the search by patients for alternative forms of health care. Trends toward "natural" foods, psychological counselling, and acupuncture, among others, have been growing and challenging the traditional health-care system. They could have a significant impact on the environment in which pharmacists operate.

Demographics

The science of demography deals with the occurrence of the main events of personal and family life within human groups, as well as with the population structures that result from them. Pharmacists must possess a basic knowledge of demographic analysis, particularly with regard to consumers, if they are going to be able to understand their environment and make rational business decisions.

THE AGING OF OUR POPULATION

As we saw in Chapter 23, the increasing percentage of the elderly in our society is a phenomenon that will have a profound impact on the health-care environment. It is estimated that our total population should reach some 28.5 million by the year 2000; also by that time, the number of elderly persons in our country will have doubled, to represent 14 percent of the total population.[5]

While more than half of our non-institutionalized population suffers from health problems, the proportion of persons in poor health increases with age. In addition, women have more health problems than men in adulthood and old age.[6]

SOCIOLOGICAL CHANGES

Recent figures on lone-parent families are even more intriguing. Just over 150,000 males and 700,000 females were raising a child (or children) single-handedly in 1986.[7] Such a major societal shift has had and will continue to have an enormous effect on the pharmacist's marketplace. Both elderly people and single parents will possess distinctive attitudes and will require specialized care and service.

EPIDEMIOLOGICAL TRENDS

New epidemiological trends are also emerging. It is generally accepted, for instance, that the incidence of Crohn's disease and, therefore, the number of ostomates, has been on the rise for the last 20 years.[8] Also, more high-risk patients (for example, premature infants, cancer patients) are surviving than ever before, placing new demands on our health-care system.

CONSUMER BEHAVIOUR PATTERNS

Chapter 15 explained consumer behaviour and the ways in which pharmacists can benefit from analyzing their consumer market and targeting promotion, products, and services to a specific group or groups. Understanding the consumer is perhaps the most essential aspect of understanding the environment in which you work.

---

[5] Statistics Canada, Catalogue #91-520; also M. Blanchet, *Aging with Limited Health Resources: Proceedings of a Colloquium on Health Care*, May 1986 (Ottawa: Supply and Services Canada, Catalogue #EC22-139/1987E, 1987), p.88.

[6] Y. Peron and C. Strohmenger, *Demographic and Health Care Indicators: Presentation and Interpretation* (Ottawa: Statistics Canada, Catalogue #82-543E, 1985), p. 146.

[7] Peron and Strohmenger, *Demographic and Health Care Indicators*, p. 81.

[8] G. Schoepp, "Home Sweet Home: First-Hand Tips on How to Make It in Home Health Care," *Drug Merchandising* 66, no. 8 (August 1985): 22.

Changes in Lifestyle

Preventive medicine is more a state of mind than a precise consumer concept. As we saw in Chapter 23, the importance of self-care is being recognized as people learn to eat better, exercise more, and smoke less. To reinforce positive attitudes, the provincial governments have embarked on new legislative approaches and public-awareness campaigns. Despite pressure from tobacco lobbyists, Ottawa passed its Tobacco Products Control Act (Bill C-51) in 1988. The restrictions on cigarette advertising contained in the legislation signalled a real change in our society's attitudes toward smoking. About the same time, Ontario developed a "health-goals concept" aimed at ways to promote health and reduce the incidence of diseases that are largely avoidable.

For many years, pharmacists have been encouraging healthful behaviour with innovative programs like the CPhA's "Stand Up and Be Counted" program, conducted in conjunction with the federal government. Similarly, many pharmacies supply information on diet and exercise on the request of physicians and nurses.

Managing Your Environment

Some management strategies that address the environmental factors we have outlined will now be discussed. What can you do to accommodate a changing environment?

Demographics

An understanding of demographic factors is applied in various critical choices made by the pharmacist-owner: selecting a location (see Chapter 3), marketing (see Chapter 15), and identifying new service opportunities (see Chapter 23). Here we shall point out only a few examples of further strategies to employ in relation to demographics.

With respect to the elderly, you should keep in mind that the number of products used does not increase with age, but gradually shifts to more specific age-related categories (for example, toward laxatives and skin-care products). Selecting products prudently, providing a free delivery service, and mailing follow-up letters outlining your services to older clients will help you win on this front of the demographic wars.

As our population ages, more people than ever before will need care in nursing homes or extended-care hospitals. Develop contacts in government who can inform you of upcoming tenders for nursing-home contracts. Competition may be such that, in order to win a tender, a pharmacy will have to be equipped with the professional-support software programs that were described in Chapter 20 (see pp. 326-332).

Companies such as Compusearch Market and Social Research Ltd. can give interested pharmacists a good picture of their potential clientele by employing data supplied by the Census of Canada. If you think you need some help in identifying how your services are perceived by patients and physicians, watch for the periodic pharmacy surveys conducted and published by such companies as Schering Canada Inc. or the Upjohn Company of Canada.

Privatization

The consensus among political analysts today is that private organizations may be equally if not better equipped than government to administer certain necessary guidelines (regarding service, administration, employment, productivity, and quality assurance) within publicly owned institutions. As a result, a large number of private administrative organizations have been established as quasi-governmental agencies. Hence, an astute assessment of needs in the political environment by a private firm can lead to its supplying services that the government has not been providing satisfactorily.

Many municipal officials favour privatization of public hospitals because it relieves them of a deficit-ridden activity and leads to upgrading of the facilities – and therefore, presumably, to better health care for the community – at no cost to the government. Consequently, the management of either entire hospitals or certain of their departments is being contracted out.

"Contracting out" is most likely to occur (1) when governments are under financial stress (and most governments in our country currently are); (2) when large cost savings are likely; or (3) when such a move is politically feasible. Contracting out to the private sector allows governments to limit themselves to the roles that suit them best: articulating demand, acting as a purchasing agent, monitoring the contractor's performance, and paying the bill. Governments then leave the responsibility to produce and deliver goods to the contractor. "Contracting in" refers to the growing practice of allowing government agencies to bid for work on a fair and equitable basis against private contractors.

One U.S. survey showed that more than 5000 individual hospital departments in the United States were being managed by 84 outside contractors.[9] The most commonly contracted functions were, in descending order: housekeeping, food service, emergency room, plant operations, respiratory services, pharmacy, laundry, and data processing.

[9]L. Punch, "Contract Management Companies Manage Growth Rate of 13.3 Percent," *Modern Healthcare* 15 (August 1984): 45–52.

In any privatization venture, attitudes have to be changed and new skills have to be acquired. Pharmacists have to become more aggressive in marketing their services by doing more lobbying. Mental-health offices, day-care centres, and other government agencies could be considering contracting out professional pharmacy services. Other potential areas of business growth might include anything from servicing a drug and alcohol treatment centre to franchising a postal substation.

Pharmacists are in a position to say to government, "We have the skills you need. Let's talk about it. Let's sign a service contract."

Negotiating with Government

Negotiations with government will not be easy in the years ahead, whether actual acquisition cost (AAC) or best available price (BAP) is used in calculating prescription drug claims.

If gross margins continue to fall or hover around the 30 percent mark, future negotiations for pharmacies working with AAC schemes could well be centred on limiting the quantities of drugs dispensed or decreasing the co-payment from, say, 75 percent to 50 percent of the professional fee. At the same time, formularies may be introduced in AAC provinces to intensify competition among manufacturers.

Rebates and discounts for prompt payment given by wholesalers or manufacturers to AAC pharmacies in British Columbia do not have to be incorporated into the invoice cost. If the Ontario government increases its power to estimate best available price, pharmacists in that province may negotiate to expand their rebate and discount programs offered by manufacturers or wholesalers.

Promoting Professional Services

Given the disparities in the "actual acquisition costs" of many drugs for various pharmacies (resulting from the range of possible wholesale promotions, dating deals, volume discounts, and timing of purchases immediately prior to price increases), together with the prevalence of unscrupulous professional-fee discounters among pharmacies in the marketplace, pharmacists must buy their pharmaceuticals frugally and convince the bargain-hunting consumer that he or she should be asking for quotes on the *total* prescription price, rather than on the dispensing fee alone. (A pharmacy managing its operation to get the cheapest possible AAC could meet the discounter's total prescription price if the difference between their AACs equals the difference between their professional fees.) Motivated members of our profession may not wish to play the discounter's game and prefer instead to promote themselves to consumers on the basis of their unique professional services. If you choose the latter course, remember that in marketing professional services, perception is reality. If people feel they are getting the highest quality of service and if they believe you will be there to serve them and their families even better five or ten years from now, they will usually be willing to pay you an above-average market price for your efforts.

Pharmacists wishing to establish a physician-oriented pharmacy practice must employ specific tools to promote themselves and their profession. Publishing a drug-information bulletin or newsletter, assertive use of the telephone, and promotion of drug-information memos to physicians can make a big difference in attempting to sell professional services.

Increasing Pharmacy Size

While there has not been an increase in the number of pharmacies in Canada over the past few decades, those in existence have grown substantially in size. Many pharmacies have been forced to expand because of pressure from "superstores" or large grocery stores, which are delving into the pharmacy business. With some operations employing five to ten pharmacists, bureaucracy has escalated and management of such an environment has become more complex.

Health-Care Perceptions

As we saw in Chapter 23, there is little doubt that the trend toward self-care will lead to expansion of the home health-care market.

Because it requires unique marketing strategies, product knowledge, and selling skills, home health care is an entirely new enterprise, with which pharmacists should become familiar.

The bulk of the business is generated by referrals from key health-care personnel, such as enterostomal therapists, hospital emergency departments, physiotherapists, or community-care facilities. A home health-care pharmacy typically draws from a trading area three times larger than the prescription-drug trading area.[10] Making consumers aware of a home health-care pharmacy may be difficult because advertising a service is seldom as effective as advertising a product. It is worthwhile knowing that the majority of home health-care purchases will likely be made by persons over 65 years of age.

In addition to being a business that involves much paperwork, home health care can have a few other drawbacks. Government benefit lists or taxation policies for home health-care goods have historically changed from year to year.

Home health-care products can be classified into two general groups: durable medical equipment (DME) and durable medical supplies (DMS). Representative items, such as lumbosacral braces, walkers, anti-embolism stockings, cervical traction kits, or ostomy equipment cannot simply

[10] Schoepp, "Home Sweet Home," p. 24.

be purchased "off the shelf." They require person-to-person selling, counselling, or fitting.

In the past, home health-care pharmacies had to cope independently with inventory management, but now shrewd wholesalers carry complete product lines or offer well-designed marketing programs (for example, Medis' Mobility Medical). Selecting a home health-care wholesaler is probably more crucial than selecting a pharmaceuticals wholesaler, because price fluctuations on the same item tend to be more substantial and more common in the home-care industry. Look for consistency of service and quality of goods when choosing a supplier.

Pharmacies that do not introduce a home health-care capacity may find soon enough that they are losing potential business to non-pharmacy outlets. Aggressive recreation and leisure marketing should be part and parcel of any home health-care management strategy. People using tennis courts, golf courses, or swimming pools will be more likely to need surgical supplies and sports-medicine devices, such as tennis elbow braces and hot-cold packs. In assessing your inventory requirements, keep in mind that 23 percent of sports injuries involve the knee; 19 percent, the legs; 16 percent, the back; and 15 percent, the ankles and arms.[11]

Changes in Lifestyle

Because of the lifestyle changes taking place in our society, preventive medicine may finally be a salable idea. The emergence of Acquired Immune Deficiency Syndrome (AIDS) has brought health-care issues into sharp focus. Pharmacists have a social responsibility to stock adequate inventories and supply their clients with educational materials on all the health-care issues of the day.

Today's consumers are more informed and looking for ways to improve their health status. Most laypeople, however, need assistance from the pharmacist in interpreting media coverage of a new drug or of new medical findings.

A patient consultation conducted professionally by a pharmacist can be a real asset to the business, because it becomes an instrument through which to sell services. Let's look at a few examples. The major American clinical trial published in the *New England Journal of Medicine* in early 1988,[12] which showed that aspirin could prevent heart attacks in previously healthy males, provided pharmacists with an opportunity to counsel patients about ASA dosage, toxicity, patient selection, and so on. The controversy surrounding the ability of fish oils to prevent coronary heart

---

[11] Schoepp, "Home Sweet Home," p. 24.
[12] C.H. Hennekens et al., "Preliminary Report: Findings from the Aspirin Component of the Ongoing Physicians' Health Study," *New England Journal of Medicine* 318, no. 4 (28 January 1988): 262–64.

disease could also be clarified by the pharmacist. So, not only can pharmacists sell products, they can also counsel patients and thereby further promote the range of their services.

Pharmacists should be watchful of the changing consumer preferences that accompany lifestyle changes, and make inventory choices based on their observations. For example, in 1988, "hot" items included vitamin A acid cream or gel for wrinkles, minoxidil (Rogaine) for hair loss, and digital thermometers.

Summary

To operate a successful business, a pharmacist must first understand the environment and then attempt to manage it. Given the current political, economic, demographic, and lifestyle trends, it is clear that if pharmacists are going to flourish in the marketplace, they
will have to sell their professional services more wisely and aggressively to governments and consumers. Refer to the Environment Checklist below for a reminder of the points that should be taken into consideration.

This chapter has attempted to provide some information that will help you to serve your community more capably and make a better living in the process.

An Environment Checklist

    A. Understanding the environment
       1. Political climate
          - government spending restraint
          - privatization
          - free-trade agreement
       2. Economic climate
          - provincial prescription-drug plans
          - methods of R̠ drug pricing: BAP versus AAC
          - role of insurance companies
          - tax reform
       3. Health-care perceptions
          - development of the home health-care industry
          - emergence of "walk-in" clinics
       4. Demographics
          - aging of the population
          - sociological changes
          - epidemiological trends
          - consumer trends
       5. Lifestyle changes
          - preventive medicine: role of the individual; role of government

B. Managing your environement
   - identify your dominant consumer demographic segment; understand consumers' product preferences
   - be a more active lobbyist; look into signing service contracts with government
   - negotiate with governments and insurance companies for a professional fee that is truly representative of the cost of providing the service
   - promote your professional services; diversify into home health care; improve product knowledge; make use of manufacturer promotions and "franchises"
   - make inventory selections based on lifestyle trends, such as those promoting self-care
   - think of patient counselling as a method of selling your pharmacy's services

RECOMMENDED READING

Home Health Care Marketing – A Manual for Retail Pharmacies. Johnson and Johnson, in co-operation with the National Association of Retail Druggists, 1983.

Peron, Y., and Strohmenger, C. *Demographic and Health Care Indicators: Presentation and Interpretation.* Ottawa: Statistics Canada, Catalogue #82-543E, 1985.

Savas, E.S. *Privatization: The Key to Better Government.* Chatham, N.J.: Chatham House Publishers, Inc., 1987.

Schoepp, G. "Home Sweet Home: First Hand Tips on How To Make It in Home Health Care." *Drug Merchandising* 66, no. 8 (August 1985): 22 -27.

Selling Skills: Home Health Care Marketing. Johnson and Johnson, in co-operation with the National Association of Retail Druggists, 1984.

25

EXPANSION OR RELOCATION
OF THE BUSINESS

Introduction

A pharmacy owner must consider a range of factors before proceeding with a decision to expand or relocate the business. While each pharmacist would be facing a different set of circumstances, an approach that allows for a structured and coherent decision process is possible in all cases.

The final decision to expand or relocate always remains the subjective judgment of the pharmacy owner, but the risks involved can be advantageously reduced through an understanding of the elements involved in the decision-making process and the role that outside experts can play.

All businesspeople must learn to cope with change. A pharmacy's changing environment can be viewed in terms of the internal and external factors that precipitate the need for alterations in the established methods of operating the store.

Many of the elements that must be considered in the process of deciding whether to expand or relocate are similar to those involved in the decision to establish a new pharmacy practice or to purchase an existing one. Hence, in this chapter, we shall be reviewing aspects of location and demographic analysis, capital needs, financial assessment, and other areas discussed earlier in the book.

Let us first consider the option of business expansion, which, for the purposes of this discussion, will refer either to the enlargement of present premises or the opening or purchase of an additional store or stores.

EXPANSION OF THE PHARMACY

The initiative to expand often results from (1) awareness of customer dissatisfaction, (2) competitive pressure, or (3) an individual's entrepreneurial drive.

An increasing frequency of customer complaints relating to such things as cluttered aisles or slow check-out lines is often the first hint that change is overdue. The need for change can be caused either by rapid growth or a decline in sales activity. Rapid growth, due to consumer preference for the particular location or business practices of the pharmacy, usually results in the need to increase inventory levels and add staff, both of which may disturb a previously acceptable equilibrium within the store and demand greater space for operations. Alternatively, a recognition that the pharmacy's sales are not keeping pace with others in the industry should suggest to the pharmacist-owner that it is time to reconsider the needs of the pharmacy's most valuable resource – its customers. Staying attuned both to the customer's wishes and to developments in the market area is a fundamental rule of business.

This philosophy is illustrated in Peters and Waterman's description of Stew Leonard's Dairy in Norwalk, Connecticut.[1] Leonard believes so strongly in his customer as both a person to be served and a source of information that he regularly meets with panels of customers to seek their opinions on how to improve his store. His respect for the role that the customer plays is evidenced by the granite marker outside his store on which his personal business philosophy is inscribed: "Rule 1: The customer is always right. Rule 2: If the customer is ever wrong, reread Rule 1."

Leonard attributes his recognition of the need for expansion in his business to nothing more than listening to the customer. During an interview with a Nova Scotia pharmacist, we heard a similar opinion. The pharmacist related the story of the improved traffic pattern and 30 percent sales increase that occurred in the first year after he expanded his pharmacy from 4500 to 6500 square feet and remerchandised the complete store. Customer comments were very positive about the wider aisles and the generally more comfortable atmosphere in the larger store. "And," said the pharmacist, "we can now look forward to a new period of growth as the new space has given us more room to merchandise and display a wider range of products. Besides," he noted, "we had little choice in the timing of the move as we had one chance to take adjacent space that may not have been available again for some time."

Once the pharmacy owner is aware that something must be done to

---

[1] Thomas J. Peters and Robert H. Waterman Jr., *In Search of Excellence* (New York: Warner Books, 1984).

maintain or improve customer satisfaction, a framework should be employed within which the alternatives can be reviewed and which can serve as a guide to reaching a decision.

Our discussion in this chapter is based on a framework that takes into consideration both the internal and external factors influencing the business. Three internal factors must be explored: (1) the present facility, including physical and operational considerations; (2) customer needs; and (3) financial considerations. When combined with the analysis of external factors, represented largely by the existing competition and developments in the industry, the pharmacy owner should be able to reach a rational business decision regarding the option to expand the practice. Figure 25.1 graphically depicts the elements that comprise the decision-making framework.

Internal Factors

PRESENT FACILITY: PHYSICAL CONSIDERATIONS

Land:

1. Is there sufficient land for expansion?
2. Is additional land available?
3. Can a "land swap" be arranged?
4. Can an option be arranged for a future purchase?

Parking:

1. Will an expansion or new location have sufficient parking to accommodate present and future customers?
2. Is there nearby municipal or on-street parking?
3. Will new parking patterns allow ease of entry and exit to or from the store?

Street traffic:

1. Will the present or proposed vehicular flow past your store allow for easy ingress/egress to and from the pharmacy property? One can easily be misled by traffic surveys that show high traffic counts near a proposed location: if the average vehicle speed near the proposed location is too great to allow for easy exit from the traffic pattern, then the store cannot gain the full benefit of high exposure to traffic.
2. Are any municipal alterations expected in the main artery that directs automobiles toward your store? Failure to review municipal plans could result in a newly expanded store being removed from the main

Figure 25.1   EXPANSION OF THE PHARMACY: A FRAMEWORK FOR
DECISION MAKING

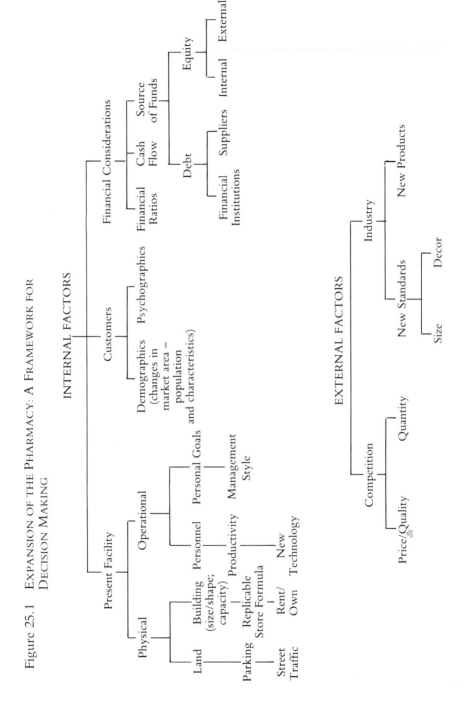

flow of traffic. For instance, a planned new by-pass road could alternatively create a new opportunity for expansion or for a move from an existing location.
3. Will the new or expanded store be convenient for walking traffic? This is not a major consideration for most shopping-mall locations, but it is most certainly crucial to a free-standing pharmacy or one in a medical building. To survive economically, pharmacies in clinics or office buildings must be located near the main entrance of the building and/or on the floor with the highest pedestrian traffic volume.

Building:

1. Is the present building in a satisfactory state of repair? If not, would it be less expensive to build a totally new building, assuming that the present business can be retained in the interim? An architect, along with mechanical and electrical engineers or contractors, can provide expert opinions on the feasibility of expanding the present building.
2. Is the size or shape of the building conducive to internal or external expansion? Physical expansion of the retail area can sometimes be accommodated by reducing the size of the stockrooms and other underutilized space within the present facility. This is clearly a less costly approach than the addition of a new wing. Imaginative architects and builders have been successful in combining two adjoining buildings into a single retail space. This option may be considered if an adjoining building is available.
3. If the present store is in a mall or larger building, will adjacent space for expansion be available at a time that is convenient to the pharmacy owner or should he or she opt to rent additional space when it becomes available, even if this is earlier than planned?

PRESENT FACILITY: OPERATIONAL CONSIDERATIONS

Personnel

The impact on human resources cannot be overlooked in an expansion decision. Its staff members are critical to any business, and the need to recruit and train new staff, as well as to reassure and motivate existing staff, must be taken into consideration. Existing staff members may feel threatened when new job openings become available in the expanded store. They should be informed of plans as they develop in order to minimize this natural insecurity in face of the unknown. It may also be helpful in this regard to enlist the aid of existing staff members in orienting and training new staff. Enhanced opportunities for long-time staff members that might arise with the expansion should also be pointed out.

The pharmacy owner should bear in mind that job descriptions may require revision as a result of the expanded operation.

Equally important is the training of management staff to meet the needs of the growing business. If the pharmacist-owner is to devote his or her time to overseeing expansion plans and activities, a manager should be in place to whom responsibility for the basic business operations can be delegated.

The pharmacy owner, with the assistance of management staff, must provide pharmacy personnel with adequate training, effective incentives, and up-to-date technology in order to yield improved productivity in the newly expanded operation.

Productivity

Many authors have attempted to define productivity, but it may best be viewed as a simple matter of doing the right tasks better. In the case of the community-pharmacy practice, productivity means improving the execution of those tasks that enhance the consumers' exposure to products and services and facilitate their movement through the store, in the aim of increasing customer satisfaction and, hence, sales.

Improvements in productivity can be achieved by utilizing modern design techniques that enhance traffic flow throughout the store. Improvements in check-out flow and stock-receiving procedures are also critical. Pharmacy might benefit from the model of the grocery industry in North America, which has effected some of the greatest productivity improvements of the past decade. It has, for example, been at the forefront of the retail industry in its implementation of new technology, such as computerized cash registers with price-look-up (PLU) capability and point-of-sale scanning systems, which allow staff to move customers through the check-out areas faster and more efficiently.

The capacity to prepare personnel adequately and to increase productivity through updated store design and computerization should therefore be viewed as a critical consideration in any pharmacy owner's plans for expansion.

Like our counterparts in the grocery industry, pharmacies must be prepared to handle more volume at a lower gross margin in future years. An owner's anticipation of this reality could be the source of an expansion decision. This philosophy is advocated by Arthur Levitt, who states that "healthy growth occurs when productivity advances allow output to rise faster than the amount of work required to produce it."[2]

[2] Arthur Levitt Jr., "Industrial Policy: Slogan or Solution?" *Harvard Business Review* 62, no. 2 (March–April 1984): 6.

Goals and Responsibilities of the Owner

Plans for expansion of a pharmacy practice are often motivated by the entrepreneurial drive of a pharmacist-owner. Entrepreneurs are driven by the need for personal satisfaction, independence, and the sense of control over their lives that comes with owning a business. The most familiar example of a modern-day pharmacist with these entrepreneurial characteristics is Murray Koffler, founder of the Shoppers Drug Mart pharmacy chain. Frank Raskey, in his book entitled *Just a Simple Pharmacist*, describes Koffler as a "visionary" who initiated the mass-merchandising style of drugstores in Canada and applied this philosophy to expand from a single pharmacy into Canada's largest drugstore chain.[3]

Assuming that the pharmacist-entrepreneur has weighed the risks versus the potential return of additional investment in the enterprise, the benefits he or she could expect to derive from growth would include (1) higher sales, (2) improved staff productivity, and (3) increased awareness of the business by potential customers. Each of these should contribute to increased profitability.

Unfortunately, sales growth may not always lead to higher profitability if underlying management systems are not in place. Higher sales mean increased frequency and quantity of purchases, and unless adequate systems, such as purchase orders, claim forms, and receiving logs are in place, inventory levels and mix may become unbalanced. Increased purchasing and inventory also create a need for additional staff and enhanced security procedures.

A fast-growing business demands well-honed managerial skills on the part of the owner. For example, careful monitoring of cash flow becomes critical as inventories and overhead rise. Similarly, the ability to delegate duties and responsibilities becomes a necessity in a larger operation. A review of one's management style is hence a prerequisite for successful expansion. Writing in the *Harvard Business Review*, William Fruhan cautions that a business owner must "think real" and aim at sustaining a greater-than-inflationary rate of growth in order to derive rewards from the extra time and resources required to fuel the growth of the business.[4]

The key, then, is controlled growth, stimulated by the combined goal of satisfying both customer needs and one's own personal entrepreneurial drive.

[3] Frank Raskey, *Just a Simple Pharmacist: The Story of Murray Koffler, Builder of Shoppers Drug Mart Empire* (Toronto: McClelland and Stewart, 1988).

[4] William E. Fruhan, "How Fast Should Your Company Grow?" *Harvard Business Review* 62, no. 1 (January–February 1984): 6–8.

CUSTOMERS

One challenge facing the pharmacy owner who plans to expand the business is to detect growth opportunities in the market, identifying niches that are currently underserviced or require improved service. The pharmacist, then, as a business owner, must be aware of general population trends and monitor demographic changes within his or her market area. Let us, therefore, briefly review the relevant points on this subject, which has been discussed in greater detail in earlier chapters of the book.[5]

In the late 1980s, two growing market segments offer opportunities for pharmacy owners. First, the post–World War II "baby boomers" – the 20–39 age group – have evolved into the largest market segment. The combination of high expectations for personal satisfaction, the resulting spending patterns, and the frequency of two household incomes makes this category of consumers most attractive to retailers. This group's high level of spending on personal-care products in particular offers a favourable opportunity for pharmacies to increase sales by offering both a wider selection of such products and better prices. Second, the growing number of elderly people in the population is leading to higher government and private expenditures on health care. As discussed earlier, this provides increased opportunities not only for prescription services but also for support services in areas such as home health care.

Today, market researchers are not only studying changes in age and income (demographics) but are also investigating customer preferences through psychographic analysis, as described in Chapter 15. Market segmentation has also been analyzed in the market-research literature in terms of employment, financial status, original nationality, and purchasing habits. Pharmacy owners planning expansion will benefit by familiarizing themselves with the results of ongoing market research and by conducting their own investigations through the use of sources such as Statistics Canada, trade journals, monitoring of the competition, discussion with suppliers, and close observation of the pharmacy's own clientele. The latter is critical if the pharmacy owner is to predict major changes in the market area accurately and at the right time. Internal customer information should be updated regularly, to monitor changes in such factors as age, household size, and mobility.

FINANCIAL CONSIDERATIONS

Once a need to expand has been established, the pharmacist-owner must determine if the project is financially feasible.

There are at least four areas of funding that may be used singularly or in combination to finance expansion, including (1) existing cash flow,

[5] See, specifically, Chapters 3, 15, 23, and 24.

(2) additional debt capital, (3) additional equity capital, and (4) extended terms from suppliers.

Some businesses generate sufficient cash internally to support the capital costs of construction and the cost of additional inventory. The decision to finance an expansion project through internal funds may stem from a reluctance to take on debt or from a belief that a further investment in one's own business will bring a greater return than would investment in outside money-market instruments, such as investment certificates, stocks, or bonds.

Taking on new or additional debt requires that a business owner convince a lending institution that his or her project is worthy of their trust. To inspire confidence in the banker that the pharmacy is able to generate sufficient revenues to repay the debt, the pharmacy owner must prepare a business plan.[6] Lending institutions require the commitment of the owner in the form of equity and/or personal guarantees. Some financial institutions are more restrictive than others, so the pharmacy owner should be prepared to shop around.

Another alternative for meeting the capital requirements of growth is the infusion of new equity capital into the business. This may come from personal savings, from the sale of part of the business to new partners, or from offering a new location to a franchisee. Should an owner decide to franchise an additional location, he or she can expect to obtain some up-front cash to offset opening costs, but the most important goal would be to enhance both the short- and long-term profitability of the new store by aligning with a success-oriented franchisee.

The pharmacist-owner should, however, be aware of the costs involved in acquiring funds through partners or franchisees. With external equity, there comes a reduction in control over the enterprise; that is, some portion of ownership (equity) is given up to gain access to the new funds. On the other hand, there are also benefits in sharing the future profits of the firm, such as increased support and enthusiasm and the commitment of the new investor-managers to the endeavour. The latter could, in the end, lead to even greater profits by affording more time for the original owner to investigate new opportunities. To quote Arthur Levitt once more, "fostering entrepreneurship is essential to healthy sustainable growth."[7]

Suppliers will benefit from a pharmacy's expansion through its ability to purchase and display more of their products. They may therefore be receptive to requests for extended dating or special terms in light of the expansion, and would thereby become another source of funding. The delays in payment that they conceded would allow the pharmacy to

---

[6] Review the material in Chapter 5, "The Business Plan" and Chapter 6, "Meeting Capital Needs."

[7] Arthur Levitt Jr., "Industrial Policy: Slogan or Solution?", p. 8.

generate more internal cash through a grand opening sale and other promotions.

A word of caution is in order: failure to keep a supplier fully informed if the pharmacy's capacity to pay current invoices is temporarily constrained may result in a discontinuation of credit, product shortages, and, ultimately, dissatisfaction among the store's customers.

External Factors: The Competition and the Industry

A critical evaluation of the local competition according to criteria such as location, parking, accessibility, capacity to expand, and merchandising style should be undertaken before finalizing an expansion decision.

Reaction to competitors can be classified as offensive or defensive. An offensive strategy is guided, first and foremost, by the goal of maintaining or increasing customer satisfaction; a defensive strategy is more concerned with counteracting the activities of one or more of a pharmacy's competitors.

If the competition is aggressive, then the decision to expand may be motivated by a desire to protect existing sales or market share (a defensive approach). On the other hand, if competitors are less than aggressive, then an expansion decision may be motivated by the desire to fill a perceived void in the market (an offensive approach).

A merchandising policy of always making available the newest of products and services is an offensive or self-driven strategy, which often results in a decision to expand because increased space is required for new products and services and, it is hoped, for increased traffic flow. Also contributing to the need for expansion is the rapid growth of the pharmaceutical industry, which now offers such a vast range of non-prescription drugs and self-diagnostic and home health-care products.

In addition to personally surveying the activities of competing stores and regularly reviewing their advertising, the pharmacy owner can acquire a thorough knowledge of competitors' activities from trade associations, suppliers' representatives, and industry journals. Such information about the competition's product and service range, pricing and merchandising policies, and perhaps even about their plans for the future, combined with a strong desire to improve customer satisfaction, will prevent the pharmacy owner from potential misjudgments about the timing or direction of ongoing expansion plans.

If one can define defensive strategy as the reaction to an initial move made by the competition, then defensive reasoning alone as the basis for an expansion decision may place the pharmacy owner at too great a risk. Without a thorough evaluation of the full range of criteria that we have discussed thus far, such a decision can result in an excessive financial drain on the resources of the core business, with too little assurance of the necessary return on the investment in the future.

Although there are ultimately no assurances in business, the well-researched and carefully assessed expansion decision will generally enable the business owner to benefit from real opportunities rather than to suffer losses as a result of emotional or reactive decisions aimed mainly at offsetting a competitive move. To quote the *Harvard Business Review*, "the first principle of strategy is not to beat the competition, but to deliver value to customers."[8]

RELOCATION

The relocation decision can be addressed by reviewing at least three additional criteria that have not been fully discussed in the expansion model: (1) market strategy; (2) opportunity; and (3) rent versus equity. Further considerations regarding personnel are involved, and, finally, the importance of professional expertise in the project of relocation must be recognized.

MARKET STRATEGY

Efforts to maintain or improve existing sales may precipitate a move. The declining capability of an established retail space to service the needs of existing customers can lead an owner to search for a new location. If the pharmacy owner is confident that a core customer base will follow the established business to a nearby building, then the move is probably recommended, since it will allow for an improved layout yielding benefits in traffic flow and security and leading to increased sales.

A change in location may also be necessary if the neighbourhood in the current market area is experiencing a decline in population generally or in the pharmacy's target customer group specifically. Consideration, in these circumstances, should be given to a move outside the old market area. An interview with an East Coast pharmacist provided a clear example of the factors that can precipitate the relocation of a pharmacy. This pharmacist told the story of a declining and aging residential population that was being forced out of the market area by increasing commercial development. During the last three years in the location, the pharmacy's annual sales volume had dropped by 10 percent each year. On moving to a new store in a new and growing neighbourhood, sales volume increased by 75 percent in the first year, and the pharmacist expects a further 25 percent increase by the end of the second year in the new location.

[8] Kenichi Ohmae, "Getting Back to Strategy," *Harvard Business Review* 66, no. 6 (November–December 1988):134.

OPPORTUNITY

The pharmacist in our example took advantage of an opportunity to purchase a piece of land at a busy intersection in a growing part of the community. If he had failed to assess the new area and make his decision to purchase at the time the land was available, his only alternative may have been to close his declining business and seek employment elsewhere.

Opportunities surround us constantly. Although luck can sometimes play a role in a new and better space becoming available, astute businesspeople more often make their own luck by staying aware of developments in their own and other market areas – in other words, by being informed opportunists. Occasionally, the potential to relocate arises without prior notice, as a result of the decisions or misfortunes of others. Some examples of this would be the illness or death of a pharmacist-owner, insolvency, or the closing of stores by a corporate head office. A recent example of this was the withdrawal of Boots Drug Stores Ltd. from Canada in 1988, following which groups of stores and individual locations were offered to new investors. For some pharmacists, this led to the sudden availability of space that had advantages over their existing locations.

The pharmacy owner who operates with a business plan is at an advantage to make the quick decisions that are necessary when such opportunities become available.

RENT VERSUS EQUITY

A pharmacist might choose to relocate for the opportunity to build equity in an owner-occupied building. This opportunity would permit the pharmacy owner to make long-range plans for increasing productivity and meeting customer needs, without fear of losing the space because a lease could not be renewed.

Shopping-centre managements have been known to evict tenants or force them to relocate to allow for expansion of the development. It is important that pharmacists clearly understand all clauses of a shopping-centre lease if they are to avoid the unpleasant experience of forced relocation. It may be possible to include a clause in such a lease to protect the owner and commit the management of the centre to compensate for costs associated with forced relocation.

PERSONNEL

The pharmacy owner must not neglect the concerns of employees in any decision to relocate. Such a move will disrupt established work patterns and may also lead to resignations among long-term employees if relocation overcomplicates their travel arrangements. Hours of operation may also change to accommodate consumer demand, resulting in altered shift schedules that may present difficulties for some employees. The pharmacist-owner should be aware of such concerns and of the general insecurity that news of relocation can create among staff members. The owner should be prepared to discuss the reasons for the changes with staff and involve them in the process. The positive aspects of relocation and growth, including greater opportunities for advancement and potentially higher wages, should be stressed. A motivated staff with a sense of participation in the project can be invaluable in making relocation a smoother, less disruptive process.

PROFESSIONAL ASSISTANCE

Once a decision to relocate has been made, the pharmacy owner must seek expert advice to help reduce the risks involved. A well-informed real estate broker is certainly invaluable, and should be engaged as soon as the need to relocate becomes evident. Legal advice should be sought to review all contracts and leases and an accountant should be engaged to assist with cash-flow projections and other information required by lending institutions. Insurance coverage must be updated to allow for a larger inventory and additional equipment. Suppliers, too, can be of assistance, not only in extending purchase deals associated with the opening of the new pharmacy, but also because they can arrange for the shipment of merchandise to coincide with a new store's readiness to deal with the increased inventory.

CONCLUSION

In conclusion, it might be valuable to review some of the critical points made in Chapter 3 on location analysis. With expansion or relocation, the tools of location analysis are no less important than with the initial search for a viable pharmacy site. The following should be viewed as essential steps in site evaluation:

1. Estimating the amount of business potential within a defined trading area.
2. Determining if the store is strong enough to generate all its own business or if it would benefit more from proximity to other businesses; in other words, the choice of a free-standing site versus a shopping-centre location must be made.
3. Investigating whether there is a promising population growth in the trading area.
4. Locating closer than the competitor to the population source or to a significant attraction, such as a medical clinic.

5. Assessing the competitor's location in comparison to your chosen site with the objective of minimizing a competitive hazard.
6. Evaluating the site economics, such as occupancy costs.[9]

As we suggested earlier, the decision to expand or relocate is ultimately a subjective one, substantiated by a thorough analysis and knowledge of the local market. And, as William Fruhan states, "The key to the value of a business is profitability. If you've got it, flaunt it. If you haven't got it, try to get it. If you can't get it, get out."[10] The same theory applies to the choice of expanding or relocating a pharmacy.

RECOMMENDED READING

Beaumont, John R. "Retail Location Analysis: Some Management Perspectives." *International Journal of Retailing* 2, no. 3 (1987): 22–29.
Churchill, Neil C., and Lewis, Virginia L. "The Five Stages of Small Business Growth." *Harvard Business Review* 3 (May–June 1983): 30–50.
Fruhan, William E. "How Fast Should Your Company Grow?" *Harvard Business Review* 62, no.1 (January–February 1984): 6–8.

[9] Ronald R. Gist, *Management Perspectives in Retailing*, 2nd ed. (New York: John Wiley and Sons, 1971), pp. 204–207.
[10] Fruhan, "How Fast Should Your Company Grow?", p.93.

26

CONTINUING EDUCATION: A LIFELONG COMMITMENT TO LEARNING

INTRODUCTION

At one time it was accepted that there were only two certainties in life – death and taxes. In the latter half of the twentieth century, it is probably more accurate to add a third – change. Perhaps nowhere has the impact of change been more evident than in the professions. For most professions, the increasing number of changes is further compounded by a corresponding decrease in the length of time available to adjust to them. As a result, adaptation to change is shifting from an intergenerational to an intragenerational struggle. For example, the half-life of professional knowledge in medicine and engineering has been estimated to be as short as five years. (The half-life of professional knowledge is the period of time within which fifty percent of the knowledge base of a profession has become outdated by refinements, discoveries, and advances in technology.)

As much as we might wish otherwise, pharmacy is not immune to change in its practice environment. It does not take long for new graduates to discover that their original competence does not come with a lifetime guarantee. An illustration of the impact of change on pharmacy can be found in a 1988 advertisement for the annual publication *Compendium of Pharmaceuticals and Specialties*, which emphasizes that the new edition has "more than 200 new products" and a "70 percent content

425

change."[1] Community pharmacy is further complicated by continual refinements in the merchandise mix and merchandising practices, and by an increasing variety of competitors, such as food and drug superstores and deep discounters. Similarly, hospital pharmacies, in addition to coping with a seemingly endless array of new drugs and procedures, are being required to adopt private-sector practices such as marketing and group buying as they compete for shrinking resources in an era of cost containment.

In this constantly changing environment, pharmacists will be required to continuously update and upgrade their clinical, administrative, and management knowledge and skills. Failure to do so will mean lost opportunities for innovation, professional advancement, and business expansion. For the laggard, there will be a decrease in career satisfaction because of a feeling of being "left behind." In the worst-case scenario, if no corrective action is taken, a gradual but steady loss of competence will occur, eventually leading to obsolescence (see Figure 26.1).

What must a pharmacist do to maintain professional competence? Competence has been defined as "the ability to accomplish an essential performance characteristic in a satisfactory fashion."[2] Too often continuous learning is seen as a panacea for professional incompetence or obsolescence. There is no doubt that continuing to learn is vital to maintaining competence, but it is a prerequisite, not an ironclad guarantee. Competence is not merely knowing what to do, how to do it, and when to do it: it is also manifesting that knowledge in action. It is in their performance that health professionals prove their competence.

You may have noticed that the emphasis in our discussion so far has been on "continuous learning," not "continuing education." This distinction is made to illustrate a very important point. Education is formalized instruction; learning is the desired outcome of education. But not *all* learning is the result of education: a substantial amount occurs outside the formal instructional setting. Therefore, to restrict our discussion to continuing education would be to eliminate what for many professionals is a major portion and, perhaps the most significant portion, of their battle against obsolescence. A large part of a professional's learning will occur incidentally, as the result of reading professional literature, having discussions with patients, co-workers, and industry representatives, and addressing the problems that arise in daily practice. In the rapidly changing world of pharmacy, practitioners cannot rely exclusively on organized continuing-education programs to upgrade their knowledge. They must not only place continuous learning high on their list of professional responsibilities but also become very self-reliant and

[1] *Canadian Pharmaceutical Journal* 121(1988), p. 755.
[2] "The Continuing Competence of Pharmacists," *Journal of American Pharmaceutical Association* NS15, no. 8 (1975): 436.

Figure 26.1 TIME-DEPENDENT KNOWLEDGE GAPS FOR TECHNICALLY EDUCATED PEOPLE (NEED FOR UPDATING AND BROADENING)

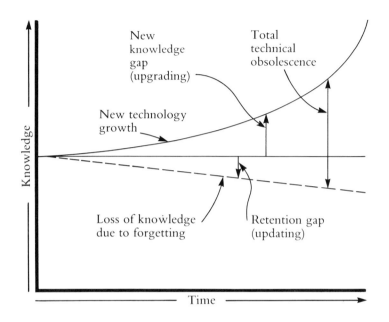

Source: Reprinted from "Continuing Engineering Education," *The Military Engineer* 71 (1979): 180.

self-directed in seeking out opportunities and avenues to help them maintain their abilities.

As important as self-directed learning is to continuing competence in pharmacy, the extent to which it is practised has remained largely undocumented. The scope of self-directed learning in some of the other health professions is now beginning to be described in the literature. Table 26.1 summarizes the results of a study on the learning resources used by physicians as they pursue their learning projects. While formalized instructional techniques (including lectures, home-study programs, and programmed texts) were found to be important, one cannot help but be struck by the vast array of independent, self-directed approaches to learning that the surveyed physicians adopted (consultations, discussion, investigation, mentoring, and so on). Very similar means are available to the pharmacist, and the new graduate should waste no time in cultivating a network of resources to assist in his or her continuous learning program.

Table 26.1. LEARNING RESOURCES USED BY PHYSICIANS

Learning resource	Description or examples
Formal instruction	Structured teaching activities including lectures, courses, and individual lessons.
Reading	Journals, textbooks, package inserts, old notes, files, etc.
Investigation	Visits to other hospitals, reviewing patient charts, phoning, "digging out" the information.
Discussion	Informal conversation with colleagues or other professionals. Most frequently one-to-one but sometimes in groups.
Experimentation	Learning by doing, such as assisting in surgery or trying out equipment.
Observation	Watching a colleague or seeing an exhibit. Frequently mentioned in conjunction with experimentation.
Consultation	Formal written and verbal interaction with other professionals in which specific information is sought.
Suppliers	Talking to salespersons, reading detail sheets and advertising.
Note taking	Pulling "pearls" from articles, encouraging critical thinking.
Media	Audio tapes, T.V., etc.
Family	Mostly cited for non-vocational projects.
Demonstration	Watching someone else and then being guided through the specific steps or principles in a structured manner.
Library resources	Ordering literature searches from a librarian and obtaining books and journals from the library.
Committees	Serving on hospital committees or committee work for community and professional organizations.
Mentoring	Direct personal coaching from a colleague.
Home study	Instructional materials designed to be studied at home.
Writing	Preparing an article for publication, writing a committee report or protocol.
Programmed text	Using a structured textbook with a question and answer format.
Teaching	Reviewing and organizing a subject prior to giving a lecture or presenting a teaching case.
Professional and social organizations	Personal contacts, literature, and meetings of organizations to which the individual belongs.

Source: L.J. Hummel, "An Investigation of Physician Self-Directed Learning Activities" (Unpublished dissertation, Michigan State University, 1985). Reprinted in Robert K. Richards, "Physicians' Self-Directed Learning: A New Perspective for Continuing Medical Education," *Möbius* 6, no. 4 (October 1986): 11.

Relicensing Requirements

The fact that practising pharmacists have to maintain their competence is self-evident. However, the mechanisms adopted by the provincial licensing authorities to ensure the continuing competence of their professional members vary. Depending where you practise, the licensing body may rely on one of three methods as the principal means of ensuring competence: mandatory continuing education, voluntary continuing education, or competence assessment.

In North America, a requirement that pharmacists participate in continuing education is by far the most predominant approach to maintaining competence. Forty U.S. states and four Canadian provinces (Alberta, Saskatchewan, Manitoba, and Prince Edward Island) have legislated participation in continuing education as a condition of relicensing. Mandatory continuing education requires the pharmacist to complete a given number of continuing education units (C.E.U.'s) in a prescribed period of time, usually one to three years. One C.E.U. approximates one contact hour of involvement in continuing education. To receive credit, an activity must be sponsored by an approved provider of continuing education or be assessed to ensure that it meets previously agreed-upon standards. What qualifies for continuing education and the maximum number of C.E.U.'s permitted for different types of continuing education and in different subject areas may vary. For example, some provinces restrict the type of business-management courses that can qualify for C.E.U.'s; some also restrict the number of C.E.U.'s that can be obtained from business-management courses. Other provinces allow continuing-education credit for preparing articles for publication and for presenting continuing-education lectures.

In jurisdictions with mandatory continuing-education requirements, pharmacists who fail to obtain the necessary number of C.E.U.'s in the prescribed period of time will not have their licences renewed. In such situations, the licensing body may permit the individual to write a challenge examination to demonstrate his or her competence to practise or it may require the individual to take specifically designed continuing-education programs.

In provinces where continuing education is voluntary (Ontario, New Brunswick, Nova Scotia, Newfoundland, and Quebec), no minimum requirement is set for participation and continuing education is not tied to relicensing. Some of these provinces do recognize pharmacists who engage in organized continuing-education activities by providing a "Certificate of Recognition" for those who acquire a certain minimum number of C.E.U.'s in a licence year. What qualifies for credit may vary from province to province as it does in jurisdictions with mandatory requirements. For example, Ontario permits a certain number of C.E.U.'s for reading selected journals, provided that the pharmacist submits a précis of the articles read.

The third approach to ensuring competence involves defining what is meant by "competence" and then relicensing individuals on the basis of evidence that they meet a minimal standard. Ontario, Quebec, and British Columbia have investigated the establishment of such programs. Of the three, the College of Pharmacists of British Columbia has the most experience and has been developing a relicensing program since the mid-1970s. The system in British Columbia consists of a compulsory written assessment of knowledge for all pharmacists, and, for those with potentially serious deficiencies, a subsequent peer-review process to confirm that the areas of poor performance evident from the written assessment in fact exist. Specifically developed continuing-education programs are recommended or required to address potential or confirmed weaknesses.[3]

Although the approach varies from province to province, continuing to learn and adapting to changes in the accepted standard of practice are fundamental expectations in all provinces. The national co-ordinating body, the Canadian Council on Continuing Education in Pharmacy (CCCEP), can provide further information on existing provincial requirements and national and provincial programs (see the Directory section of this book.)

SELF-EVALUATION

A very useful tool in helping to plan or direct our continuous-learning efforts is that of self-evaluation. We should regularly take stock to determine whether our expertise and knowledge are current. This may become evident to us as we respond to questions presented by our clients, co-workers, and other health professionals, as we read professional literature, as we try to keep up with our competition, or as we take on new responsibilities. We can also refer to the standards set by our professional associations and peer groups as guides to helping us select or focus our learning activities. There have recently been a number of attempts to draw up competency statements and standards of practice for pharmacy.[4] In addition to addressing clinical competencies, some of these documents recognize the importance of management and administrative

---

[3] D.W. Fielding et al., "Competency Assessment: A Progress Report on British Columbia's Program," *American Journal of Pharmaceutical Education* 45(1981): 176–83.

[4] For examples of competence statements and standards of practice, see S.H. Kalman and J.H. Schlegel, "Standards of Practice for the Profession of Pharmacy," *American Pharmacy* NS19(1979): 21–35; "Guidelines for the Practice of Pharmacy," *On Continuing Practice* 9(1982): i–x; R.K. Chalmers, "Chair Report of the Study Committee on 'Preparing Students for the Realities of Contemporary Pharmacy Practice,'" *American Journal of Pharmaceutical Education* 47(1983): 393–401; and "Internship Program Manual," College of Pharmacists of British Columbia, Vancouver, B.C., 1987, pp. 39–41.

skills in pharmacy practice. Table 26.2, for example, lists "the types of knowledge, attitudes, and skills essential for student entry and successful growth in contemporary pharmacy practice."[5] Both academics and pharmacy practitioners feel that graduates are not well prepared in many of these areas.

Competency statements, such as those in Table 26.2 and others, can be used as self-assessment tools for continuous learning. Pharmacists should be aware of and regularly compare such professional standards to their own practice to determine areas that warrant upgrading and updating. It is hoped that in the not-too-distant future such standards will be used to develop self-evaluation instruments. Pharmacists could then complete such assessments and get a good indication of their strengths and weaknesses and hence of the areas in which to focus their continuing education.

This approach of self-assessment followed by continuing education and self-directed learning will have a number of benefits. Perhaps the most important is its power to motivate: when an individual perceives the relevance of a particular idea or procedure to his or her practice, a greater motivation to engage in further learning often follows. Also, in adopting such an approach, the individual will be in a better position to adapt to change, develop new skills and knowledge relevant to contemporary pharmacy practice, be innovative, and take advantage of new opportunities. Finally, such an approach will enable the practitioner to fulfill a primary professional responsibility – maintaining competence.

SPECIALIZATION

In contrast to other professions, pharmacy does not have many recognized areas of specialization. This does not mean that career paths in our profession are limited. Rather, areas of expertise in pharmacy practice are not usually the result of formal training but, often, of learning after graduation. For example, the career path of a hospital pharmacist may begin with the performance of staff-pharmacist duties. Over time, however, the pharmacist can develop special skills in total parenteral nutrition, I.V. additives, pediatrics, geriatrics, intensive care, drug and poison information, or supervision and administration. Similarly, a community pharmacist might begin as a dispensing pharmacist but can often develop additional expertise in areas such as drug information, home health care, or servicing long-term care facilities. In addition, while performing a myriad of administrative and management functions, the community pharmacist can develop special talents in personnel management, purchasing, or merchandising.

[5]Chalmers, "Chair Report," p. 396.

Table 26.2. PHARMACY MANAGEMENT COMPETENCIES

A. Knowledge of the role of fiscal management for the efficient and effective operation of a practice system.
   1. Read and interpret financial statements.
   2. Perform a financial analysis of pharmacy operations.
   3. Develop a budget.
   4. Perform a cost analysis.
   5. Develop a pricing structure.
   6. Demonstrate purchasing and inventory-control ability.
   7. Perform store planning/layout.
   8. Market professional services.
   9. Maintain a management-information system.

B. Knowledge of the role of personnel management for the efficient and effective operation of a practice system.
   1. Motivate personnel.
   2. Hire, fire, co-ordinate, evaluate, and direct personnel.
   3. Manage conflict.
   4. Plan.

C. Knowledge of systems of practice for provision of needed pharmaceutical-care services.
   1. Knowledge of the system of health-care delivery:
        a. role of pharmacy.
        b. role of other units.
   2. Knowledge of structure and organization of pharmacist's environment.
   3. Knowledge of drug-distribution systems.
   4. Knowledge of information systems.
   5. Understanding the use of advanced technology systems.
   6. Understanding and using computers in pharmacy service and product delivery.
   7. Knowledge of programs aimed at quality assurance of pharmacy programs.

D. Demonstrate ability to identify needed services that may be lacking or deficient at the place of practice.

E. Knowledge of legal principles pertaining to pharmacy.

F. Knowledge of programs, policies, and procedures aimed at providing appropriate drug-use control.
   1. Controlled substances.
   2. Drug-use review.
   3. Investigational drugs.

Source: Adapted from Robert K. Chalmers, "Chair Report of the Study Committee on 'Preparation of Students for the Realities of Contemporary Pharmacy Practice'," *American Journal of Pharmaceutical Education* 47(1983): 393–401.

Figure 26.2   AN EMERGING MODEL OF PROFESSIONAL EDUCATION

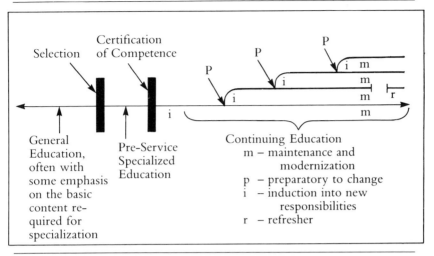

Source: Cyril O. Houle, *Continuing Learning in the Professions* (San Francisco: Jossey-Bass Inc., 1980), p. 106.

The role of lifelong learning in developing and maintaining these special skills should not be underestimated. Figure 26.2 presents a model to illustrate the importance of continuing education for professionals acquiring new skills, roles, and specialties. As the model suggests, continuing education is vital not only to maintaining the currency of our original skill: it also prepares us for changes in our responsibilities, plays a role in our on-the-job orientation into these new responsibilities, and fosters the "maintenance and modernization" of our new roles and skills. Furthermore, continuing education is important in "refreshing" those who return to a role or responsibility after an absence.

SUMMARY

Lifelong learning is especially critical for those who are faced with managing a pharmacy, since – as practitioner groups throughout North America have indicated – pharmacy graduates are generally very poorly prepared in this area. In addition, a majority of respondents in a recent survey of both hospital and community pharmacists indicated that, in the last five years, their need for continuing education in the area of management had increased.[6] The resources for continuous learning in this area are

[6]M.S. Ortiz and D.W. Fielding, "Pharmacy Management Learning Aids" (unpublished data, University of British Columbia, 1988).

growing rapidly as the need for them becomes more widely recognized.

Some of the available means for pharmacists to enhance their skills and knowledge in management and administration as well as in other areas are summarized in the Checklist of Continuous-Learning Resources below. In this list one can find a source of information to assist in meeting most, if not all, learning needs and to suit most learning styles. There are many formal continuing-education programs offered yearly by universities, professional associations, and government agencies. There are also numerous independent-study opportunities, including microcomputer packages, audio or video cassette programs, and correspondence courses.[7] In addition, a vast range of possibilities exists for self-directed study – through texts, journal articles, and consultations with colleagues in both pharmacy and other business endeavours.

Although we can recommend no single most effective method for maintaining competence, we do suggest that pharmacists remember these important points:

1. In a dynamic profession, continuing to learn to grow and to develop is an important element of maintaining competence. This is an indisputable fact of professional life.
2. It is critical that professionals stay alert for changes in their profession and for potential deficiencies in their knowledge base and skills.
3. Continuing education is most effective when there is an immediate application evident for what has been learned.
4. In a future of escalating change, individuals will have to be prepared to accept a greater responsibility for their continuous learning.

The importance of lifelong learning in all aspects of a pharmacist's practice, but particularly in his or her management and administrative role, cannot be overemphasized. Professional contentment, if not survival, will depend on the development of a lifelong commitment to learning.

A CHECKLIST OF CONTINUOUS-LEARNING RESOURCES

- Professional association meetings
  National: Canadian Pharmaceutical Association
          Canadian Society of Hospital Pharmacists
  Provincial: licensing body
          pharmaceutical society

[7] An extensive list of independent study programs is prepared each year by the Ontario College of Pharmacists, 483 Huron Street, Toronto, Ontario M5R 2R4, and also by the American Council on Pharmaceutical Education, Chicago, Illinois.

- University
    Continuing pharmacy education programs
    Business/commerce faculty continuing-education programs
- Community college business management programs
- School boards' evening programs in small business development
- Federal Business Development Bank programs
- Provincial government ministries' programs for small business
- Continuing-education programs sponsored by pharmaceutical companies
- Consulting with pharmacist colleagues
- Consulting with other businesspeople in your community
- Consulting accountants, lawyers, and bankers
- Pharmacy journals such as *Drug Merchandising; Canadian Pharmaceutical Journal; American Journal of Hospital Pharmacy; Canadian Society of Hospital Pharmacy Journal*
- Business/management/administration journals
- Business/management/administration texts
- In-house training programs such as the Shoppers Drug Mart Academy
- Hospital in-service programs

RECOMMENDED READING

Chalmers, R.K. "Chair Report of the Study Committee on 'Preparing Students for the Realities of Contemporary Pharmacy Practice.'" *American Journal of Pharmaceutical Education* 47(1983): 393–401.

"The Continuing Competence of Pharmacists." *Journal of the American Pharmaceutical Association* NS15(1975): 432–57.

Dubin, S.S. "Obsolescence or Lifelong Education: A Choice for the Professional." *American Psychologist* (May 1972), pp. 486–98.

"Guidelines for the Practice of Pharmacy." *On Continuing Practice* 9(1982): i–x.

Houle, C.O. *Continuing Learning in the Professions.* San Francisco: Jossey-Bass Inc., 1980.

"Internship Program Manual." College of Pharmacists of British Columbia, Vancouver, B.C. 1987, pp. 39–41.

Kalman, S.H., and Schlegel, J.H. "Standards of Practice for the Profession of Pharmacy." *American Pharmacy* NS19(1979): 21–35.

Quinlan, G. "Professional Competence – No Lifetime Guarantees." *Canadian Vocational Association Journal* 12(1976): 7–9.

27

PERSONAL GOALS, QUALITY OF LIFE, AND FINANCIAL PLANNING

PERSONAL GOALS

The vast majority of people have no specific goals in life. More than half of the population have not drawn up last wills and many people have no idea of their financial worth. Many don't even know what benefits are provided by their employers.

By putting their affairs in order, people can achieve significant accomplishments for themselves and their families. People who set goals tend to be more successful and suffer less from stress; they are able to manage their careers in a way that allows them to work more efficiently and productively toward desired results.

Personal goal setting is a prerequisite for personal growth, self-improvement, and success. Goals add purpose and lend direction to life; without them, we drift. It is essential to develop goals for all stages of our lives – throughout our educations and careers, as well as for retirement. And, not least, structuring our lives around goals may very well contribute to extending lifespan.

Goal setting is a long-term proposition that addresses questions such as the following: Where do I want to be in ten years? What sort of home

437

do I wish to buy, or am I happy to rent? What dollar value in investments do I hope to accumulate? Do I want to operate a single pharmacy practice or establish a chain of pharmacies?

Goal setting is not as difficult as it may seem. It is a matter of looking down the road and determining specifically what one would like to derive from life. Becoming a millionaire within ten years is a goal that has little chance of becoming a reality – unless the planning starts now.

If becoming a millionaire is a personal goal, write it down and choose a deadline date – say, January 1, 1999. There will of course be other long-term goals in the plan, but we shall focus here on the best approach to becoming a millionaire. The first step is to break the goal down into short-term objectives, in order to reach the long-term goals by meeting smaller, achievable aims. For example, to become a millionaire, a pharmacist must accumulate personal assets and, possibly, pharmacy assets. Personal assets can be accumulated with the salary or dividends taken from the pharmacy business and a properly developed savings plan. Weekly and monthly amounts should be set aside in an investment port-folio that will accumulate interest and / or dividends and capital appre-ciation (the increasing value of shares) over the next ten years. For example, if you put aside $870 per month for ten years, with accumulated interest, dividends, and capital appreciation of 12 percent per annum (which is modest), you would have $200,000 by the end of the ten-year period. Furthermore, the value of a pharmacy will increase with increased profits. Depending on location, economic conditions, interest rates, and other economic factors, the pharmacy's operating assets – inventory, fixtures, equipment, and goodwill – can be worth anywhere from four to five times its annual pre-tax profits.[1] Thus, if the annual pre-tax profit of the pharmacy is $100,000 after paying a reasonable salary to the pharmacist-owner, then the business will be worth anywhere from $400,000 to $500,000. This tells the pharmacist-owner that his or her personal fi-nancial planning must attempt to increase equity in personal investments, real estate, home, and so on, to approximately $500,000 to $600,000 in order to achieve the goal of becoming a millionaire. The planning exercise will then tell the pharmacist whether the goal is a realistic one – if all indicators point to the problem that too great a risk would be involved in attempting to increase equity to $600,000, the clear signal is that the ultimate goal, or the time period within which it is to be achieved, must be revised to something more realistically attainable.

Only by setting realistic goals with reasonable deadlines and having the commitment and discipline to follow through on them can individuals hope to realize their ambitions.

A great deal can be achieved by the organized and determined indi-

---

[1] You may find it helpful to review the discussion in Chapter 4 on estimating the value of an established pharmacy.

vidual, given the time and motivation to do so. But first, the question "What do I really want out of life?" must be answered. To get started in this type of self-analysis, put together a "wish list," then assign a level of priority to each individual item on the list. Next, break each of these goals into short-term objectives. The real secret of success is to make each objective a challenge that forces one to stretch a little and makes each accomplishment rewarding and motivating. Goals and objectives should be well thought out and put in writing. They must be reasonable, attainable, measurable, and compatible with one another and with the individual's desired lifestyle. Self-discipline is required to pursue each short-term goal relentlessly, focussing on the rewards of the eventual achievement and not on the temporary discomfort of the pursuit. It is imperative that goals be written down, as a tangible aid to differentiating between real priorities and the vast number of other activities that can distract us from our goals.

If a goal cannot be expressed in writing, it is unlikely that it can be achieved. It is therefore important to be specific: don't say, "I want to be rich"; say, "I want to be a millionaire by January 1, 1999." All goals should be measurable: don't write, "I want to achieve happiness, success, and independence," but determine what specific accomplishments you believe would bring you these qualities in life.

Another goal-setting exercise involves taking inventory of oneself. For example, list details of your personal situation under headings such as income, important personal possessions, family situation, hobbies and leisure activities, and accomplishments. Then envision what your situation would be ten years from now if you continued along the same course. Under the same headings, list what you would really want to see happening ten years from now. If the two lists differ, it is time to take a hard look at personal goals, and to make some changes.

Goal setting will help to increase motivation and enable the pharmacist to become more result-oriented and hence to plan and gain greater control over his or her destiny. It will also provide a framework for self-evaluation. Most of all, it will increase the pharmacist's chances of success, financial independence, and a comfortable retirement.

A pharmacist-owner's goals must be reflected in the business goals of the pharmacy. The desire to achieve a specified level of income within a given period of time must be in the forefront of the pharmacist's mind when preparing the pharmacy's operational plan for the next year. In other words, the level of sales required to satisfy the first objective of the long-term plan must be determined, and the best ways to achieve that sales volume considered. Should new product lines be taken on? Or should some of the less profitable lines be discontinued to achieve the specified goal? By posing and effectively answering such questions, then following through with the resulting plans from year to year, the pharmacist can realize business-related and personal aspirations.

MANAGING PERSONAL FINANCES

Goal setting is the first step in the personal financial-planning process. Clearly, personal financial planning is critical if the desired lifestyle and quality of life to which the pharmacist and his or her family aspire is to be achieved. The best approach is a simple one: manage personal finances as you would a successful business – through constant planning and monitoring. Start by preparing a statement of net worth that lists the current value of personal or family assets and liabilities. (Refer back to the form given in Chapter 6, Figure 6.1, for this purpose.) This is the equivalent of a balance sheet, only that it represents personal rather than corporate wealth. It should be updated every year.

It is then necessary to determine how your money is being spent. To do this, analyze your chequebook for the past twelve months. Where credit-card payments have been made, review the last year's billing statements to determine what was purchased and record your findings in broad categories, such as clothing, entertainment, gasoline, and so on. Remember that separate credit cards should be kept for personal and business use.

Ideally, these expenses should be summarized by the month. Expenses will fall into four categories:

1. *Regular expenses*: regular monthly items, such as rent, mortgage, utilities, gas, telephone, groceries, and entertainment.
2. *Irregular expenses*: items that occur randomly throughout the year or only in certain months, such as property taxes, insurance, clothing, and gifts.
3. *Emergency expenses*: unexpected expenses, such as car or home repairs.
4. *Major-event expenses*: items such as vacations, home furnishings, or elaborate Christmas parties.

The most difficult item to assess is likely to be the pocket money that is spent on lunches, haircuts, parking, and small occasional purchases. Unitemized spending can be controlled by keeping cash on hand to a minimum and using a credit card as a personal bookkeeper. (In the latter case, of course, credit-card charges should be paid as they come due, in order to avoid excessive carrying charges.)

Finally, it is necessary to establish priorities. Setting priorities should ideally be a decision process that involves the whole family, and each family's priorities will be different. For example, it costs more to own a home than to rent accommodation. Some people prefer to rent and spend the extra cash on vacations and more luxurious cars. Others prefer to own their homes, and to sacrifice some of the luxuries.

Figure 27.1 Six-Month Family Budget-Control Form

Month	July		August		September		October		November		December		Total	
	Budget	Actual	Budget	Actual	Budget	Actual	Budget	Actual	Budget	Actual	Budget	Actual	Budget	Actual
Income														
Spouse #1														
Spouse #2														
F/Allowance														
Dividends														
Interest														
Pension														
Annuities														
Rentals														
Other														
Total														
Expenditures														
Increase (+)														
Decrease (−)														
Bank Balance														
Opening														
Closing														
Transfer to Savings														

Figure 27.2 SIX-MONTH FAMILY BUDGET EXPENDITURES

Month	July		August		September		October		November		December		Total	
	Budget	Actual	Budget	Actual	Budget	Actual	Budget	Actual	Budget	Actual	Budget	Actual	Budget	Actual
Regular– Monthly														
Rent/ mortgage														
Electricity														
Heating														
Telephone														
Cable														
Groceries														
Allowances														
#1★														
#2★														
Dry clean/ laundry														
Car–payments														
–gas														
Entertainment														
Bank loan														
Savings														

Irregular – Monthly												
Property taxes												
Insurance												
– home												
– car												
– life												
Clothes												
– #1												
– #2												
– children												
Birthdays												
Car licences												
Gifts												
Major Event												
Vacation												
Home furnishings												
Emergencies												
Car repair												
Home repair												
Total												

★ Allowance is pocket money for lunches, parking, haircuts, cosmetics, etc.

The Family Budget Plan

To monitor and control personal finances, it is necessary to implement a family budget plan. First, list the total annual budgeted expenses according to stated goals and priorities. Then list annual income from all sources, such as salaries, interest, dividends, rent, and family allowances. Some portion of income must go directly into savings. To successfully attain goals, savings must be considered as essential an expense as food or rent. Total expenses (including savings) must equal total income (unfortunately, individuals cannot operate in a deficit position the way the government can). The family budget plan can be implemented using a six-month budget-control form as shown in Figure 27.1, in conjunction with a six-month expenditures record, as shown in Figure 27.2.

Note that in each form there are two columns under each month: "budget" and "actual." Regular, irregular, and major-event expenditures should be anticipated and recorded in the budget column of the month of expected disbursement in Figure 27.2, which breaks expenses down into the four main categories, giving a clearer picture of spending habits and assisting in the preparation of more realistic budget plans. The resulting figures should be entered in the monthly budget expenditures columns of Figure 27.1. Similarly, anticipated income should be recorded in the budget column for the month of expected receipt in Figure 27.1. The budgeted monthly closing bank balances can be calculated by recording the opening balance from your bank statement for the first month and tallying anticipated income and expenditures, including the amount to be transferred to savings, for each subsequent month.

To monitor the plan, record actual monthly expenditures, including emergency expenses, in Figure 27.2, and transfer the resulting totals to Figure 27.1. During the year, some expenses will be higher than budgeted, and cutbacks in other areas will be required. However, avoid the common mistake of cutting back on vacations – everyone needs a vacation. Try trimming away some of the pocket-money expenses instead. Finally, balance your monthly bank statement and record the actual closing bank balance in the appropriate position in Figure 27.1.

PERSONAL VERSUS BUSINESS FINANCES

Pharmacy owners should recognize that they are in effect conducting two separate business – the pharmacy business and the personal "business." But owning a pharmacy can be a somewhat overwhelming endeavour, as the business consumes so much time and energy. As a result, the distinction between personal and pharmacy finances can easily become muddied. It is therefore essential to differentiate between the two, especially at the outset. There are too many examples of small business ventures that fail due to the owner's neglect of personal financial planning.

Pharmacy owners must think of themselves as employees of their businesses, earning a set remuneration. It is very easy – and often tempting – to withdraw that extra $500 or $1000 from the company account to cover personal wants and expenses and still stay within the bank-loan limit. But the cost of such withdrawals will be much higher when the accountant does the year-end tally. Too many business owners find themselves at the end of the year having to repay large "shareholder advances" as a result of these borrowings, because they have failed to consider tax implications, that is, the personal income-tax liability that accrues with such "borrowed" funds. At a 45 percent marginal income-tax rate, the tax department will view a withdrawal of $10,000 from the business as a net payment to the owner of $10,000 – for which the owner's gross pay would have to be $18,181. Thus, that $10,000 results in a tax liability of $8181. The total of $18,181 ultimately becomes a charge against the company's net profits – an unwelcome surprise that could cause serious problems with the banker.

Long-Range Personal Financial Planning

A successful business looks well beyond the short term in its financial planning. Long-term planning is also required in the area of personal finances. If a personal goal is to become financially independent within ten years, it is necessary to determine how much cash will have to be available by that time, either in the pharmacy business or in personal savings, investments, or equity in a home. Long-range personal financial planning must also take into account the funds that will be required to ensure the continuation of the pharmacist's desired quality of life through the years after retirement. This critical consideration will be discussed in greater detail later in the chapter.

A word of caution to pharmacy owners: do not manage finances on an ad hoc basis. Base your planning on a reasonable salary from the business, one that the pharmacy can afford – your accountant can help determine that amount. In addition, review your personal financial planning with the accountant, who can provide objective advice. Operating personal finances on the model of a successful business will provide a better and less stressful lifestyle and will ensure that the pharmacy's success as a business venture is not jeopardized by a lack of control over personal financial planning.

INVESTMENTS

Wise investment of cash savings can more efficiently and quickly bring the financial independence that the pharmacist seeks. However, pharmacy owners should be aware of the "basic law of investment," which

Figure 27.3   INVESTMENT OPTIONS: EXPECTED RISK AND RETURN

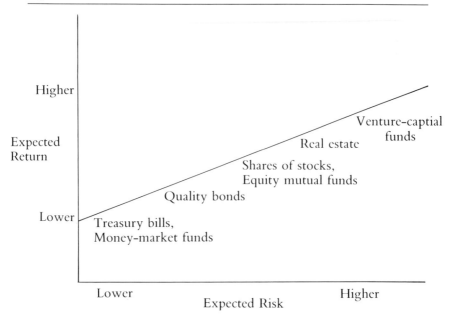

holds that return on investment will vary directly with the degree of risk involved and inversely with the liquidity of the investment. Figure 27.3 demonstrates this principle, setting out the various types of investments and the degree of risk and level of return that can be expected from each. If one's long-range personal financial planning suggests that a 15 percent annual return on investment is required to achieve financial goals, then, if the prime interest rate is in the area of 10 percent, cash savings would have to be invested in stocks, real estate, or venture-capital funds to obtain the required return. In early 1987, an investment in common shares in the stock market or, possibly, in equity mutual funds, would have been recommended as the surest way of achieving this 15 percent target. However, many individuals who followed this logic were caught in the October 1987 stock-market crash. In other words, there is no *secure* investment that will provide a yield in excess of the return on low-risk treasury bills. Some might suggest that quality bonds are a secure investment with a higher return. But it must be remembered that, if the prime rate increases, the *market value* of these quality bonds will decrease (while the yield, that is, the percentage return, will be the rate of interest at which the bonds were initially purchased). Hence, the investor could expect the market value to increase only if interest rates had fallen since the time of purchase. Check the bond price tables that are published daily in major newspapers for an illustration of this principle.

In 1987–88, real estate appeared to be a secure (and high-yield) investment for anyone. However, history tells us that no investment – not even real estate – can remain in a continual upswing: ask anyone who purchased a home in Vancouver in the late 1970s.

A caution must be raised here: young pharmacists establishing their practices, as well as older pharmacists approaching retirement, should take the least risk with their savings. Cautious investing, in treasury bills, term deposits, and Canada Savings Bonds, is the wisest option for the young pharmacist, until such time as the pharmacy has proven its continuing profitability and substantial funds are available for purposes of investment. At that time, the investment portfolio can be diversified to include a variety of higher- and lower-risk securities. Furthermore, if the new pharmacy owner's personal financial plan suggests that a rate of return higher than the prime interest rate *must* be sustained over a long period of time in order to achieve financial goals, those goals are probably unrealistic, and should be revised.

All pharmacists should thus take the time to plan their investments, in full awareness of the possible consequences of any option that promises a yield in excess of the prime bank rate. In addition, individuals who have personal debts, such as mortgages or credit-card debts, should pay them off before using available funds for investment purposes. The interest on such debts is paid out of net earnings, that is, with after-tax dollars. Hence, if your personal income is high enough to attract a marginal pre-tax rate of approximately 45 percent (this percentage will vary depending on the province), the interest is in effect being paid with 55-cent dollars. This means that if an individual is carrying a mortgage of $100,000 at 11 percent, $20,000 of his or her gross earnings per year ($100,000 × 11% = $11,000 ÷ 0.55 = $20,000) is actually required to pay the interest. If the same $100,000 were invested in treasury bills at, say, 8 percent, the interest earned, in after-tax dollars, would be $4400 ($8000 × 0.55). Hence, by investing these funds rather than paying off the mortgage, the individual would effectively lose $6600 ($11,000 – $4400) annually in after-tax dollars.

Tax Planning

Tax planning includes two basic approaches to effective financial management with regard to taxation – tax deferment and tax savings. Tax planning is considered a sign of sound management in minimizing the impact of income taxes. Tax-deferment and tax-savings measures are both fully legal, and should not be confused with measures that deliberately (and of course illegally) misrepresent taxable income.

TAX DEFERMENT

Deferring taxes means delaying the payment of income taxes on a certain portion of income for a certain period of time. Tax-deferred funds can provide interest-free financing for a pharmacy or can serve to "even out" taxable income over a period of years. Also, if inflation is high, deferred income taxes will ultimately be paid with "cheaper" dollars. The tax payment may even be delayed to a time when the pharmacist's income, and consequently the personal tax rate, are lower – for example, after retirement.

Incorporation is in fact one method of deferring income tax. A sole proprietor's income from a profitable pharmacy may incur personal taxes at a rate as high as 45 percent. By incorporating and drawing only a "reasonable" salary from the company, the owner would be retaining profits in the company, whose earnings, up to $200,000 annually, would be taxed at a rate of about 22 percent. His or her personal income would thereby also fall to a lower tax bracket. The best way to defer personal income tax is to place funds in a registered retirement savings plan (RRSP), which we shall discuss in detail later on. Some people like to consider more frivolous methods of deferment, such as limited partnerships in risky businesses. In the past, multiple-unit residential buildings (MURBS), movies, gas and oil, and similar speculative projects served as popular investment vehicles for tax deferment. Most of these are no longer advantageous for such purposes as a result of changes in recent federal budgets.

TAX SAVINGS

Too many pharmacists find tax planning methods intimidating and consequently pay more tax than necessary in an attempt to avoid any possible problems in the future. It is advisable for them to spend a few hours each year with their tax accountant to review personal and business tax affairs. The $200 to $400 cost for this service will be a small price to pay in light of the savings that could potentially be made.

Owner's Remuneration and Tax Planning Methods

One of the first questions in tax planning that the pharmacist must address is "In what form should I take remuneration to best minimize overall taxes?" There are three basic forms in which payment to the owner may be made: salary, dividends, and bonus. Depending on the size and nature of the particular pharmacy practice, either salary alone or some combination of salary, dividends, and bonus, can bear the greatest advantages in terms of taxation. We shall point out several of the considerations involved in such decisions, but we must stress that no single solution is appropriate for all pharmacies, since all situations differ in critical respects. Matters of taxation can be very complex and it is recommended that pharmacy owners discuss the various options in detail with a tax accountant before proceeding.

A salary is handled very simply. First, the amount that the pharmacy can afford to pay its owner, either on a weekly, bi-weekly, or monthly basis, must be determined. The appropriate deductions for income tax and Canada or Quebec Pension Plan must be calculated (pharmacy owners do not qualify for unemployment insurance deductions). In certain cases – for example, during the early years of a pharmacy's operation – drawing a salary may be the most advantageous option.

Dividends represented a popular method of remuneration for pharmacy owners before the federal budget of 1981 was passed. Until that time, certain tax savings were available to small-business owners if they took dividends instead of salary in accordance with the "dividend tax-credit" system. This is no longer the case. However, dividends can be an advantageous form of payment if shares in the pharmacy are divided between spouses: this can provide an excellent opportunity for income splitting to minimize taxes (see p. 451).

One approach to deferring corporate taxes is to set up a company bonus to the owner or nominees (a spouse or dependants) at the end of the fiscal year, to be paid out of net profits before income taxes. The bonus would be deducted as a salary expense in the given fiscal year, thus lowering taxable income and the corporate income tax payable. The bonus must then be paid out to the pharmacist or nominees within 180 days of the year-end, and personal taxes on the funds would be payable at that time. Note that this deferment is advantageous only if it serves to reduce the amount of corporate income that exceeds $200,000 and that is thereby ineligible for the lower small-business tax rate. If income is already below $200,000, there would be little sense in declaring a bonus, because it would be taxed at a higher rate as personal income. There are certain legal requirements connected with bonus payments that can be clarified for the pharmacy owner by a tax adviser.

The point to remember is that remuneration from the pharmacy should be structured in the way that best accommodates the financial needs and tax liability of both the business and its owner.

Registered Retirement Savings Plan (RRSP)

This is perhaps the best method of deferring tax on personal income. The 1988 federal budget has provided an added advantage by increasing the limit on the total contributions that can be made annually to an RRSP.

The maximum contribution allowed in 1988 was $7500 or 20 percent of earned income, whichever is lower. Contributions to an RRSP are deductible from taxable income. This means, for example, that for anyone in the 45 percent tax bracket, the government is in effect paying 45 percent toward that individual's pension plan.

It is important to note that investment income, including dividends from the pharmacy owner's company, does not qualify as earned income. One must therefore take remuneration in the form of a salary or bonus rather than dividends to have sufficient earned income to allow for contributions to the RRSP fund.

RRSPs have some disadvantages. One is that RRSP funds cannot be used as collateral for personal or business loans. Another is that, when funds are withdrawn, they will attract full tax rates, including full rates on any capital gains that might have been deposited in the fund.

Don't think of an RRSP only as a method of tax deferment; it is first and foremost a valuable personal retirement fund. In this regard, another important consideration concerning RRSPs must be raised. To ensure substantial personal tax savings during retirement years, it is advisable to split RRSP contributions by creating a separate spousal fund (in cases, of course, where the spouse earns a smaller income). Contributions to an RRSP in the spouse's name will be deductible from the pharmacist's own personal income, but will belong solely to the spouse. The value of such planning will be discussed in further detail in the following section on retirement planning.

Self-Administered RRSP

An individual in the 45 percent tax bracket would normally have to earn $1818 for every $1000 used for investment purposes, but through an RRSP, the full $1818 can be invested and allowed to accumulate, tax-free.

There are various methods of establishing an RRSP. The most common method is to purchase certificates from a chartered bank or trust company. Another method is to establish a self-administered plan. This can be done through trust companies or stockbrokers, who allow flexibility in the way the RRSP funds will be invested. The types of investments available are cash deposits, shares in public companies, term deposits, guaranteed certificates, mutual funds, bonds, and mortgages. In fact, with a self-administered RRSP, one can invest in a mortgage in one's own home. Items that do not qualify for investment through an RRSP are precious metals, gems, commodities, art, antiques, and undeveloped land.

Income Splitting

Income splitting involves reducing overall income tax by paying other family members a salary or, in accordance with legal guidelines, making them shareholders of the company who thereby receive dividend income. Sound advice from a tax accountant is critical in these matters. Income splitting may serve to reduce either the pharmacist's personal income or the company's net profit, if necessary, to a level that qualifies for the small-business corporate rate. This approach depends, of course, on the tax situation of the husband, wife, or children, and, in the case of paying salaries, on the actual contribution of labour on the part of family members to the business. In the case of paying dividends to family members, legal restrictions must be explored with the assistance of a tax accountant.

Loans to Shareholders

A pharmacist considering the purchase of a home should borrow the required funds through the incorporated pharmacy, as an interest-free shareholder's loan. Granted, at the end of each year, imputed interest will be added to the personal tax return at the going rate, but the after-tax cost will only be the tax on the interest. For example, if the mortgage is $100,000 and the interest rate is 11 percent, the after-tax amount required to pay the interest will be $11,000. The rate of imputed interest, on the other hand, hovers around 9 percent, for $9000 in imputed interest. The tax payable, at 45 percent, would therefore be $4050 for a savings in after-tax personal income of $6950. The ability to take out a shareholder's loan for the purchase of a home is one of the advantages a pharmacy owner has over salaried employees.

It is important to remember that all mortgages should be paid off at the earliest possible time. However, tax planning would involve weighing the advantages of paying off a shareholder's loan as opposed to investing money in an RRSP. Since the appropriate alternative will depend on the particular situation, the pharmacy owner should review the benefits of each option with a tax adviser.

Medical Expenses

Dental work and certain major medical expenses that are not covered by provincial health insurance plans can represent substantial after-tax costs. Premiums paid to insurance companies to provide coverage for these additional dental and medical costs are deductible for tax purposes. It is therefore advisable to establish a company plan to provide the additional coverage.

Capital Gains

There is a lifetime capital-gains exemption of $100,000 for every Canadian. This applies to revenues on the sale of any investments, including real estate, stocks, and bonds.

In addition, there is a $500,000 lifetime capital-gains exemption on the sale of shares in Canadian-controlled private corporations, which, of course, include pharmacies. This has created a new approach to tax planning called "capital-gains splitting," which capitalizes on the advantages of income splitting between spouses. Hence, if a pharmacist is selling the shares of the pharmacy and each spouse owns 50 percent of those shares, each will be eligible for the $500,000 capital-gains exemption on the revenues from the sale. In provinces where the pharmacist must own over 50 percent of the pharmacy operation, shares should be split 51 percent to 49 percent.

Although this can be a significant advantage for the seller of the pharmacy, it must be pointed out that most pharmacies are sold on the basis of operating assets – inventory, fixtures, equipment, and goodwill – rather than shares,[2] and the exemption does not apply to revenues gained from the sale of assets. In the latter case, earnings on the sale of inventory, fixtures, and equipment are not taxable if these assets are sold at book value, which is normally done. Income tax is payable, however, on 75 percent of the value of goodwill at the pharmacy's corporate tax rates (in Ontario, for example, this would mean 22 percent for the first $200,000 of taxable income and about 44 percent thereafter). If goodwill is valued at, say, $400,000, the taxable portion will be $300,000 (75 percent), and the tax payable (in Ontario) would be $88,000 ($44,000 on the first $200,000 at 22 percent and $44,000 on the remaining $100,000 at 44 percent).

Since income-tax regulations change with every provincial and federal budget, it is once again advisable to engage the services of an accounting firm that can provide expert advice in this area.

RETIREMENT PLANNING

Retirement planning is often ignored by pharmacists until they reach 45 to 50 years of age. This is usually too late to plan for a comfortable retirement. Long-range planning should consider not only the amount of money required to maintain a desired quality of life through the years of retirement, but also the need to divide pension funds between the two spouses on an equal basis, as mentioned earlier, in order to minimize personal income taxes at retirement.

[2] You may find it helpful to review the material on structuring the purchase of a pharmacy in Chapter 4.

On December 31 of the year one turns 71, funds held in RRSPs must be withdrawn. Unless those funds are promptly rolled into an annuity or a registered retirement investment fund (RRIF), the full amount withdrawn will be taxed at prevailing income-tax rates. Note also that such funds cannot be divided between spouses at that time; they must be held in separate RRSPs to be converted into separate annuities or RRIFs. Consider the following example: based on current interest rates, a joint survivor annuity guaranteed for the life of each spouse runs at about $6000 per $50,000 in the fund. Thus, if $1 million has accumulated in an RRSP by the time of retirement, it could be converted to a pension plan for life that provides $120,000 annually ($1,000,000 ÷ $50,000 × $6000). With proper planning, this income could be split, with each spouse receiving $60,000 annually, resulting in a substantial personal-tax saving throughout the retirement years.

We have mentioned the two options of guaranteed annuities and RRIFs. A guaranteed annuity provides a prescribed annual income calculated on the basis of total funds invested. The pension is therefore set, and the individual is locked into receiving the prescribed amount of money annually. An RRIF, which functions much like an RRSP and which can similarly be established as a self-administered fund, offers its holder more flexibility and greater control over future earnings, in that the individual can determine how to invest the funds. Also, while the individual is committed to withdrawing a certain minimum amount annually, that minimum is relatively small and the size of annual withdrawals beyond that stipulated amount is at the individual's discretion. The advantages of one option over the other will vary depending on prevailing interest rates and, once again, the aid of a tax accountant would be valuable in balancing the options.

Long-range personal financial planning should take into consideration the amount of savings that must be accumulated to ensure a comfortable retirement. Determining this amount is very simple. We shall base our example on the option of a guaranteed annuity, but the same principles would apply if funds were to be invested in an RRIF. Annuity tables can be reviewed from time to time to determine the costs of a guaranteed annuity on a joint survival basis. As mentioned earlier, the present annuity rates hover in the area of $6000 per year per $50,000 invested.

To start, current family budget expenses should be reviewed. On retirement, certain expenses, including mortgage payments, clothing, and children's expenses, will decrease. Others, however, such as vacations and entertainment, may increase. Such changes should be considered and the budget adjusted accordingly. The funds that should be available at the time of retirement can then be calculated. For example, if a pharmacist is 40 years old and wishes to retire at age 65, that is, 25 years later, what amount of capital will be required in order to purchase an annuity that will provide an annual income allowing his or her current

Figure 27.4. CALCULATION OF FUNDS REQUIRED ON RETIREMENT

Adjusted annual expense budget	$ 40,000
Estimated income taxes	15,000
Gross amount required in current dollars	$ 55,000

Inflation at 5% (3.386)

Gross amount required in future dollars,
25 years later ($55,000 × 3.386) $ 186,230

Funds required to finance retirement
at $6000 per $50,000 invested:

$$\frac{x}{\$50,000} \times \$6000 = \$186,230$$

$$\frac{x}{\$50,000} = \frac{\$186,230}{\$6000}$$

$$x = 31.038 \times \$50,000$$

$$x = \$1,551,916 \text{ rounded off to} \qquad \underline{\$1,550,000}$$

lifestyle, as adjusted, to be maintained? Figure 27.4 assumes a required after-tax income of $40,000 annually, plus an estimated income-tax liability of $15,000, for a total gross income of $55,000 per year, in today's dollars. The inflation rate during the 1980s has been fluctuating between three percent and twelve percent. If the average rate of inflation over the next 25 years is estimated to be five percent, then the compounded factor for 25 years is 3.386. This increases the $55,000 in today's dollars to $186,230 in future dollars 25 years from now. Assuming an annuity of $6000 per year per $50,000 invested, the amount of funds required at the time of retirement would be $1,550,000. These calculations are reflected in Figure 27.4.

This may strike you as a shocking amount, but it is indeed in line with the effects of inflation that we have witnessed over the past 25 years: consider, for example, the increase in pharmacists' salaries since 1964, as well as the increased value of property, automobiles, and so on. Our example should make evident the importance of taking retirement needs into account in personal financial planning during the earlier years, in order to avoid what could be an overwhelming surprise at middle age.

FINANCIAL-PLANNING ADVISERS

In most cases, pharmacists are unable to take the time and lack the expertise necessary to prepare an effective personal financial plan that will ensure their financial independence and a comfortable retirement. However, the needed assistance is abundantly available. The following is a list of financial planners who can provide assistance in this regard:

1. Insurance agent or broker
2. Mutual-fund salesperson
3. Accountant
4. Lawyer
5. Stockbroker
6. Investment counsellor
7. Real estate agent
8. Mortgage broker
9. Bank manager
10. Trust officer
11. Financial planners

You will find that some of these advisers display initials after their names, such as C.F.P. (Certified Financial Planner) and R.F.P. (Registered Financial Planner). These individuals have special training in personal financial planning. However, many of them are also involved in selling some sort of product. It is important to consider what may be motivating a personal financial planner and to exercise caution by seeking references before engaging the individual to prepare the plan. It is suggested that a proper plan can only be prepared by an individual who operates on a "fee-for-service" basis and has no connection to companies that sell products, which may ultimately be included as part of the overall plan. It should be noted, finally, that certain pharmacy organizations, such as the Canadian Pharmaceutical Association as well as some of the provincial associations, offer their members financial-planning assistance by way of information on specific plans (for example, RRSPs) or on investment companies and financial services.

Conclusion

The choice of becoming a pharmacy owner implies that an individual is interested in achieving and maintaining a certain degree of independence and a satisfying and rewarding quality of life. Self-evaluation and a clear outline of attainable and measurable personal goals, supported by closely monitored long-range planning, will enable the pharmacist to realize those aspirations throughout his or her career and retirement.

RECOMMENDED READING

Enterprise System III: RRSP. Ontario Pharmaceutical Association, n.d.
"A Guide to Personal Financial Planning." *Canadian Pharmaceutical Journal* (September 1983), p. 378.
Snyder, J. Christopher. *It's Your Money.* 6th ed. Toronto: Stoddart Publishing Co. Ltd., 1989.
Zimmer, Henry B. *Making Your Money Grow.* 3rd ed. Toronto: Collins Publishers, 1984.

DIRECTORY

The following is a list of national pharmacy organizations, provincial statutory organizations, provincial voluntary organizations, faculties and schools of pharmacy, organizations in the Canadian drug industry, and selected listings of the Health Protection Branch of Health and Welfare Canada.[1]

This Directory does not list the names of individuals currently holding office in the various pharmacy organizations, since such information is subject to change. We recommend, however, that graduating pharmacists and practising pharmacist-owners subscribe to the Canadian Pharmaceutical Association's annual *Pharmacy Directory* for the valuable information it contains on the current officers and other resource personnel in the regulatory, voluntary, educational, and government organizations.

National Pharmacy Organizations

CANADIAN PHARMACEUTICAL ASSOCIATION (CPhA)

The Canadian Pharmaceutical Association is the national association of the profession, comprising pharmacists in all walks of pharmaceutical

---

[1] These listings are adapted from the 1989 *Pharmacy Directory*, published by the Canadian Pharmaceutical Association.

457

endeavour, their provincial and national member associations and related organizations, pharmacy students, and persons interested in the advancement of the profession and its endeavours in Canada.

Restructured under new by-laws in August 1972, the association is representative of its comprehensive membership in its purpose of enhancing the status of the profession as a prominent contributor in the delivery of health care and the quality and scope of pharmaceutical service provided to Canadian society.

The CPhA acts as a liaison and co-ordinating organization to represent the profession of pharmacy at the national level and, at all levels, to assist with administrative problems related to the rendering of pharmaceutical services. The CPhA publishes materials of interest to pharmacy, most notably the *Canadian Pharmaceutical Journal*. Interested parties may contact the organization's director of publications and / or the editor of the journal, at the address given below:

Canadian Pharmaceutical Association   (613) 523-7877
    1785 Alta Vista Drive
    Ottawa, Ontario
    K1G 3Y6

ASSOCIATION OF DEANS OF PHARMACY OF CANADA (ADPC)

The ADPC is the national organization comprising the nine deans and directors of the faculties, schools, or colleges of pharmacy in Canada. It is headed by an annually elected president. This organization serves as a forum for liaison and co-ordination of pharmacy education activities. Communication is maintained with the pharmaceutical industry, professional associations, federal cabinet ministers, chain stores, and the Association of Universities and Colleges of Canada, of which it is an associate member. ADPC also serves as a committee of the Association of Faculties of Pharmacy of Canada.

CANADIAN ASSOCIATION OF PHARMACY STUDENTS AND INTERNS (CAPSI)

CAPSI, a national organization of students in Canadian schools of pharmacy, provides a medium for liaison and exchange of information concerning academic and student-interest matters. It promotes and represents the interests of pharmacy students to organized bodies in pharmacy, government, and the community. The executive secretary of CAPSI may be contacted through the Canadian Pharmaceutical Association.

CANADIAN COUNCIL ON CONTINUING EDUCATION IN PHARMACY (CCCEP)

CCCEP was formed in May 1973 to serve as the national co-ordinating body for continuing pharmacy education. Its members are the provincial regulatory organizations. Its objectives are to act as the national accrediting organization of continuing-education programs and their providers, promote interprovincial exchange of information on continuing pharmaceutical education, act as a national resource centre, develop national programs, determine standards and requirements, and undertake continuing-education research. While there is no consensus on voluntary or mandatory continuing education for pharmacists, each province has designated a person to be responsible for co-ordinating continuing-education activities. Information on current co-ordinators may be obtained from the CPhA's annual *Pharmacy Directory* or through the provincial regulatory or voluntary organizations.

CANADIAN FOUNDATION FOR PHARMACY (CFP)

The CFP is a philanthropic association, annual membership in which is open to all individuals and corporations in every branch of the profession of pharmacy.

The philanthropic mission of the foundation is to encourage progress in Canadian pharmacy education, research, and practice by providing financial assistance to programs designed to help practising pharmacists, the faculties or colleges of pharmacy, and pharmacy students, both graduate and undergraduate. The CFP may be contacted at the following address:

Executive Director   (416) 979-2024
Canadian Foundation for Pharmacy
   603-123 Edward Street
   Toronto, Ontario
   M5G 1E2

CANADIAN SOCIETY OF GOVERNMENTAL PHARMACISTS (CSGP)

The CSGP is a CPhA Member Association and has as its members pharmacists who pursue their careers at all levels of government service, including the armed forces.

CANADIAN SOCIETY OF HOSPITAL PHARMACISTS (CSHP)

The CSHP, with provincial or regional branches responsible to the national council, is a voluntary organization of hospital pharmacists formed to enhance the standards of practice in hospitals and the role that pharmacists play in the general organizational pattern of hospitals.

CANADIAN SOCIETY OF INDUSTRIAL PHARMACISTS (CSIP)

The CSIP, a CPhA member association, is a voluntary professional organization of pharmacists employed in the Canadian pharmaceutical industry. The society provides an exchange of information and ideas on professional and technical problems pertaining to the industry.

CONFERENCE OF PHARMACY REGISTRARS OF CANADA (CPRC)

The CPRC provides for administrative liaison on regulatory matters in an organization comprised of the registrars of provincial statutory associations and the executive director of the CPhA.

PHARMACY EXAMINING BOARD OF CANADA (PEBC)

The PEBC conducts a national examination to fulfill its principal purpose of establishing academic qualifications for pharmacists that are acceptable to participating licensing bodies. This board was incorporated by federal statute on 21 December 1963.

Provincial Statutory Organizations

These organizations are recognized under their respective provincial pharmacy acts. Their regulatory obligation includes registration, licensing, and professional discipline of pharmacists, to standardize the practice of pharmacy and the conditions under which pharmaceutical services and products are provided to the public.

College of Pharmacists of British Columbia (COPBC)
    240-1575 W. Georgia Street,
    Vancouver, British Columbia
    V6G 2V3   (604) 683-6588
Alberta Pharmaceutical Association (APhA)
    10615-124 Street,
    Edmonton, Alberta
    T5N 1S5   (403) 488-8152
Saskatchewan Pharmaceutical Association (SPhA)
    301, 2631-28th Avenue,
    Regina, Saskatchewan
    S4S 6X3   (306) 584-2292
Manitoba Pharmaceutical Association (MPhA)
    187 St. Mary's Road,
    Winnipeg, Manitoba
    R2H 1J2   (204) 233-1411

Ontario College Of Pharmacists (OCP)
483 Huron Street,
Toronto, Ontario
M5R 2R4 (416) 962-4861
Ordre des Pharmaciens du Québec
266 Ouest rue Notre-Dame, Bureau 301,
Montréal, Québec
H2Y 1T6 (514) 284-9588
New Brunswick Pharmaceutical Society (NBPhS)
Place Heritage Crt., 204-95 Foundry Street,
Moncton, New Brunswick
E1C 5H7 (506) 857-8957
Nova Scotia Pharmaceutical Society (NSPS)
P.O. Box 3363(S), 1526 Dresden Row,
Halifax, Nova Scotia
B3J 3J1 (902) 422-8528
Prince Edward Island Pharmacy Board
P.O. Box 1084,
Charlottetown, Prince Edward Island
C1A 7M4 (902) 368-4905
Newfoundland Pharmaceutical Association (NPhA)
Apothecary Hall, 488 Water Street,
St. John's, Newfoundland
A1E 1B3 (709) 753-5877

Provincial Voluntary Organizations

These organizations have no regulatory authority but exist to represent the views of employee and employer pharmacists. They may also sponsor continuing-education programs, salary surveys, negotiation for professional fees, and a variety of insurance benefits for their members.

British Columbia Pharmacists' Society (BCPhS)
604-1200 W. 73rd Avenue, Vancouver, British Columbia V6P 6G5
Manitoba Society of Professional Pharmacists Inc. (MSPPI)
187 St. Mary's Road, Winnipeg, Manitoba R2H 1J2
Ontario Pharmacists' Association (OPA)
707-99 Avenue Road, Toronto, Ontario M5R 2G5
Association Professionnelle des Pharmaciens Salariés du Québec (APPSQ)
C.P. 609, Succursale N., Montréal, Québec H2X 3M6
Association Québécoise des Pharmaciens Propriétaires (AQPP)
1031, rue St-Denis, Montréal, Québec H2X 3H9
Atlantic Provinces Pharmacy Council (APPC)
P.O. Box 3363 (s), Halifax, Nova Scotia B3J 3J1

New Brunswick Pharmacists' Association
  Place Heritage Court, 204-95 Foundry Street,
  Moncton, New Brunswick E1C 5H7
Pharmacy Association of Nova Scotia (PANS)
  P.O. Box 3214(S), 1526 Dresden Row,
  Halifax, Nova Scotia B3J 3H5
P.E.I. Pharmaceutical Association
  P.O. Box 2225, Charlottetown, Prince Edward Island C1A 8B9
Committee of Newfoundland Community Pharmacies (CNCP)
  Apothecary Hall, 488 Water Street, St. John's, Newfoundland
  A1E 1B3

Canadian Faculties and Schools of Pharmacy

There are nine faculties or schools of pharmacy in Canada. Each has its
own admission requirements and procedures and each provides individual programs for product research and study.

British Columbia	University of British Columbia	(604) 228-2343
	Faculty of Pharmaceutical Sciences	
	2146 East Mall	
	Vancouver, British Columbia	
	V6T 1W5	
Alberta	University of Alberta	(403) 492-3362
	Faculty of Pharmacy &	
	Pharmaceutical Sciences	
	Edmonton, Alberta	
	T6G 2N8	
Saskatchewan	University of Saskatchewan	(306) 966-6328
	College of Pharmacy	
	Saskatoon, Saskatchewan	
	S7N OWO	
Manitoba	University of Manitoba	(204) 474-9306
	Faculty of Pharmacy	
	Winnipeg, Manitoba	
	R3T 2N2	
Ontario	University of Toronto	(416) 978-2889
	Faculty of Pharmacy	
	Toronto, Ontario	
	M5S 1A1	

Quebec	Université Laval École de Pharmacie Québec, Québec G1K 7P4	(418) 656-3211
	Université de Montréal Faculté de Pharmacie C.P. 6128, succ. A Montréal, Québec H3C 3J7	(514) 343-6422
New Brunswick Nova Scotia P.E.I.	Dalhousie University College of Pharmacy Halifax, Nova Scotia B3H 3J5	(902) 424-2097
Newfoundland	Memorial University of Newfoundland School of Pharmacy St. John's, Newfoundland A1B 3V6	(709) 737-6571

Organizations in the Canadian Drug Industry

These are associations that represent drug manufacturing and / or distributing companies in Canada.

Canadian Drug Manufacturers Association (CDMA)
   1120 Finch Avenue W., Suite 604,
   Downsview, Ontario M3J 3H7   (416) 663-2362
Canadian Wholesale Drug Association (CWDA)
   1110 rue Sherbrooke ouest, Suite 307,
   Montréal, Québec H3A 1G8   (514) 842-8627
Council for Accreditation of Pharmaceutical Manufacturer Representatives of Canada (APRM)
   3466 Ashby Street, St. Laurent, Québec H4R 2C1 (514) 333-8362
Pharmaceutical Advertising Advisory Board (PAAB)
   345 Kingston Road, Pickering, Ontario L1V 1A1   (416) 286-2275
Pharmaceutical Manufacturers Association of Canada (PMAC)
   302-1111 Prince of Wales Drive,
   Ottawa, Ontario K2C 3T2   (613) 727-1380
Nonprescription Drug Manufacturers Association of Canada (NDMAC)
   830-1600 Carling Avenue,
   Ottawa, Ontario K1Z 8R7   (613) 722-4500

Federal Government Contacts

The following departments and personnel are responsible for pharmaceutical issues that concern the federal government. They supply the link between the federal government and pharmacists, pharmaceutical organizations, and the pharmaceutical industry.

HEALTH AND WELFARE CANADA, HEALTH PROTECTION BRANCH

Assistant Deputy Minister   (613) 957-1804
Health Protection Building
Tunney's Pasture
Ottawa, Ontario
K1A OL2

Director General
Drugs Directorate   (613) 957-0368
Health Protection Building
Tunney's Pasture
Ottawa, Ontario
K1A OL2

Director
Bureau of Drug Quality   (613) 957-1831
Health Protection Building
Tunney's Pasture
Ottawa, Ontario
K1A OL2

Senior Pharmacy Consultant   (613) 957-1482
Health Protection Building
Tunney's Pasture
Ottawa, Ontario
K1A OL2

Director
Bureau of Dangerous Drugs   (613) 954-6522
Jackson Building
122 Bank Street
3rd Floor
Ottawa, Ontario
K1A 1B9

Director
Bureau of Human Prescription Drugs   (613) 991-0107
355 River Road
Tower B, Place Vanier
Vanier, Ontario
K1A 1B8

Director
Bureau of Nonprescription Drugs   (613) 954-6493
355 River Road
Tower B, Place Vanier
Vanier, Ontario
K1A 1B8

Director
Bureau of Biologies   (613) 957-8065
Virus Building
Tunney's Pasture
Ottawa, Ontario
K1A OL2

Director
Bureau of Veterinary Drugs   (613) 957-3824
Tunney's Pasture
Ottawa, Ontario
K1A OL2

Provincial Drug Programs

Each of the provinces and territories of Canada has a drug-benefit program in place. Each is different from the other in some way. The tables
on the following pages are designed to describe, in a concise way, each
of the programs. From the available information, similarities and differences can be identified.

The source of this information is a report entitled "Provincial and
Territorial Drug Reimbursement Plans," prepared by Lori Anderson of
the Bureau of Drug Quality, Health Protection Branch, Health and Welfare Canada, as of September 1987.

The tables are intended to identify each provincial drug-benefit program, the relevant legislation and regulations that apply, the eligible
beneficiaries and payment mechanisms under each program, and the
address of the drug-plan manager responsible for each.

Table 1.   GENERAL DRUG-BENEFIT INFORMATION

Province/ Territory	Program Name	Date of Implementation	Legislation	Manager's Address
British Columbia	British Columbia Pharmacare	1 January 1974	GAIN Act	Manager, Pharmacare Govt. of B.C. 301-1275 W. 6th Ave. Vancouver, B.C. V6H 1A6
Alberta	a. Prescription Drug Program b. Alberta Blue Cross Plan for Seniors	a. 1947 (original program); 1961 (current program) b. 1 July 1974	None	N.W. Regional Manager Institutional Operationals Branch Alberta Hospitals & Medical Care P.O. Box 2222 11010-101 St. Edmonton, Alta. T5J 2P4
Saskatchewan	Saskatchewan Prescription Drug Plan	September 1975 New Saskatchewan Prescription Drug Plan, 1 July 1987	The Prescription Drugs Act	Executive Director Saskatchewan Prescription Drug Plan Dept. of Health T.C. Douglas Bldg. 3475 Albert St. Regina, Sask. S4S 6X6
Manitoba	a. Pharmacare b. Personal Care Home Drug Program c. Social Allowances Health Services	a. 1 July 1973 b. 1 July 1973 c. prior to 1950	a. Prescription Drugs Cost Assistance Act b. Health Services Insurance Act c. The Social Allowances Act	Pharmaceutical Consultant Manitoba Health Services Commission 599 Empress St., Rm. 227 P.O. Box 925 Winnipeg, Man. R3C 2T6
Ontario	Ontario Drug Benefit	September 1974	Ontario Drug Benefit Act, 1986 Prescription Drug Cost Regulation Act, 1986	Director Drug Programs and Policy Branch Ministry of Health 7 Overlea Blvd., 6th fl. Toronto, Ont. M4A 1A8
Quebec	*Programme de Médicaments du Québec*	1 August 1972	*la Loi de l'assurance-maladie*	Directeur général Conseil consultatif de pharmacologie 1125 chemin St-Louis Sillery, Qué. G1S 1E7
New Brunswick	a. Prescription Drug Program b. Health Services Pharmaceutical Program	1975	a. Prescription Drug Payment Act and Regulations b. Health Services Act and Regulations	Director Prescription Drug Program Dept. of Health P.O. Box 5100 Fredericton, N.B. E3B 5G8
Nova Scotia	Nova Scotia Medical Services Insurance Pharmacare	a. 1 October 1974 b. 1 September 1981 c. 1 September 1981 d. 1 October 1976 e. 1 December 1978 f. 1 October 1980	N.S. Health Services and Insurance Act and Regulations	Executive Director Health Services & Insurance Commission Joseph Howe Bldg., 8th fl. P.O. Box 760 Halifax, N.S. B3J 2V2

Province/ Territory	Program Name	Date of Implementation	Legislation	Manager's Address
Prince Edward Island	a. Social Services Drug Program b. Diabetes Control Program c. Drug Cost Assistance Plan	a. n/a b. n/a c. 1 January 1987	a. n/a b. n/a c. Drug Cost Assistance Act	Director Pharmacy Services Dept. of Health P.O. Box 2000 Charlottetown, P.E.I. C1A 7N8
Newfoundland	Newfoundland and Labrador Prescription Drug Program	a. Social services: 1970 b. Senior citizens: 1980	None	Manager Nfld.-Labrador Prescription Drug Plan P.O. Box 8070 Station A St. John's Nfld. A1B 4A6
Northwest Territories	Pharmacare	1 July 1979	N.W.T. Pharmacy Act	Program Policy Officer Health Programs & Standards Dept. of Health Govt. of N.W.T. Yellowknife, N.W.T. X1A 2L9
Yukon	a. Pharmacare b. Chronic Disease and Disability Program	a. 1 July 1981 b. 1 February 1987	Health Care Insurance Plan Act and Regulations	Director Health Services Govt. of Yukon Box 2703 Whitehorse, Yukon Y1A 2C6

Table 2.   CLIENTELE AND BENEFITS OF PROGRAMS

Province/ Territory	Beneficiaries	Residency Limitations	Benefits	Formulary	Therapeutics or Formulary Committee
British Columbia	Group 1 – Full Assistance: a. Residents of licenced long-term care facilities b. Holder of valid Human Resources Medical Benefits Program W card, issued on basis of need Group 2 – Partial Assistance: a. Residents 65 + b. All residents of B.C.	90 days	All provincial & federal R schedule drugs, plus a limited number of non-R drugs and medical supplies, e.g., syringes, ostomy and prosthetic appliances	None	None
Alberta	a. Persons receiving social assistance, Assured Income for the Severely Handicapped, and Guardian Social Allowance b. Persons 65 +	None	All drugs listed in the CPS, with some exclusions	None	None

Province/ Territory	Beneficiaries	Residency Limitations	Benefits	Formulary	Therapeutics or Formulary Committee

Saskatchewan	a. Standard: all residents of province with a valid Health-Services Card
	b. Residents of special-care homes *not* receiving social assistance
	c. "Unique circumstance" individuals with extraordinarily high up-front costs under the deductible program
	d. Special diseases: paraplegics, cystic fibrosis, and end-stage renal-disease patients
	e. Social assistance:
	   1. General
	   2. Residents nominated on basis of need; dependants of Plan 1 recipients under the age of 18
	   3. Social assistance recipients in special-care homes
	f. Wards of the province and inmates of provincial correctional facilities
	g. Patients receiving palliative care
		3 months	Drugs listed in formulary, plus those approved under exception drug status, selected extemporaneous compounds, oxygen, and selected nutritional products approved on a case-by-case basis
			
			Antituberculosis and anticancer drugs, AZT for AIDS, cyclosporin for transplants, epidural morphine, deferoxamine, calcitonin, lupreolide acetate, menotropins, and synthetic growth hormone are available at no charge
				Saskatchewan Prescription Drug Plan Formulary	Saskatchewan Formulary Committee and Drug Quality Assessment Committee

Manitoba	a. Residents of Manitoba not covered by other federal or provincial benefits b. Residents in personal-care homes c. Persons financially indigent	None	All drugs for which a ℞ is required by law, plus a limited number of non-℞ drugs	Manitoba Drug Standards and Therapeutics Formulary	Manitoba Drug Standards and Therapeutics Committee
Ontario	a. Residents 65 + b. Persons receiving home care c. Residents of homes for special care (outpatients of psychiatric institutes) d. Persons receiving daily care in an extended-care facility e. Persons receiving benefits under provincial Family Benefits Act f. Persons receiving municipal General Welfare Assistance	a. 1 year prior to approval of an appli-cation, if not in receipt of federal Old Age Security pension. b,c,d,e, and f: Ontario residents in receipt of benefits under these programs.	Drugs listed in formulary plus special authorizations (e.g., oxygen, allergenic extracts, other drugs), influenza virus vaccine, and approved non-℞ drug products distributed in bulk to nursing homes for the aged	Ontario Drug Benefit Formulary/ Comparative Drug Index	Drug Quality and Therapeutics Committee

Province/ Territory	Beneficiaries	Residency Limitations	Benefits	Formulary	Therapeutics or Formulary Committee
Quebec	a. Persons 65 + b. Persons receiving social assistance	90 days	Drugs in *La liste de médicaments de la Régie de l'Assurance Maladie du Québec*	*La liste de médicaments de l'Assurance Maladie du Québec*	*Conseil consultatif de pharmacologie*
New Brunswick	a. Residents 65 +, diagnosed cystic fibrosis patients, home-care patients, licensed N.B. nursing home residents, organ transplant recipients receiving cyclosporin, AIDS patients (AZT), and patients receiving human growth hormones b. Social Services recipients and dependents, child-welfare recipients, and some mental health patients	None	All drugs for which a ℞ is required by law (except certain cough and cold remedies, laxatives, and antacids), a limited number of non-℞ drugs, plus specific drugs for special beneficiary groups	N.B. Product Selection Formulary (Prescription Drug Program) and Common Usage Drug Schedule	Product Selection Committee
Nova Scotia	a. Residents 65 + b. Persons receiving Family Benefits c. Persons receiving Diabetic Assistance d. Cystic fibrosis patients e. Diabetes insipidus (neurogenic persons) f. Cancer Assistance Program, dependent on financial basis	90 days; resident in province for at least 6 months per year	a and b: All drugs requiring a ℞ by law, plus supplementary benefit list of non-℞ drugs, diabetic supplies and testing materials, and ostomy supplies c. Diabetic supplies and testing materials d, e, and f: Particular coverage of medications related to the condition	Nova Scotia Prescription Drug Formulary	Drugs and Therapeutics Committee, N.S. Health Services and Insurance Commission
Prince Edward Island	a. Persons receiving social assistance b. Diabetics c. Persons 65 + upon application	a. none b. none c. 3 months	a. All drugs for which a ℞ is required by law, plus a limited number of non-℞ drugs b. Diabetic supplies c. Benefit-list products only	a. None b. None c. Benefits List	None
Newfoundland	a. Residents who receive social assistance benefits b. Residents 65 + who receive Guaranteed Income Supplement (G.I.S.)	None	*See* Common Usage Drug Schedule	Nfld. Interchangeable Drug Products Formulary	Formulary and Therapeutics Committee
Northwest Territories	a. persons 60 + (non-native and Métis) b. Non-native and Métis persons diagnosed as having certain disease conditions[2] c. Non-native and Métis persons designated by Dept. of Social Services as medically indigent	3 months	Drugs listed in formulary, plus those available under exception drug coverage	Northwest Territories Pharmacare Formulary	N.W.T. Formulary Advisory Committee

[2]N.W.T. Plan B Diseases: cancer, tuberculosis, venereal disease, celiac disease, cystic fibrosis, pernicious anemia, rheumatoid arthritis, rheumatic fever, epilepsy, chronic psychosis, diabetes mellitus, phynyketonuria, cleft lip/palate, congenital anomalies and chronic diseases of the urinary system, spina bifida, osteoarthritis, congenital cytomegalovirus, cerebral palsy, multiple sclerosis, diabetes insipidus, asthma (up to age 19), hypertension, rickets.

Table 2.   CLIENTELE AND BENEFITS OF PROGRAMS

Province/ Territory	Beneficiaries	Residency Limitations	Benefits	Formulary	Therapeutics or Formulary Committee
Yukon	a. Yukon residents 65 + or aged 60 + and married to Yukon resident who is 65 +	Residents eligible under Yukon Health Care Insurance Plan	a. All drugs for which a ℞ is required, plus a limited number of non-℞ items	a. None	a. None
	b. Yukon residents who have a chronic disease or a serious functional disability		b. ℞ drugs only, as controlled under the Food and Drugs Act and the Narcotic Control Act, plus biologicals	b. Benefit list	b. Chronic Disease Advisory Committee

Table 3(a)   FINANCIAL ASPECTS OF PROGRAMS

Province/Territory	Government Payment	Beneficiary Co-payment
British Columbia	a. Residents 65 + : 25% of the professional dispensing fee, plus 100% of drug cost	a. 75% of the professional dispensing fee to a maximum of $125 per person per year
	b. Residents of long-term care facilities: 100%	b. None
	c. Holders of Human Resources Medical Benefits Program W card: 100%	c. None
	d. All residents: 80% of costs exceeding $275 per family unit	d. $275 per family unit per year, plus 20% thereafter
Alberta	a. Social assistance recipients: 100%	a. None
	b. Persons 65 + : premiums for Alberta Blue Cross coverage	b. 20% of ℞ charge
Saskatchewan	a. Under 65: 80% over $215 per family; 80% over $75 per senior family; 80% over $50 per single senior	a. Under 65: $125 plus 20% thereafter per family; 65 + : $75 plus 20% thereafter per single senior
	b. 100% of drug ingredient cost, plus partial assistance on professional fee	b. Maximum of $3.95 per ℞
	c. 80% of ℞ cost	c. 20% of ℞ cost
	d. 100%	d. None
	e. 1. 100% for selected drugs; 100% of drug ingredient cost, plus part of professional fee for remainder of formulary drugs;	e. 1. $2 maximum per ℞
	2. 100% of Formulary drugs	2. None
	3. 100% of all ℞'s	3. None
	f. 100% of all ℞'s	f. None
	g. 100% of all formulary drugs or exception-status approved drugs	g. None
		Diabetics pay $1 per package for insulin and urine-test agents, and only the 20% up-front for blood glucose test agents
Manitoba	a. Persons 65 + : 80% over $75 per family; persons under 65: 80% over $125 per family	a. 65 + : $75, plus 20% thereafter per family; under 65: $125, plus 20% thereafter per family
	b. Residents of personal-care homes: 100%	b. None
	c. Financially indigent residents: 100%	c. None
Ontario	100%	None
Quebec	100%	None

Province/Territory	Government Payment	Beneficiary Co-payment
New Brunswick	a. Persons 65 +: 100%, less co-payment; home-care patients, etc.: 100%	a. 65 +: $3 per ℞ under $45/yr. of co-payment: cystic fibrosis and home-care patients, nursing-home residents, transplant recipients, etc.: none
	b. Social services, child welfare, etc.: 100%, less co-payment when applicable	b. Social services recipients: adults pay $2 per ℞; children pay $1 per ℞; child welfare: no co-payment
Nova Scotia	100%	None
Prince Edward Island	a. Social assistance recipients: 100% b. Diabetics: 100% c. Persons 65 +: balance of ingredient cost	a. None b. None c. Dispensing fee, plus first $4 of ingredient cost
Newfoundland	a. Social assistance recipients: 100% b. Residents 65 +: cost of drug ingredients	a. None b. Professional dispensing fee
Northwest Territories	100%	None
Yukon	100%	None

Table 3(b)   FINANCIAL ASPECTS OF PROGRAMS

Province/ Territory	Professional/ Dispensing Fee	Fee Expiry Date	Definition of Drug Costs	Reimbursement Recipient	Pharmacy Contract
British Columbia	$6.03	Current fee on 31 August 1987	Actual acquisition cost, i.e., the net cost to the pharmacy after discounts, rebates, etc.	*Group 1:* Pharmacy *Group 2:* Patient	Yes
Alberta	$6.05	30 June 1988	Cost to the wholesaler, plus 25% for the size most frequently purchased	Blue Cross	Yes
Saskatchewan	$5.50 Insulin: 33 1/3% markup Urine test agents: 50% markup	30 June 1988	Actual acquisition cost, plus markup to allowable maximums, depending on ingredient cost. (Actual acquisition cost may include an 11% markup allowed to the wholesaler by contract.)	a. Patient All other plans: pharmacy contract holder	Yes
Manitoba	$5.25	(Negotiations pending)	Price listed in formulary or cost of smallest package size	a. Patient b. Pharmacy c. Pharmacy	No
Ontario	$5.95	30 November 1987	As described in the Drug Benefit Formulary/ Comparative Drug Index ("Best Available Price"), plus percentage (Currently BAP + 10%)	Pharmacies, dispensing physicians oxygen/ allergen suppliers some participating hospital out-patient dispensaries	No; there are pilot capitation projects, however.

Province/ Territory	Professional/ Dispensing Fee	Fee Expiry Date	Definition of Drug Costs	Reimbursement Recipient	Pharmacy Contract
Quebec	$4.34 on first 20,000 ℞'s; $3.74 thereafter	31 May 1987	Manufacturer's price as listed in *La liste de médicaments de la Régie de l'assurance maladie du Québec*	Pharmacy	Yes: contract with AQPP
New Brunswick	$6.34; extemporaneous preparations: $9.51	30 June 1988	Price listed in formulary or net cost to pharmacy

Non-℞ items: some are charged at customary retail price, others at cost price, plus dispensing fee | Pharmacy/ dispensing physician | Yes |
Nova Scotia	$7.53 $11.30 (specified compounds) $3.60 (dispensing physicians)	30 June 1989	Actual acquisition cost: net cost to the pharmacy after all rebates, allowances, free products, etc.	Pharmacy; Dispensing physicians	Pharmacy Association of Nova Scotia
Prince Edward Island	a. $6.15 $3.50 (O.C.'s) $9.22 (Extemp.) b. Insulin: 25% markup c. $5.90	31 October 1987	a. Actual acquisition cost b. Actual acquisition cost c. Same as negotiated with Blue Cross of Atlantic Canada	a. n/a b. n/a c. Pharmacy	a. No b. No c. Yes
Newfoundland	a. $5.56/$5.90 b. $6.00 (*Average*, fee not negotiated) O.C.'s: $3.50/ $3.71 Extemp.: $8.34/ $8.85 Diabetic supplies: 33 1/3% markup. Surcharge of 10% when ingredient cost exceeds $30	a. 31 March 1989 b. 31 March 1989	Price of smallest quantity to pharmacist, except for prices quoted in the Nfld. Interchangeable Drug Formulary	Pharmacy	a. Yes b. No
Northwest Territories	$7.55	30 June 1988	Cost to wholesaler, plus 25% for the size most frequently purchased; cost, plus 35% for Inuvik and Frobisher Bay	Pharmacy	Yes
Yukon	$7.25	30 April 1988	Not defined	Pharmacy	No

Table 4   DISTRIBUTION OF DRUGS

Province/Territory	Quantity Restrictions	Product Selection Legislation	Product Selection Liability
British Columbia	Usual prescribing practice: 100 days' supply limitation	Yes: permissive. Physician may write "No substitution"	Pharmacist
Alberta	Up to 34 days, except for 8 therapeutic classes (e.g., anticonvulsants) where up to 100 days' supply is provided	Yes: permissive. Physician may write "No substitution"	Pharmacist

Province/Territory	Quantity Restrictions	Product Selection Legislation	Product Selection Liability
Saskatchewan	a. No limit; should be consistent with good pharmaceutical practice *All other plans:* up to 180 days' supply. One dispensary fee for every 34 days supply, with the following exceptions: Two-month list – O.C.'s, oral estrogens; 100-day list – digitalis preparations, phenobarbital, anticonvulsants, oral hypoglycemics, calcium preparations, gold compounds, antithyroid and thyroid preparations	Yes: mandatory. Pharmacist must dispense standing-offer drug, unless physician writes "No substitution" Pharmacist is reimbursed at acquisition cost to the lowest-cost product in formulary for all others, unless "No substitution" is indicated	Protective legislation
Manitoba	No limit; should be consistent with good pharmaceutical practice	Yes: mandatory for drugs listed in formulary, unless physician writes "No substitution"	Protective legislation
Ontario	Municipal general welfare recipients (Plan f): a quantity sufficient for a 35-day course of treatment For senior citizens and all other plan types: a quantity sufficient for a 250-day course of treatment	Yes: permissive. However, pharmacist is reimbursed at the cost of lowest product in formulary, unless physician writes "No substitution," and in cash market, there is virtually mandatory "price" substitution	Protective legislation; government accepts liability
Quebec	No limit; should be consistent with good pharmaceutical practice	Yes: permissive. Physician may write "No substitution"	Pharmacist
New Brunswick	a. Normally dispensed in quantities sufficient for 34 days' supply, except in cases where smaller quantities are sufficient for the normal course of treatment b. Quantities up to 100 days' supply may be dispensed	Yes: permissive. Physician may write "No substitution"	Protective legislation
Nova Scotia	Maximum of 180 days per prescription	No	Pharmacist
Prince Edward Island	a. Maximum of 60 days' supply for all items b. Maximum of 90 days' supply for all items c. 34 days for most items, except those on an approved list	No	n/a
Newfoundland	a. In accordance with ℞, up to 34 days' dosage or 120 doses, whichever is greater b. Up to a maximum of 100 days' supply	Yes: must charge lowest price listed for interchangeable drugs. Physician may write "No substitution"	Protective legislation
Northwest Territories	Same as Saskatchewan (Plans b,c,d,e,f, and g)	No	Pharmacist
Yukon	No limit; should be consistent with good pharmaceutical practice	No	Pharmacist

GLOSSARY

Accounts payable: a term applied to the aggregate of amounts owed to the creditors of a business.

Accounts receivable: a term applied to the aggregate of amounts due from the customers of a business.

Assets: those items owned by a business.

Automated counting system: automatic system for counting tablets or capsules by which technical personnel can obtain the exact count of the medication prescribed.

Average collection period: average length of time required to collect accounts receivable.

Average inventory: the amount calculated when the beginning inventory and ending inventory are added together and divided by two.

Average payable period: average length of time taken to pay invoices.

Balance sheet: a statement of the financial condition of a business at a certain date showing its assets, liabilities and capital.

Basic law of investment: a principle which holds that a return on investment will vary directly with the degree of risk involved and inversely with the liquidity of the investment.

Bay shelving: a storage facility of open shelving found in the prescription department.

Beginning inventory: the total inventory on hand at the beginning of a specified period.

Blister package: a protective package of clear plastic that conforms roughly to the shape of the contents and is attached to a firm cardboard backing allowing the entire contents to be displayed.

474

Book value: the dollar worth of an asset appearing on the balance sheet after deducting a specified percentage per year for depreciation.

Break-even analysis: a procedure that determines the degree of business volume at which total revenue equals total expense or, in other words, at which sales equal fixed costs plus variable costs.

Business interruption insurance: a type of insurance that provides a continuation of income to the pharmacy in the event of fire or other serious disruption that causes the pharmacy to be unable to render services for a period ranging from a few days to a few months.

Business plan: a report that consists of a descriptive section outlining the nature of a business and the marketing approach that is planned for it, as well as a financial report detailing past operations and the latest interim monthly financial statement, together with projected monthly income statements and projected monthly cash flow statements for the upcoming year.

Capital: wealth (money or property) which is used or capable of being used to produce more wealth.

Capital gains: gains that result from the disposition of capital property.

Capitation: A method of determining fees, by which a pharmacist claims a fixed fee per patient for a specified time, regardless of the amount of care required.

Carrying costs: the costs associated with holding products in inventory (also called holding costs or maintenance costs).

Cash flow: a summary of cash receipts and disbursements of a business, for a defined period of time.

Cash management: Freeing up funds for operating purposes by minimizing assets and maximizing liabilities, specifically accounts payable.

Census Agglomeration (CA): the main labour market of an urban area of at least 10,000 population.

Census Metropolitan Area (CMA): the main labour market area of an urban area of at least 100,000 population.

Central computer system: a computer system by which the pharmacist contracts for full service with a computer service company and thereby transfers the responsibility for management reports to that company.

Citizen's arrest: a provision (Section 449) of the Criminal Code of Canada which allows any person to make a citizen's arrest and to deliver that person to a peace officer. The citizen must see the crime occur to make such an arrest.

Collective ownership: a form of business enterprise popularly known as a cooperative, by which interested parties band together to buy or sell products or services.

Comprehensive general liability and shop malpractice insurance: a type of insurance that covers both the corporation as an entity and all its employees for legal liability in case of a possible suit (may also be referred to as third-party liability insurance or casualty insurance).

Computer hardware: the physical equipment of a computer system.

Computer software: the programs that instruct the computer hardware to perform various functions.

Consumer market: the potential of a selected group of consumers to purchase the goods or services offered to them.

Continuing education unit (C.E.U.): terminology used in the field of continuing education. One C.E.U. approximates one contact hour of involvement in continuing education. In provinces and states where continuing education is mandatory, the pharmacist must complete a given number of C.E.U.'s in a prescribed period of time.

Corporation: a form of business enterprise in which ownership is represented by stock or shares in the firm. Shareholders are not financially liable for the business beyond the cost of the shares they have purchased (limited liability).

Cost of goods sold (COGS): the cost of merchandise sold to customers during a specified period, usually one year; calculated by adding the net cost of purchases during the period to the beginning inventory, and deducting the ending inventory.

Cost-based pricing: the process of establishing a price based on costs by totalling all the costs associated with an item offered for sale, including the product cost itself, the freight cost, allowances for advertising, and the cost of labour involved in getting the product to the shelf and maintaining it.

Current assets: assets that can be converted into cash within a twelve-month period.

Current liabilities: liabilities that will be paid within a twelve-month period.

Current ratio: a key ratio that bankers use to determine the liquidity of a business; calculated by dividing the total current assets by the total current liabilities.

Debt capital: the amount of money that must be borrowed to finance a business.

Depreciation: the decrease in value of a fixed asset due to wear and tear or obsolescence.

Destination store: stores which generate most of their own traffic, i.e., customers consciously choose the store as their destination.

Diagnostic kit: a test kit which can monitor for a specific disease or medical condition and which is designed for use at home by the patient or in a laboratory.

Disability-free life expectancy (DFLE): the age to which the average person lives free of chronic illness or other disabilities.

Disability insurance: a type of insurance which protects against loss of income by providing for its continuance, when the loss is occasioned by illness or accident.

Discount pricing: pricing below market levels; used to attract traffic and increase sales.

Dividend: a distribution of profits to the shareholders of a corporation.

Dollar control: Any approach to controlling inventory that focusses on the amount of money invested in inventory rather than on the number of units or the particular products involved.

Dump bin: a self-standing container with a header card into which a promoted product is "dumped" randomly. They are located in high traffic aisles of the retail outlet.

Earnings multiplier: the reciprocal of the percentage return on investment that a business should be expected to bring its owner. The indicated earnings of the pharmacy are multiplied by the 'earnings multiplier' factor to determine the theoretical value of the operating assets.

Economic order quantity (EOQ): the dollar volume of purchases or level of inventory at which combined procurement and carrying costs are lowest.

End displays: displays at the ends of gondolas.

Entrepreneur: someone who organizes a business, assuming all the inherent risks, for the purpose of obtaining a profit.

Environmental scanning: the process of continually noting current events and analyzing them for their impact on the business environment.

Equity capital: the amount of money invested in a business.

Exchange value: the value of any product or service in the marketplace as determined by what an individual will pay in dollars for it.

Financial leverage: the relationship between equity capital and debt capital.

Financial ratio analysis: a simple ratio or series of ratios calculated from data in the financial statements. The ratios provide indications of how well managers are utilizing the resources available to them by comparing current year's ratios to past year's and to industry averages.

Financial statement: a statement, comprised of an income statement and a balance sheet, which provides a picture of the financial status of a business at a point in time.

Fiscal year: a twelve-month period ending with the last day of any month.

Fixed assets: assets more or less permanent in nature whose useful life is more than one year.

Franchise: a form of licensing by which the owner (franchisor) of a product, service or method obtains distribution at the retail level through affiliated dealers (the franchisees).

General partnership: a grouping of two or more people coming together to form a business. Each partner is individually liable for the business debts.

Generic products: products that are copies of an original brand-name product.

Gondolas: free-standing fixtures that hold retail merchandise for sale.

Goodwill: the value of an intangible asset; usually the difference between the purchase price of a business and the appraised value of its physical assets.

Gross margin: the difference between the selling price and the cost of the item sold (also referred to as gross profit).

Gross-margin pricing: the percentage by which the selling price exceeds the cost price.

Gross margin return on inventory investment (GMROI): a ratio that is used to assess the effectiveness of inventory management by determining the productivity of the inventory, i.e., the gross margin dollars that are generated by each dollar invested in inventory.

Halo effect: a term used to describe a phenomena by which an interviewer is biased in favour of a particular personality or physical attribute on the part of interviewees over other factors which may be more relevant to the position in question.

Hot-spot cross: the product placement area in the centre of a gondola; associated with the highest sales.

Impulse items: items that a consumer had not planned on purchasing.

Income splitting: the reduction of overall income tax which the owner of a business achieves by paying other family members a salary or making them shareholders of the business who then receive dividend income.

Indicated pre-tax earnings: pre-tax income after reasonable wages and all operating expenses have been paid; based on a review of the business' previous financial statements.

Intercept store: stores which are located between people in a 'trading area' and their traditional source of goods or services.

Inventory control: the monitoring of stock on hand in terms of stock-keeping units or dollar value and cost.

Key-person insurance: a type of insurance which upon the death of a business's 'key person' will provide the funds to attract, educate and train a replacement and keep the business in operation until this occurs.

Leasing: a financing mechanism for the acquisition by a business of premises, equipment, shelving, fixtures and computers; an alternative to renting or purchasing.

Letter of Intent: a document to be signed by interested parties that procedes the drawing up of a formal purchase agreement (to buy an established pharmacy); should include the basic elements of the purchase – price, terms of payment and structure – and an indication that the closing will be subject to the purchaser's obtaining the necessary financing.

Liquidity: the ability to turn assets into cash quickly, in order to repay debt from short-term capitalization.

Load shedding: the reduction by a government of its subsidization of certain services, i.e., privatization.

Marked money: a security measure by which identifiable bills are stored in the cash register, to be given to a robber along with the remainder of the cash register contents.

Market area: sub-area, within a geographic region, that can be defined by population, transportation networks, and economic characteristics.

Marketing: the process by which the demands of the public for goods and services are not only satisfied, but also – by means of collecting and analyzing market information – predicted and enhanced.

Market research: the study of the attitudes and beliefs that shape the consumer's response to a product or service.

Markup on cost: a method of pricing by which the markup is expressed as a percentage of the cost price.

Net/net/net/lease: a lease which makes the tenant responsible for core rent and, separately, for all other expenses defined in the offer to lease, with the possible exception of major repairs.

Net worth (individual): the value of personal assets less personal liabilities.

Occupancy costs: expenses incurred as a result of a business occupying a specific premise, i.e., rent (or the interest on a mortgage and depreciation of the building), utilities, property taxes, repairs and maintenance.

Offer to lease: a document which covers the basic terms (rent, definition of the space, any additional costs for common maintenance and property taxes) that will be included in the actual lease of a premise.

Open-to-buy (OTB) budget method: a dollar-control system based on establishing overall monthly purchase budgets in advance, monitoring actual sales and purchases during each month, and adjusting the purchase budget for the following month to compensate for documented overspending or underspending and sales declines or increases in the previous month.

Operating loan: a form of working capital financing; also referred to as a demand loan or "line of credit"; used to finance current assets.

Operational plan: the foundation for the business plan; involves gathering, analyzing and planning action around information that will assist in meeting the pharmacy owner's personnel and business goals.

Original packaging: the prepackaging by a manufacturer of a product (often prescription drugs) on the basis of a therapeutic course of treatment for which it is commonly prescribed.

Partnership insurance: a type of insurance that in the event of the death of a partner provides funds to finance a purchase from the deceased's family.

Pareto's Law: a guideline of inventory control which holds that 20 per cent of all products stocked generates 80 per cent of total dollar sales, 15 per cent of inventory generates another 15 per cent of sales, and the remaining 65 per cent of the stock generates only 5 per cent of sales.

Password system: a computer security system using appropriate passwords in order to control and limit access to information to authorized personnel only.

Pegboard: a hard backing with symetrical holes that can hold movable hooks; used to display merchandise.

Performance review: an evaluation by an owner/manager or supervisor of an employee's performance in his or her job.

Periodic inventory control systems: a manual unit-control system; involves monitoring sales of product items over specific time periods.

Perpetual system: an inventory control system that records sales as they occur, continually calculating increases in the value of inventory as products are received into stock and reductions as products are sold.

Planogram: a precise, detailed scheme for merchandise display within given-product categories.

Point-of-sale system: a combination of computer software, hardware and cash register that captures product information at time of sale or when it is received into inventory.

Policy and procedures manual: written guidelines communicating store policy and procedures for the benefit of both management and staff.

Post-marking surveillance: monitoring of new drugs after market introduction.

Procurement costs: the costs associated with purchasing merchandise.

Product facing: a product package on the shelf, facing out to the consumer, with stock of the product lined up behind the front package.

Professional fee: A fee representing the cost to the pharmacy of the service component (labour, operational, general and administrative costs) in dispensing prescriptions.

Profit and loss statement: a financial statement of a point in time showing the income and expenses of a business.

Profitability: the ability of the business to generate sufficient revenue not only to pay its expenses but also to reward its owner(s).

Reorder point: the minimum level to which stock of a product is permitted to drop before it is reordered.

Replacement insurance: a type of insurance that provides the full replacement value for fixed assets (land, building, fixtures, equipment).

Retained earnings: profits of a firm that are reinvested in the business.

Shareholders' agreement: a contractual agreement which establishes the ground rules of the relationship between a business (owner) and investors.

Shareholders' equity: shareholders' investment in a business.

Shrinkage: the variance between the book value of inventory and the physical count.

Slat wall: a slatted or grooved backing that can be fitted with either shelves or rows of hooks; used to display merchandise.

Smart card: a plastic card the size of a credit card that carries a computer chip; it can carry large amounts of information regarding its bearer, e.g., the person's complete medical and drug history.

Sole proprietorship: a business which is wholly owned by one individual, the proprietor.

Sole proprietorship insurance: a type of insurance that provides the necessary funds for a sole proprietor's surviving family members to reorganize, carry on, or sell the business in the event of his or her death.

Solvency: a measure of a firm's ability to repay debt from long-term capitalization.

Stand-alone system: an in-house computer system which includes both hardware (the microcomputer) and the rights to a software package(s).

Stock-keeping unit (SKU): the smallest distinguishable packaged unit in a product category.

Strategic plan: a plan which sets the overall direction or goal for the pharmacy and outlines the philosophy by which the pharmacy will operate.

Suscipient business: a principle of location analysis; holds that a store need not generate its own traffic nor depend on neighbouring stores for its customers but that having a location in a place where people circulate for reasons other than shopping can bring in its business.

Term loan: a type of loan used primarily to finance the purchase of capital or long-term assets, such as buildings, fixtures, and equipment, whose value will not fluctuate, but will depreciate over time.

Trial balance: a list taken of the account balances in the general ledger to prove the accuracy of the postings to the ledger and to establish a summary of data for the preparation of financial statements.

Turnkey operation: a type of franchise in which the franchisor undertakes all that is necessary to establish the operation, and the franchisee simply opens the door and begins doing business.

Turnover rate (TOR): a theoretical number of times during a specified period, usually one year, that inventory is bought and completely sold.

Unit control: any approach to controlling inventory that focusses on the number of units of particular products carried in inventory.

Universal Product Code (UPC): an identification code consisting of a series of bars and numerals located on a lable or outer package which makes it possible to scan products on scanning counters in order to register all necessary product information and appropriate prices.

Venture capital: a source of capital for a new business; viable only if the business requires financing well in excess of $500,000 but shows promise of great profits in the future. Venture capitalists usually require a percentage of the ownership of the business, an annual return on their investment and a seat on the board of directors.

Visual balance: the appealing arrangement of products on shelves according to size or colour.

Visual system: a method of inventory control that consists simply of examining the merchandise on the shelves and reordering if it is below a desired level or out of stock.

Walk-in medical clinics: clinics often found in shopping malls which supply fast medical care without the need of an appointment.

Working capital: the value of current assets less current liabilities.

PERMISSIONS

Table 3.1   Reproduced with the permission of the Minister of Supply and Services, Canada.

Table 3.2   Reprinted with permission of John Wiley & Sons, Inc., New York, New York.

Table 3.3   Reproduced with the permission of the Minister of Supply and Services, Canada.

Figure 3.1   Reprinted with the permission of Medical Economics Company Inc., Oradell, New Jersey.

Location Analysis Checklist, Chapter 3   Reprinted with the permission of Medical Economics Company Inc., Oradell, New Jersey.

Figure 4.1   Reprinted with the permission of the Canadian Pharmaceutical Association, Ottawa, Ontario.

Figure 4.2   Reprinted with the permission of the Canadian Pharmaceutical Association, Ottawa, Ontario.

Figure 4.3   Reprinted with permission of John Wiley & Sons, Inc., New York, New York.

Figure 4.4   Reprinted with the permission of the National Association of Accountants, Montvale, New Jersey.

Figure 8.1   Reprinted with the permission of the Grain Insurance and Guarantee Company, Winnipeg, Manitoba.

Figure 9.1   Reprinted with the permission of Vic Store Fixtures, Inc., Victoriaville, Quebec.

Table 11.1   Reprinted with the permission of the Ontario College of Pharmacists, Toronto, Ontario.

Table 11.2   Reprinted with the permission of the Federal Business Development Bank, Montreal, Quebec.

Table 11.3   Reprinted with the permission of the Ontario College of Pharmacists, Toronto, Ontario.

Figure 11.1   Reprinted with the permission of Hoffmann-La Roche Limited, Etobicoke, Ontario.

Figure 11.2   Reprinted with the permission of H.J. Segal, Toronto, Ontario.

Figure 11.4   Reprinted with the permission of Marion Laboratories, Inc., Kansas City, Missouri.

Figure 15.1   Reprinted with the permission of Shoppers Drug Mart, Willowdale, Ontario.

Figure 15.2   Reprinted with the permission of Sandoz Pharmaceuticals Corporation, East Hanover, New Jersey.

Figure 15.6   Reprinted with the permission of H.J. Segal, Toronto, Ontario.

Figure 15.7   Reprinted with the permission of Drug Trading Company Limited, Scarborough, Ontario.

Figure 15.8   Reprinted with the permission of Hoffmann-La Roche Limited, Etobicoke, Ontario.

Figure 18.1   Reprinted with the permission of the National Association of Accountants, Montvale, New Jersey.

Figure 21.1   Reprinted with the permission of the Upjohn Company of Canada, Toronto, Ontario

Table 21.1   Reprinted with the permission of the Upjohn Company of Canada, Toronto, Ontario

Table 21.2   Reprinted with the permission of the Upjohn Company of Canada, Toronto, Ontario

Table 21.3   Reprinted with the permission of the Upjohn Company of Canada, Toronto, Ontario

Figure 21.2   Reprinted with the permission of the Canadian Pharmaceutical Association, Ottawa, Ontario.

Figure 21.3   Reprinted with the permission of the Canadian Dental Association, Ottawa, Ontario.

Table 24.1   Reprinted with the permission of Chatham House Publishers Inc., Chatham, New Jersey.

Table 24.2   Reprinted with the permission of Drug Merchandising, Toronto, Ontario.

Figure 26.1   Reprinted with the permission of John P. Klus, Society of American Military Engineers, Alexandria, Virginia.

Figure 26.2   Reprinted with the permission of Jossey-Bass Inc., San Francisco, California.

Table 26.1   Reprinted with the permission of Taylor and Francis, New York, New York.

Table 26.2   Reprinted with the permission of the American Association of Colleges of Pharmacy, Alexandria, Virginia.